TWO-WAY RADIO

TWO-WAY RADIO

ALLAN H. LYTEL

Manager of Proposal Coordination
Crosley Division, Avco Corporation
Senior Member, STWE
Member, IRE
Member, ALA

McGRAW-HILL BOOK COMPANY, INC.

New York   Toronto   London

1959

TWO-WAY RADIO

Library of Congress Catalog Card Number: 59-7314

II

39380

THE MAPLE PRESS COMPANY, YORK, PA.

to

ELAINE GREENABAUM LYTEL

FOREWORD

The history of two-way radio communications in some ways parallels the development of commercial radio broadcasting. Signal Corps radio equipment was installed in vehicles as far back as 1904, and communications from aircraft to the ground were demonstrated in 1908. The first presidential election covered by radio was the Harding-Cox campaign of 1920. A year later Station KOP was placed in operation by the Detroit Police Department.

But the truly large-scale growth of two-way radio communications has taken place since World War II. Today there are at least 1,500,-000 transmitters in use in the United States, and with every transmitter there are one or more receivers. Along with the tremendous increase in equipment has come the introduction of such revolutionary things as transistors and other solid-state devices that have made possible, for the first time, small-size, highly reliable mobile equipment with very low power drains. The potentialities of these new techniques are just beginning to be exploited. As a result, in commercial equipment, hand-held transceivers are replacing the more bulky equipment for emergency use, and many types of vehicular radios are now being made with transistorized power supplies.

In the armed forces, where advanced technical features often are an overriding consideration, transistorized equipment is now in production for several types of mobile-communication equipment.

The past two years (1957–1958) have seen a great many changes in two-way-radio rules and regulations by the FCC. These have been concerned largely with more effective utilization of the radio spectrum, which is in a very real sense one of our most precious natural resources.

In the 30–50 Mc band, for example, channels are now established with a 20-kc spacing rather than the old 40-kc spacing; the assigned frequency must be kept within 0.002 per cent; and the deviation is usually limited to ±5 kc.

In the 152–162 Mc band, instead of the former 60-kc channel spacing, the new channels are now set up for a 15-kc spacing, with every other channel in use. Thus, there will be a channel every 30 kc; the frequency must be held to within 0.0005 per cent; and the deviation limit is ±5 kc.

In the 450–460 Mc band, the channel spacing has been changed from 100 to 50 kc with a frequency tolerance of 0.0005 per cent and the deviation is limited to ±15 kc.

There is, of course, a great deal of commercial two-way-radio equipment in use which does not conform to the standards listed above. And according to the FCC, all systems in use after Oct. 31, 1963, must conform to these new regulations. Any new system which is authorized after Aug. 1, 1958, must conform to the new regulations. There is a provision that any equipment which was in use as of Aug. 1, 1958, may have new units added to it based upon the old standards up until the cutoff date of Oct. 31, 1963.

The technical requirements listed above, as well as others, are only part of the changes made by the FCC in the last several years. There also has been a modification of some of the types and classes of radio service which have been available.

A Business Radio Service was established as of Aug. 1, 1958, to accommodate any legitimate business enterprise. A Manufacturer's Radio Service, available as of Aug. 1, 1958, is designed for material handling, which once came under the Special Industrial Radio Service; the Low Power Radio Service has been eliminated, but the users will find accommodations in the new Business Radio Service; the Special Industrial Radio Service has been modified to include certain specialities such as farms, ranches, contractors, and the like; and the Local Government Radio Service is available to cities and towns as of June 30, 1958, for use by police, fire, street, and water departments.

Thus, there are three factors which point the way toward a vastly increased use of two-way radio in the near future. These are the new technical innovations in circuit design and solid-state circuit elements; the new technical requirements on channel spacing, frequency tolerance, and deviation limitations as imposed by the FCC; and the revisions of the various classifications of radio service which have opened this means of communication to many types of business and industrial enterprise.

According to the FCC report as of June, 1958, radio permits and licenses grew by almost 200,000. There were more than 2,100,000 authorizations and over 1,500,000 transmitters in actual use. This is almost 250,000 more transmitters than were in use in 1957.

Safety and Special Services Radio alone, with its more than 40 groups, includes 465,000 authorizations with more than 1,407,000 mobile and fixed transmitters. Public safety groups such as police, fire, and the like operate almost 300,000; industrial services 420,000; amateur and disaster 184,566; aviation 81,335; land transportation 341,753; and marine 79,000.

Among these authorizations for transmitters, as of June 30, 1958, were: buses, 2,700; auto emergency, 9,000; special emergency, 13,000; highway maintenance, 28,000; forestry conservation, 34,000; fire departments, 60,000; railroads, 65,000; taxicabs, 100,000; citizens, 125,000; and police departments, 167,000.

There were 185,000 amateur radio operators, and the number of licensed commercial radio operators exceeded 1,500,000 at the end of June, 1958.

In writing this book on Two-way Radio, Allan H. Lytel of the Crosley Division, Avco Corporation, has performed a unique service. He has covered both mobile (vehicle) and base-station (fixed) radio transmitters and receivers and their test equipment (AM is included as well as FM) both in theory and practice, thus filling a need for a comprehensive volume that will be useful to the amateur and professional alike.

F. C. REITH
Group Executive
Crosley and Nashville Divisions
Avco Corporation

PREFACE

The purpose of this book is to explain the growing field of two-way radio communications to the technicians and maintenance men who will be responsible for installation, servicing, and repair. This book is aimed at the Technical Institute level, and it is written with a minimum amount of mathematics so that it may be used either for home study or as a classroom textbook. Examples of equipment are used wherever possible.

There are many different types of mobile-radio equipment which are presently on the air. Some were produced by manufacturers who are no longer in this business, but whose equipment continues to provide reliable and economical communications. The newest equipment, of course, is manufactured by those companies who are currently in the mobile-radio business. And this diversity of two-way-radio equipment provides a challenge for the technician. I hope that many technicians will be encouraged to enter this field. The installation and maintenance of mobile radios is a rapidly growing electronic business. Throughout this book, the circuits and equipments which are discussed apply to many of the commercial receivers and transmitters. The same thing is true for test equipment.

This book has been in process for more than ten years. It was started when I was teaching at Temple University Technical Institute in Philadelphia. Most of the book was actually written while I was with General Electric in Syracuse, New York, and it was completed while I was with Avco/Crosley in Cincinnati. I gratefully acknowledge my debt to the manufacturers of the radio equipment for their kind permission to include photographs and schematic drawings of their products. Special acknowledgments must be made to Edward Noll and Matt Mandl, who helped me learn more about two-way radio while we were all teaching at Temple University, and to Judy Valentine, of the General Electric Electronics Laboratory, for her typing and suggestions.

ALLAN LYTEL

CONTENTS

TWO-WAY RADIO

CHAPTER 1

AN INTRODUCTION TO TWO-WAY RADIO

1-1. Two-way Communications

Two-way radio is the fast-growing two-way voice communication between two stations at least one of which is mobile or moving. Usually each installation has both a transmitter and a receiver; frequency modulation (FM) or amplitude modulation (AM) may be used; both types are on the market.

Every two-way communications system is assigned a certain frequency on which to operate, as with broadcasting. The simplest system has a base (fixed) station and one or more mobile stations in automobiles, trucks, or other vehicles.

Two-way radio covers a very wide field with many different types and models of receivers and transmitters. The usefulness of two-way radio extends to many industrial applications including delivery of fuel oil, as in Fig. 1-1; construction and building, as in Figs. 1-2 and 1-3; utilities, as shown in Figs. 1-4 and 1-5; railroads, as in Fig. 1-6; and automobile road service, as in Fig. 1-7.

And these are but some examples. Over two million transmitters have been authorized by the Federal Communications Commission (FCC) for the many uses of today's radio communication systems.

Two-way radio has two basic types of transmitter-receiver units: A *mobile* is a unit designed for use in a vehicle or as a portable unit. These are compact radios with battery power supplies. A two-way radio *station* is a base-station unit designed for use with a fixed antenna as a headquarters unit to be used in a fixed location.

Calls can also be made, in some cases, from a vehicle to a telephone by dialing a number in a local telephone system. Anyone in that local system can call the vehicle in exactly the same way as in making a house-to-house call. But when placing a toll call the long-distance operator must be called first.

Such systems consist of a dial radiotelephone in a vehicle, with a two-way-radio system as a carrier to the local-telephone-company installation.[1] A transmitter-receiver base station is connected to the local

[1] Ramsey McDonald, "Dial Direct" Automatic Radiotelephone System, *Trans. IRE, PGVC*-11, p. 80, July, 1958.

FIG. 1-1. Fuel-oil delivery truck with driver using mobile radio.   (*General Electric.*)

FIG. 1-2. Crane operator showing microphone in use. (*General Electric.*)

telephone system.   Termination and switching equipment at the base station automatically transfers the radio calls to the telephone system and telephone calls to the radio system.

Calls can also be made from vehicle to vehicle.   Two telephone lines are required to connect the base-station equipment with the telephone company's central office.   One line is for calls from telephone to radio; the other, for radio to telephone.

A typical mobile-radio transmitter-receiver combination is illustrated in Fig. 1-8. This is designed for use in a vehicle. An adjustable mounting bracket fits several different types of installations. The *on-off switch, the volume control,* and the *squelch control* are the only ones available to, or required by, the operator. A *push-to-talk switch* on the microphone is used during transmission.

A unit such as this can be used in several different mountings. It may be placed in the trunk (Fig. 1-8) with the controls next to the driver as illustrated in Fig. 1-9. The entire unit may be placed next to the driver (Fig. 1-10) or installed on the seat of an industrial vehicle as in Fig. 1-11. These are all variations in the methods of installing a radio in a vehicle.

Base stations are transmitter-receiver units for use in fixed locations such as in buildings and may be remotely controlled. A unit may be located next to a desk (Fig. 1-12) or, by use of a 117-volt a-c power supply, a vehicle radio can be converted into a base station, as shown in Fig. 1-13.

Frequency bands cover several regions starting from 25 Mc and

Fig. 1-3. Radio mounted in waterproof case on top of truck cab. (*General Electric.*)

FIG. 1-4. Radio contact speeds utility repairs. (*General Electric.*)

extending through 470 Mc. Frequency assignments in each band are usually on a nonexclusive basis; several transmitters may share the same frequency even though they are geographically close together. The FCC is the agency responsible for licensing and control of mobile radio, just as it also controls the technical features of AM and FM radio and television broadcasting. The FCC approves commercial mobile and base-station equipment, issues the station licenses, and provides the licenses for operating and maintenance technicians.[1]

FM is becoming increasingly important as the method of transmission, but AM is still in use in some applications. FM (phase modulation changed to FM) has important advantages over AM for mobile use. The most important single advantage of FM is freedom from noise, which is important in low-power operation.

Two-way radio goes back to the very early days of radio. Early

[1] E. H. Singer, FCC Rules and Their Enforcement, *Trans. IRE, PGVC-3*, p. 129, June, 1953.

FIG. 1-5. Water-works pickup truck talks to dispatcher.   (*General Electric.*)

spark transmitters were installed in Signal Corps vehicles in 1904, air-to-ground communications operated experimentally in 1908, and in 1921 station KOP (Detroit police) was active in land mobile radio. FM started in the radio industry in 1936, and in 1941 the FCC authorized FM for vehicular communications.   During World War II many excellent FM communication sets served all branches of the Armed

FIG. 1-6. Train movements under radio control. Note loudspeaker to overcome noise. (*General Electric.*)

Fig. 1-7. Emergency road service reaches a stranded motorist with the help of radio. (*General Electric.*)

Forces, and since the end of the war mobile FM radio has grown very rapidly.

The gradual emphasis has been toward higher frequencies, which have certain advantages. High frequencies, above 100 Mc, have a limited range. There is no skip interference as with some transmissions at lower frequencies, which can be reflected by the ionosphere and be received at other locations, some at a great distance from the transmitter. But stations above 100 Mc on the same frequency do not normally interfere when they are 50 to 100 miles apart. Because many radio channels are on a shared basis, it is important that no two transmitters on the same frequency cause interference.

The UHF 450-Mc two-way-radio band has less static and less man-made noise. Foliage and trees have a greater tendency to attenuate the UHF signal, but the reflection characteristics are higher at UHF. The radio signals at these frequencies tend to bounce, or reflect, and so fill in dead spots in the radiation pattern. UHF also has the ability to get in between buildings in cities; for these reasons there is increased interest in, and use of, UHF.

Citizens Radio Service (460 to 465 Mc and 27 Mc) is an important branch of mobile radio. This service is intended for private or personal short-distance radio communication and for those not eligible under other FCC rules. Any citizen of the United States who is

Fig. 1-8. Trunk mounting of a radio transmitter showing transistorized power supply at the left. (*General Electric.*)

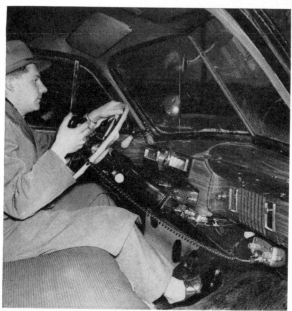

Fig. 1-9. Controls, alongside the driver, for a trunk-mounted radio. (*General Electric.*)

FIG. 1-10. Front-mounted radio showing controls within reach of the operator. (*General Electric.*)

eighteen or more years old may obtain a station license in this service, providing, of course, that his application meets the general requirements of the Commission's rules and regulations governing the Citizens Radio Service. The licensee may authorize the use of his station (or stations) by other persons, but he is still responsible for the operation of his station. One license application covers an entire system.

The increased use of two-way radio has brought this field its most important technical problem—how to allow more transmitters on the

FIG. 1-11. Business radio as used on materials-handling truck. (*Du-Mont.*)

FIG. 1-12. Base-station radio shown alongside the dispatcher's desk. (*General Electric.*)

air in the assigned bands which are already crowded. Some possible solutions to this are sharp IF filters for greater selectivity, two-level power operation, where reduced transmitter power is used wherever feasible, possible single-sideband operation for reduced bandwidth, directional antennas, or reduced power. The trend is toward more narrow-band equipment (less than 15 kc) to allow more transmitters without interference.

Two-way radio is a natural field for the serviceman. Many of the receiver circuits resemble those found in radio and television receivers. Transmitters are new to most servicemen, and some receiver circuits are also new, but mobile radio has a number of advantages as a new field.

Modern radios for two-way communication are well designed, and reliability is built-in as far as possible. New transistor power supplies are increasing system reliability. Many servicing troubles found in radio and television receivers seldom occur in mobile radio, because the equipment is designed for rugged service. Some of the test equipment

FIG. 1-13. Mobile radio, from a vehicle, used here as a base station. (*General Electric.*)

now in the service shop can be used for mobile work, such as meters, scopes, and tube testers. Some new items will be needed, but there are excellent types on the market which are not high-priced. Such instruments as a modulation meter or a highly accurate signal generator will soon pay for themselves.

1-2. Why FM?

FM has proved to be most suitable for most two-way radios. FM provides greater coverage for reception of usable signals than AM. The fact that reception of unusable signals is not possible with FM is an advantage, because this characteristic minimizes interference with usable signals.

FM, because of its "capture effect," has extensive possibilities for reuse of the same frequency at adjacent locations. This effect prevents interference within the service area of one station from transmissions of another station outside this area. It also ensures clean, reliable communications between two stations at close range without interference from stations at greater distances. On the other hand, with standard AM there is no way of rejecting interfering signals on the same frequency.

FM has a decided advantage over AM in overcoming interference from adjacent-channel operations (cross talk) and from intermodulation components. FM will provide reception of a desired signal which is only slightly stronger than an undesired signal. AM requires a much higher ratio between desired and undesired signals.

FM equipment is no more expensive than AM equipment. Present-day FM sets are simple and economical to manufacture, to install, to operate, and to maintain. They have proved extremely reliable. With the exception of those cases in which AM equipment has already been installed, the similar costs between AM and FM equipment favor the use of FM equipment.

Rejection of ignition noise by FM equipment is another significant factor of superiority over AM, especially in mobile service. As a result, the modification of the vehicle in which the FM equipment is installed is held to a minimum, and interference from the ambient ignition noise of nearby vehicles is greatly reduced.

1-3. A Typical Radio System

A system begins with a fleet of trucks, for example, used for local delivery in a metropolitan area. One fixed base station and several mobile stations are used as the basis for a small two-way-radio network. More mobile stations can be added, and as the need for increased traffic arises, the system of mobile communications can be expanded, using repeater stations located at several strategic points in order to gain greater coverage. These stations can pick up all messages and rebroadcast them at greater power in both directions.

A single system usually has one frequency, but it may have several different frequencies. In some installations there is a need for several channels. A typical case would be a large installation where vehicles are speaking to each other and at the same time the base station wishes to call a third mobile unit on a different frequency.

Various types of control are possible; local or direct control is usually used where the transmitter-receiver unit is located close to the controls. In extended local control the distance between the radio and the control point is about 50 ft or less, so that an audio amplifier is not required.

Remote-control operation, such as where the transmitter is located at a distance as on a hilltop, is used in some cases. A speech amplifier provides a strong audio signal over the wire line to the transmitter location.

In A of Fig. 1-14 a typical arrangement is shown. The base

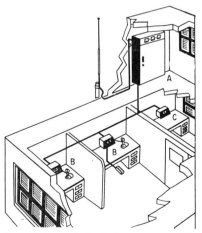

FIG. 1-14A. A basic two-way mobile radio system. Base station (A) is near the fixed antenna. Remote-control points (B) and a monitor (C) are shown. A vehicle may communicate to and from the station. (*DuMont.*)

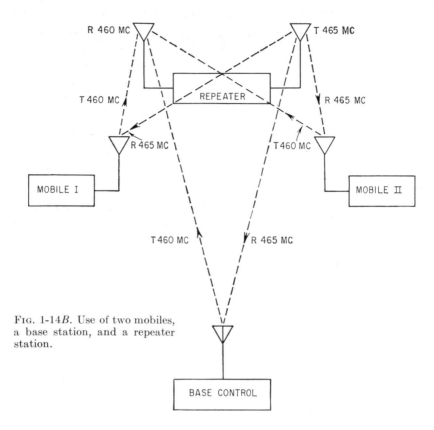

FIG. 1-14B. Use of two mobiles, a base station, and a repeater station.

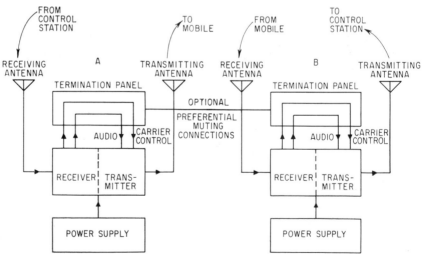

FIG. 1-14C. Repeater interconnections, showing the signals to and from the mobile station.

station (A) is located at any point near the fixed antenna.   Dispatching or two-way conversation may be originated from a local control point at the base station of one or more of the remote-control units at (B) or from both the local and remote position.   The remote controls at (B) permit two-way conversation through the base station to any vehicle.   A floor control switch is shown freeing both hands of the operator.   The monitoring unit (C) is shown in another location which permits personnel to hear both the transmitted and received messages of the base station.   The vehicle equipped with the mobile unit may also speak to the other vehicles on the road.

In *B* of Fig. 1-14 a one-way repeater is shown; this arrangement retransmits in one direction only.   The carrier-operated transmit relay is actuated by the associated receiver, controlling the transmitter in the same cabinet.   This is the simplest form of a repeater, requiring only one repeater station, but separate antennas for reception and transmission.

All base and mobile units, as an example, transmit on 460 Mc and receive on 465 Mc.   The repeater transmits on 465 Mc and receives on 460 Mc.   A message from the base, on 460 Mc, is received by the repeater, which transmits the message on 465 Mc to any mobile.   A mobile transmits on 460 Mc, and the message is received by the repeater and transmitted to the base on 465 Mc.   A two-way system is shown in *C* of Fig. 1-14.   Here two complete repeater stations in separate cabinets are operated together to relay messages in opposite directions. Four antennas are required, two receiving and two transmitting, to handle the two-way traffic.   Preferential muting connections may be used to permit one direction of operation to take preference over the other direction, overriding any retransmission possibly under way.

Two complete repeater stations are operated on noninterfering frequencies to permit communication in both directions.   Station A is then considered as an extension of the original control station, while station B would be the extension of the mobile unit.

As an example of preferential muting, the station A receiver could be connected to override the operation of the station B transmitter, allowing the control station to interrupt at any time this is necessary.

Frequency bands which are of greatest current interest and activity in mobile radio are 25 to 50 Mc, 152 to 162 Mc, and 450 to 470 Mc.

Equipment for the 152- to 162-Mc band can also be used for the 162- to 174-Mc government band and the 144- to 148-Mc amateur band.   (See Appendix A.)

Radio amateurs, who have made important contributions to the radio art, number over 185,000.   They have several different frequency allocations near the mobile bands including:

26.96–27.23 Mc   144–148 Mc
28.00–29.70 Mc   220–225 Mc
50   –54   Mc   420–450 Mc

There are a great many variations in mobile radio equipment. A fixed (nonmobile) base station is usually operated from a-c power lines and has a transmitter power of between 30 and 250 watts. A mobile station is operated from the vehicle battery, which is 6 or 12 volts direct current. In most cases the mobile-transmitter power is between 25 and 100 watts, although it can be higher. There are usually several mobile stations for each base station.

Receivers are single-frequency-tuned, but provisions can be made for two-channel operation using two different local oscillators. The receivers are adjusted at the factory so that, when they are installed, they can receive only their assigned frequency. Typical receivers have crystal control for the local oscillator frequency; some receivers have automatic-frequency-control (AFC) systems. Single, double, and triple superheterodynes are used. Selectivity is between 20 and 40 kc or better, and a sensitivity of 1 μv or less is common. Mobile-radio receivers have squelch circuits, to prevent an output from the speaker when no transmission is being received, and some systems have selective calling arrangements to enable the base station to choose between several receivers on the same frequency.

One interesting feature of mobile communications is the great number of different equipments which can be made from a very few basic units. The beginner may be overwhelmed by the number of different types of equipment in a line of a given manufacturer. As an example, a basic transmitter-and-receiver combination is a single mobile unit. Any number of different operating frequencies can be used. Any transmitter can have any of several different power ratings. Power sources such as vibrators, dynamotors, transistors, combinations of these, and 117-volt a-c power (for base stations) each make an installation different. Equipment can also be mounted in any of several ways.

All these variations mean that a single basic combination can be used in a hundred different ways. But, from the servicing point of view there is fortunately a great similarity, and aside from minor considerations an entire group may be treated in the same way.

Mobiles have different-sized cases depending upon the equipment in addition to the basic transmitter and receiver. This added equipment includes selective calling for individual receiver response to a coded signal, an audio amplifier for a loudspeaker for outdoor use, or two receivers in a single case for special applications.

Fig. 1-15. Radio mounted in outdoor weather-pro-tected case. (*General Electric.*)

Some units are available with waterproof cases for outdoor use in all types of weather as the pole-mounted unit in Fig. 1-15, rack-mounted and desk-side units for station use, and the various mobile mountings.

1-4. Users of Two-way Radio

Two-way radio comes under the Safety and Special Services author-ized by the FCC.

While mobile radio began as a tool for emergency communications, it has expanded because of the cost-saving and timesaving features of radio. The increased use of two-way radio has created a demand for more competent servicemen with proper FCC licenses for maintenance and repair.

These services of business, safety, industry, and land transportation make up most of the nonbroadcast radio authorized by the FCC. The number of transmitters in use has expanded year after year; as of the end of fiscal 1958 there were 2,100,000 authorizations.

These Safety and Special Services, shown on the following page, may be divided as follows:[1]

[1] As of August 1, 1958, the Business Radio Service became active. This service is for "any person engaged in a commercial activity," and it absorbed the Low Power Industrial Service as well as parts of both the Citizens Radio Service and Special Industrial Service.

Service		FCC rules
Aviation	All commercial and private aircraft and ground stations......................	Part 9
Amateur	Noncommercial hobbyists and experiments	Part 12
Citizens	All citizens not otherwise eligible for other licenses.............................	Part 19
Experimental	Commercial research and development....	Part 5
Industrial	Business enterprises....................	Part 11
Power	Electric, gas, steam, and water public utilities	
Petroleum	Petroleum product prospectors, producers, refiners, and pipeline operators	
Forest Products	Timber and logging companies	
Relay Press	News services and newspapers	
Motion Pictures	Motion-picture studios	
Business	Any business enterprise	
Special	Any manufacturing, construction, or production activity in a rural area (including farming) or in an urban area within limitations	
Land transportation	Common and contract carriers of passengers and freight......................	Part 16
Railroad	Railroad-operating companies	
Taxicabs	Taxicab operators	
Motor Carrier	Common or contract carrier transportation	
Auto Emergency	Public garages and auto clubs	
Marine	All commercial and private land stations for maritime communications...........	Part 7
	All marine utility (portable) stations on land or shipboard	
	All commercial and private radio-equipped vessels.............................	Part 8
Public Safety	Agencies protecting life and property.....	Part 10
Police	Municipal, county, and state police	
Fire	Municipal and volunteer fire departments	
Forestry Conservation	Governmental and private forest protection	
Highway Maintenance	Governmental operation, supervision, and maintenance of public roads	
Special	Disaster-relief organizations	
Emergency	Physicians and veterinarians in rural areas	
	Ambulance and rescue squads	
	Communications common-carrier standby	
	Isolated-area communications	
	Communications common-carrier emergency	

1-5. The FCC Rules and Regulations[1]

The Federal Communications Commission is the government agency created by Congress in 1934 and charged with regulating communication by means of radio and licensing nongovernment radio stations and their operators. The Commission is not under any government department but is an independent Federal establishment reporting directly to Congress.

The FCC functions in the interest of all those having a need to use radio communication by ensuring that the limited amount of spectrum space, or usable channels, is not used indiscriminately and by increasing the general public benefit of instant communications, thus preventing a situation of confusion.

The FCC has two types of control over mobile radio: One is the licensing of equipment and operators, and the second is the regulation of the technical operation of the equipment.

Station licenses, given by the FCC, allow the station to operate on an assigned frequency. The equipment used by the station is FCC approved. The licensee agrees to keep his station on the proper frequency and to prevent interference with other stations. Operators' licenses are issued to any individual who successfully passes the written FCC examinations.

Repairs, adjustments, and tests made on transmitters during installation, servicing, or testing must be made only by, or under the supervision of, a licensed radio operator holding a first- or second-class radiotelephone license.

Operators of mobile radio in land mobile service (above 30 Mc) do not require licenses where radiotelephone (voice) is used. But only properly authorized operators (classes 1 and 2) can make adjustments which affect the operating frequency or make any repairs to the radio.

There are four parts or elements to the FCC Commercial Radio Telephone examination. These are (1) basic law, (2) basic theory and practice, (3) radiotelephone, and (4) advanced radiotelephone. There are two classes of licenses. A first-class license requires all four elements, and a second-class license requires the first three elements. All classes require United States citizenship and the ability to read and write English; examinations may be taken at any local FCC office.

There are specific items included in the FCC requirements for two-way-radio maintenance. The important requirements are listed below.

1. *Frequency.* The operating frequency must be measured when (1) the transmitter is installed, (2) change is made in the transmitter

[1] See Appendix B, FCC Information.

which affects the operating frequency, and (3) at regular intervals. The regular intervals must not exceed one month when the transmitter is not crystal-controlled and six months when the transmitter is crystal-controlled. Below an operating frequency of 50 Mc the tolerance is 0.01 per cent, and above 50 Mc the tolerance is 0.005 per cent of the assigned frequency for most transmitters. Closer tolerances for transmitters, under narrow-band operation as proposed by the FCC, will be required: 0.002 (25 to 50 Mc) and 0.0005 per cent (50 to 1,000 Mc).

2. *Modulation.* A modulation check is required at the same time the frequency is measured. For FM transmitters the frequency of the carrier must not change more than 15 kc from the assigned center frequency. Narrow-band standards call for 5 kc deviation. For AM transmitters modulation must be between 70 and 100 per cent (for negative peaks of modulation).

3. *Power.* The plate power input (plate current times plate voltage) must also be measured, at the times specified above, and must never exceed the licensed value.

4. *Log entry.* The person making these measurements and checks must sign his name and address in the station log. Then he is responsible for the accuracy of his measurements.

Conformance to these FCC regulations is the direct responsibility of the licensed person making the measurements. Not only must he know the proper procedures, but he also must know the accuracy of his instruments. The FCC monitors the operation of the transmitters and sends citations to all violators. Most qualified radio servicemen can pass these FCC tests by extending what they already know to mobile receivers and transmitters through study.

All radio transmitters must be licensed by the FCC before being put into operation. The license must be posted at the radio station. The method and form of license application depends upon the radio service to be used.

Application for radio-station license required of all transmitters in the Public Safety, Industrial, and Land Transportation Radio Services is made on FCC Form 400. Copies of this form and instructions for completion of FCC Form 400 can be obtained from the FCC. There is no charge by the government for a radio-station license.

When completing FCC Form 400 the applicant must certify that he has a current copy of the Commission's rules covering the radio service named in the application. The licensee in the regular land mobile services may use any equipment in the FCC's *List of Equipment Acceptable for Licensing in the Radio Services Other than Broadcast,* as long as the equipment meets the technical limitations on the license.

A complete list of the Commission's rules and their other publications may be obtained from the FCC's Washington, D.C., office, or any of its field offices.   The following is a list of Government Printing Office publications containing the more essential provisions of law and regulation which pertain to the licensing and operation of the majority of radio stations used in the land mobile services.   Any one of or all the following can be obtained from the Superintendent of Documents, U.S. Government Printing Office, Washington 25, D.C.   They are not distributed by the Commission.

Study Guide and Reference Material for Commercial Radio Operator
    Examinations, 35 cents
Rules and Regulations of the Federal Communications Commission:
    Part 10.   Public Safety Radio Services, 15 cents
    Part 11.   Industrial Radio Services, 15 cents
    Part 13.   Commercial Radio Operators, 10 cents
    Part 16.   Land Transportation Radio Services, 10 cents
    Part 17.   Rules Concerning the Construction, Marking and Lighting of Antenna Structures, 5 cents
    Part 19.   Citizens Radio Service, 5 cents

The following is a list of FCC forms most commonly used by customers of communication service companies.   Forms are available upon request from the regional or Washington, D.C., offices of the Commission.

Form 400   Application for Radio Station Authorization in the Safety and Special Radio Services
Form 400-A   Request for Amendment of Radio Station Authorization
Form 401-A   Description of Proposed Antenna Structure(s), Services Other than Broadcast
Form 405-A   Application for Renewal of Radio License
Form 456   Notification of Completion of Radio Station Construction
Form 505   Application for Citizens Radio Station Construction Permit and License
Form 753-1   Application for Restricted Radiotelephone Operator Permit by Declaration
Form 756   Application for Commercial Radio Operator License or Permit

A valuable source of information about radio systems in use is the series published by the Communication Engineering Book Company, Radio Hill, Monterey, Massachusetts.   There are four annual listings:

the *Official Registry of Radio Systems* of (1) *Industrial Services*, FCC Part 11; (2) *Transportation Services*, FCC Parts 16 and 19; (3) *Public Safety Services*, FCC Part 10; and (4) *Common Carrier Services*. *Industrial Communications*, a weekly by Telecommunications Publishing Co., 1208 National Press Building, Washington, D.C., is also an important source of information.

1-6. Installation Techniques

Installation of mobile radio in vehicles differs with the type of equipment and the type of vehicle. Every installation should be made both for convenient operation and with consideration of the serviceman who will maintain the equipment.

Figure 1-16a illustrates the individual components of a typical mobile installation. A definite layout plan for the radio, antenna, power relay, fuse block, speaker, control head, and microphone, as in Fig. 1-16b, should be made before beginning work. Proper clearance for later removal of all units is important, and the driver should be able to reach the necessary controls without difficulty.

In a trunk installation the cables are brought through the trunk wall, under the floor mat, and up under the dash. The speaker may be mounted on the dashboard, on the fire wall, or on the steering column. Some receivers now have a transistor audio amplifier in the speaker case for operation in noisy locations. The power and battery cables should be kept away from excessive engine heat. A good, solid, firm ground connection is important. This should be to the battery ground if possible.

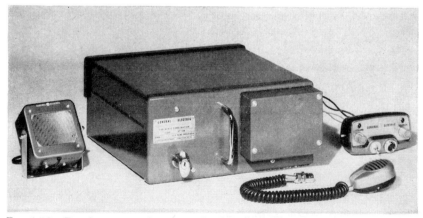

Fig. 1-16a. Receiver-transmitter case, loudspeaker, microphone, and control head for mobile radio. (*General Electric.*)

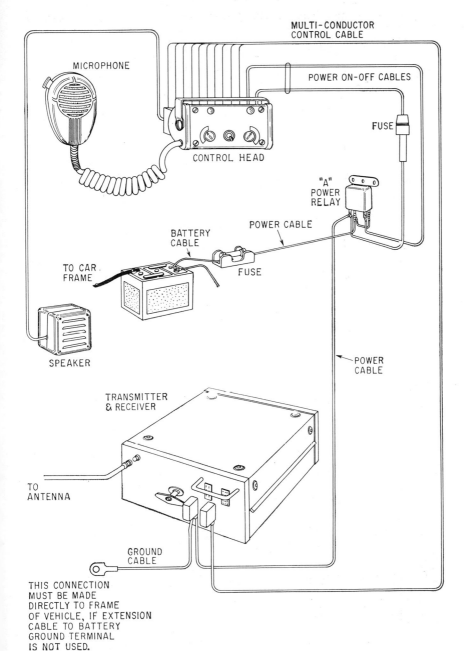

MULTI-CONDUCTOR
CONTROL CABLE

MICROPHONE

POWER ON-OFF CABLES

FUSE

CONTROL HEAD

"A"
POWER
RELAY

POWER CABLE

BATTERY
CABLE

TO CAR
FRAME

FUSE

SPEAKER

POWER
CABLE

TRANSMITTER
& RECEIVER

TO
ANTENNA

GROUND
CABLE

THIS CONNECTION
MUST BE MADE
DIRECTLY TO FRAME
OF VEHICLE, IF EXTENSION
CABLE TO BATTERY
GROUND TERMINAL
IS NOT USED.

FIG. 1-16b. Typical cable interconnections for control head and vehicle radio. (*Motorola.*)

FIG. 1-17. Standard roof-top antenna for UHF. (*Antenna Specialists*.)

The UHF antenna, as in Fig. 1-17, is usually mounted on the roof. Other band antennas are mounted on the rear fender or rear deck lid. A good ground connection is important for the antenna. A front-mount unit has the speaker and controls built-in. The microphone is mounted near the driver for convenience.

Installations in a truck may be behind the seat, under the seat, on top of the cab, or behind the cab. In the case of an outside mounting, a waterproof case is required.

Battery-charging requirements vary depending upon the amount of radio use, the equipment drain, and the amount of high-speed driving. With more than about 50 to 60 amp in transmitting position, heavy-duty generators or alternators are usually required to charge the battery. Battery voltage should not be less than 5.8 volts for a 6-volt system and 11.6 volts for a 12-volt system.

Noise reduction in vehicles is usually a problem. Suppressors and bypass capacitors plus bonding straps between parts of the car or truck are all methods for reducing noise. The success of many installations depends upon solving this problem.

1-7. After the Installation

Installation is only part of the story for successful operation. The operator must be taught how to use his radio. For most installations the steps for operator adjustment (Fig. 1-18) are as follows:

1. Operate the radio only with the motor running to prevent a dead battery.

2. Turn on the equipment. After a short warm-up (30 sec) turn squelch to minimum position.

3. Adjust volume for moderate hissing sound.

4. Adjust squelch until just beyond where the hissing sound disappears.

5. The equipment is ready to receive any message; to transmit press the microphone button when the air is free of other messages.

Careful installation and proper operator training provide the best start to a trouble-free mobile radio system. But troubles will come, and a well-trained serviceman who knows his test equipment and the systems under his care can keep these stations on the air.

1-8. Servicing and Repair

A radio or television serviceman going into the mobile-radio business will have some of the necessary test equipment but not all of it. Repairing mobile radio is more exacting than ordinary radio or television repair for several reasons. The serviceman making the required frequency checks by law must be responsible for the accuracy of his work to the FCC.

Fig. 1-18. Control head showing on-off switch, squelch, and volume. (*Motorola.*)

Mobile radio is, in many ways, quite different from broadcast radio and television. First, because the radio is an integral part of the business of the user and not a medium for entertainment, the user needs the radio for everyday use, and his equipment must have periodic checks. True, if he is a trucker, he can still use the truck if the radio does not work, but the loss of income because of missed pickups or half-empty trucks is serious, and he will be satisfied only with a rapid return to service of his radio.

In a sense, the mobile-radio user considers the periodic checks and preventive maintenance and their cost in much the same way that he considers the lubrication of his truck. Both are required for uninterrupted service.

Mobile-radio servicing has both greater rewards for the repairman and greater responsibility. One part of this responsibility concerns the use of test equipment. This equipment must be accurate, reliable, and suitable to the special requirements of mobile radio. Test equipment such as a tube tester, a vacuum-tube voltmeter (VTVM), a multimeter, RF and AF signal generators, a battery eliminator, and a capacitor checker is normally found in a television repair shop and is useful for some aspects of mobile-radio work. The signal generator should, of course, cover the necessary frequency ranges, but for some mobile servicing it must be far more accurate than ordinary test equipment. Other equipment, not used for television or radio servicing, is also required.

1. *A frequency meter* covering all bands is needed to keep the transmitter on the proper frequency, as required by the FCC, so that it will be received by other stations and so that it will not interfere with stations on a different frequency. A frequency meter designed for mobile-radio work should be accurate to 0.0005 per cent (or better) and cover the required bands.

2. *A modulation meter* is needed both for AM and FM. The modulation meter in FM measures the deviation (bandwidth) of the FM carrier. This deviation *must not exceed* the proper limit, and the meter must respond to peaks of the audio voltage, not average values. A modulation meter for AM is also useful, but the modulation in AM can be determined readily by the use of a cathode-ray oscilloscope.

3. *Dummy RF loads* are also required to simulate actual conditions of operation and, at the same time, to prevent any radiation of the signal.

4. *A grid-dip meter* is also very useful; this is a calibrated resonant circuit which permits the measurement of a tuned circuit without applying power to the equipment.

Other measuring equipment for benchwork includes various bridges, meters, and an oscilloscope.

1-9. The Future of Two-way Radio

Two-way radio has grown rapidly and has created the need for more frequency allocations by its very growth. A number of solutions have been offered for best use of the available space.

Tighter frequency tolerances (as in Sec. 1-5 above), avoiding over-modulation by restricting deviation, and audio filters which remove distortion, keep the audio passband below 3 kc, and attenuate noise are all methods for spectrum conservation. Other techniques such as pre-venting harmonic radiation, directional antennas to confine radiated energy in specific areas, reduced power for some transmitters, carrier-offset operation, great frequency sharing, and different modulation systems such as single-sideband and others are all suggested techniques for greater use of the available airspace.

Some of these techniques are gradually becoming effective under new FCC rules, and other methods will be tested, established, and become part of the expanding field of two-way radio. Cooperation between regulating agencies and the radio manufacturers will continue to extend the usefulness of this powerful industrial tool which is modern radio.

Transistors have been used in experimental radios for communications.[1] There are several advantages to the all-transistor radio. For mobile use there is at least a 10-to-1 reduction in current drain on the battery. This would permit the continuous use of the receiver even with the vehicle engine shut off for short periods. In turn, the constant monitoring of the channel will allow greater use of signaling equipment to record the reception of a calling signal and reduce the number of call-backs.

[1] S. Schwartz, Transistorized Communications Receiver, *Trans. IRE, PGVC*-7, p. 41, 1956.

For base stations, all transistor equipment would be valuable for remote radio repeater locations and emergency use where the a-c power source may fail.

Portable receiver-transmitters have several functions. They can be used for plant protection, warehouse storage, police and fire service, and specialized industrial applications. Their use, however, because of the limitations of battery size and weight and low antenna efficiency, will be restricted to a short range of up to several miles. Where the driver is communicating with several nearby hand-carried stations, as perhaps between the fire truck and individual firemen, this range limitation is not a problem. But where a number of radio-equipped policemen cover a large area, as in the case of a city, several base stations will be required for proper coverage.

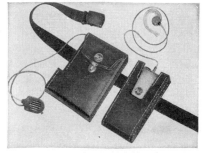

FIG. 1-19. Personalfone transistor two-way radio, showing transmitter (left) and receiver (right). (*RCA Communication Products.*)

Transistors are becoming part of the commercial mobile-radio picture. Their use demonstrates the reduction in size and weight of radio equipment as well as a smaller power drain on the battery. Many companies such as General Electric, RCA, and Motorola are beginning to use transistors in their equipment.

The Radio Corporation of America Personalfone (Fig. 1-19) is a belt radio with two transistorized units: a transmitter weighing 28 oz and a receiver weighing 14 oz. The radio is designed for short distances of up to several miles for specialized applications such as plant protection. Motorola has the Motrac (Motorola Transistorized Advanced Communications), which is also fully transistorized. This unit is a receiver-transmitter for use in vehicles. Both the Motorola and RCA radios are in the two lower-frequency bands, not the UHF band.

CHAPTER 2

PRINCIPLES OF MODULATION

2-1. FM in Mobile Radio

FM in mobile communication transmitters is phase modulation, but by conversion networks it is changed to equivalent FM.

FM in mobile receivers is related to the FM sound section of a television receiver, but the deviation, bandwidth, and frequency response are different. A brief review of the principles of FM is taken up first.

Both AM and FM are used in mobile radio, but frequency modulation provides superior reception over conventional (double-sideband) AM in the presence of noise. Mobile communication operates with low power and usually under conditions of strong noise interference. Noise, as used here, applies to natural static, man-made interference such as ignition noise, and other radio transmissions. AM[1] requires a signal-to-noise ratio of 100:1 for reasonably clear reception; FM can be clearly received at ratios of 2:1 and even less. The effectiveness of FM in overcoming noise makes possible mobile radio with many transmitters which are in the same area.

FM reduces interference because of the inherent characteristics of the FM process. Stations on the same frequency normally do not interfere provided that the stronger signal is twice the value (or even less) of the weaker signal.

Adjacent-channel interference is a problem with many transmitters on the air at the same time. Double and triple receiver conversion as well as sharp IF filter are some of the solutions to this interference.

Static and thermal noise are also prime causes of interference. Because these are, in part, AM, the limiting action of both the FM transmitter and receiver is effective in removing a portion of this noise.

For these and other reasons developed in this chapter, FM is used almost exclusively for communications between vehicles and a base station in land mobile service; AM is, however, used for marine communications, aviation radio, and low-powered industrial radio. Special forms of AM such as single-sideband are being investigated by several manufacturers, with the encouragement of the FCC, because of the possibility of reduced bandwidth and greater conservation.

[1] This applies to conventional AM.

2-2. Systems of Modulation

The three basic modulation systems are (1) AM and its several variations, (2) FM with the several methods, and (3) PM (phase modulation) which can be converted to FM.

The process of modulation, as shown in Table 2-1, involves the variation of the RF transmitted carrier in accordance with the intelligence to be transmitted, which, for communications, is usually an audio signal. A carrier has frequency, phase, and amplitude, any one of which may be varied to produce modulation.

TABLE 2-1. TYPES OF MODULATION FOR AM, FM, AND PM
A carrier may be expressed as $e = E_m \sin (2\pi ft + \Theta)$

Varying only	Produces
E_m	Amplitude modulation (AM)
f	Frequency modulation (FM)
Θ	Phase modulation (PM)

In AM (amplitude modulation) the *amplitude* of the modulated carrier is varied, and two sets of sidebands are produced; these carry the intelligence.

In PM (phase modulation) the instantaneous *phase* of the carrier is changed by the audio signal; this change is equivalent to a frequency change. In PM the equivalent frequency change is proportional to the audio frequency.

In FM (frequency modulation) the modulated carrier *frequency* varies directly as the amplitude of the audio signal.

FM is best considered by starting with an explanation of ordinary AM. A single RF frequency is the AM center frequency; this is modulated by an audio signal, and as shown in Fig. 2-1 the amplitude

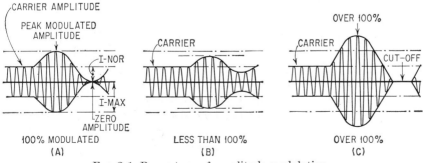

FIG. 2-1. Percentage of amplitude modulation.

of the AF varies the amplitude of the RF.   The ratio of AF to RF
amplitudes is the percentage of modulation.   This is defined as

$$M = \frac{E_1}{E_2} (100) \qquad \text{per cent}$$

where E_1 = maximum (peak) value of AF modulation
       E_2 = maximum (peak) value of RF unmodulated carrier

In A the 100 per cent modulation causes the carrier to vary between
zero and twice the unmodulated amplitude.   With less than 100 per
cent modulation the amplitude variations are less as in B.   Over-
modulation, greater than 100 per cent, causes cutoff of the carrier as
shown in C.

However, this is but one aspect of AM.   The process of modulation
creates sidebands.   If F is the original RF and f is the audio frequency,
the two sidebands are $F + f$ and $F - f$.   The vector sum of these as in
Fig. 2-2 is the amplitude-modulated carrier.   If, for example, F is 50
Mc and f is 5 kc, the three components are 50.000, 50.005, and
49.995 Mc.[1]

The bandwidth of this modulated signal is $2f$ or between $F + f$ and
$F - f$.   All of the power contained in the sidebands comes from the
modulating-signal power.

In AM the amplitude of the audio changes the amplitude of the RF
carrier, and the rate of the amplitude changes depends upon the frequency of the modulating signal.

[1] Frederick E. Terman, "Radio Engineers' Handbook," p. 532, McGraw-Hill
Book Company, Inc., New York, 1943.

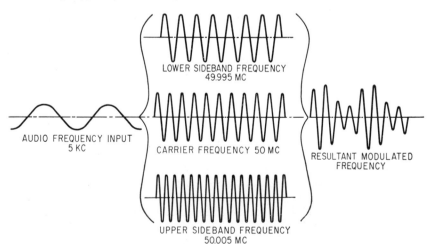

FIG. 2-2. Modulation and the AM sidebands.

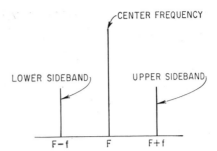

FIG. 2-3. AM showing a single set of sidebands.

Figure 2-3 illustrates another representation of AM. This is a convenient method of illustrating sidebands when explaining their relationship in FM. Here, F is the carrier, the upper sideband is $F + f$ (where f is the audio-modulating frequency), and $F - f$ is the lower sideband.

A different approach to the process is shown in Fig. 2-4. In A there

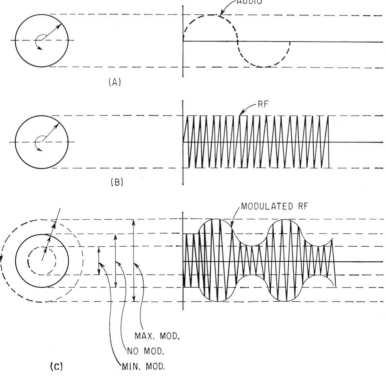

FIG. 2-4. Rotating-vector representation of AM. A is vector and one cycle of audio, B is vector and several cycles of RF, and C is the result of modulation.

is a rotating vector; as this rotates, it generates a sine wave, as shown, which is the audio signal.   In B the same representation is shown but at the radio frequency, and several cycles of the wave are shown. Audio modulation adds to, or subtracts from, this vector, and a wave, varying in amplitude, is generated, as shown in C.   This is the result-ant vector rotation.

AM, in the ordinary sense with two full sidebands (as in broadcast radio), has certain disadvantages for communications.   Transmitted power is wasted; if the unmodulated carrier power (in watts) is $2W$, an audio power of W is needed for full 100 per cent plate modulation. This audio power is divided equally between the sidebands and the total transmitted power, under full modulation, is $3W$.   But since both sidebands contain identical information, half the power is wasted (or duplicated in the other sideband), and the carrier contains no useful information.   For a 100-watt carrier, 50 watts of audio is required or 25 watts for each sideband; total output power is 150 watts.   Thus, of this 150 watts, only 25 watts is used to carry the message.

Random electrical noise and interference are a form of AM; under conditions of high noise, communications are sometimes impossible. Other AM stations, on the same or adjacent frequencies, can create interference and reduce the effectiveness of communications.

AM, in spite of its limitations, has a definite place in mobile com-munications.   While FM is superior, because of the reasons above, AM with different systems of modulation is still of importance.

In FM the center frequency is also modulated, but the frequency of the resultant wave depends upon the amplitude of the modulating signal, and the rate of this frequency change depends on the frequency of the modulation.

Figure 2-5 shows sine-wave modulation. A indicates the audio modulating signal, the unmodulated RF, and the resulting modulated, or transmitted, wave.   In B the frequency of the audio signal is unchanged but the amplitude is increased.   The frequency change in the modulated wave is greater than in A.   But in C the audio signal is unchanged in amplitude; it is the same amplitude as in A, but it is of a higher frequency.   The rate of change of the resulting modulation is higher.

Another method of representing an FM wave is shown in Fig. 2-6, where again F is the center frequency and f is the audio signal fre-quency.   In A there is modulation which produces two sets (pairs) of sidebands.   The frequency difference between the first and second sidebands, and between the center frequency and the first sidebands is f.   Thus the FM process creates $F - f, F - 2f, F + f, F + 2f$ in addi-

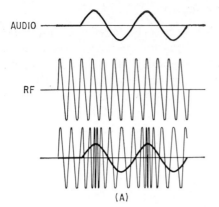

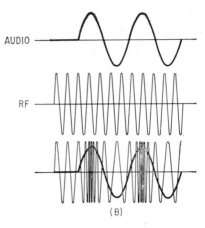

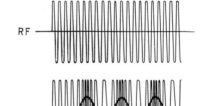

(A)

(B)

Fig. 2-5. Frequency modulation. *A* shows the audio and resulting modulation, *B* illustrates an increase in amplitude of the audio signal, and *C* has the same amplitude as *A* but an increased audio frequency.

(C)

$F-2f$	$F-f$	F	$F+f$	$F+2f$

(A)

$F-3f$	$F-2f$	$F-f$	F	$F+f$	$F+2f$	$F+3f$

(B)

$F-2f_1$ F $F+2f_1$

$F-f_1$ $F+f_1$

(C)

Fig. 2-6. Representation of the FM sidebands. With two sideband pairs in *A* the effect of increasing the audio amplitude is shown in *B* and the increase in audio frequency in *C*.

tion to the original F.   In AM there is only a single pair of sidebands; in FM there may be many sidebands.   The vector sum of all of these is equal to the power in the original (unmodulated) center frequency. Total power remains constant with or without modulation.

The *amplitude* of the center frequency varies with modulation but is constant in frequency.   The total RF output signal (the combination of all the sidebands plus the center frequency) varies in frequency under modulation.

If *only* the amplitude of the modulation changes, more sidebands are created, as in B of Fig. 2-6, but their separation remains the same.   If *only* the modulating frequency is changed (as a decrease from f to f_1) the distance between the sidebands changes directly with the change in frequency and decreases from f to f_1 as in C of Fig. 2-6.

In FM, the bandwidth depends upon two factors: the amplitude of the modulating signal, which determines the number of sidebands, and the frequency of the modulation, which determines the separation of the sidebands.

Phase modulation is a method of generating modulated waves used widely in mobile communications.   In phase modulation (PM) a crystal-controlled oscillator can be used for frequency stability. Audio-correction networks can be used to convert PM to FM and also, if desired, FM to PM.

In Fig. 2-7 the vectors for AM are shown.   The audio vector can add directly to the RF vector, with an increased *amplitude* in the resultant, as in A, or the audio vector can subtract from the RF vector and decrease the amplitude of the resultant, as in B.   The two vectors are either in phase or 180° out of phase.

But two vectors are also shown in Fig. 2-8, and as they are now 90° apart, they will create a resultant as in A or B.   The effect of this 90° addition is to rotate the resultant from its original position.

AM is produced by the rotation of the vectors in Fig. 2-7 as the RF vector is added to, or subtracted from, by the audio vector.

PM is produced by the vector sum of the RF and the audio modulating signal, as in A and B of Fig. 2-8, which changes the relative phase of the signal.

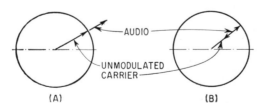

FIG. 2-7. AM rotating vectors.

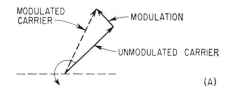

(A)

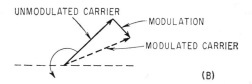

(B)

FIG. 2-8. *A* and *B* show PM from vectors 90° apart. *C* shows FM created by the shift of the center frequency.

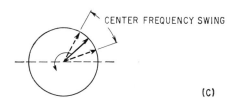

(C)

FM is produced, as in *C* of Fig. 2-8, when the RF carrier shifts ahead or behind when it is modulated.

2-3. Frequency Modulation

In FM the transmitted RF amplitude is constant, but the frequency varies directly with the amplitude of the audio signal. The rate at which the change in frequency takes place is determined by the frequency of the audio signal.

In AM the amount of modulation is expressed in per cent, but this is not possible in FM where a 150-Mc signal can be modulated ± 5 kc or ± 11 kc or $\pm$ any value, in theory, up to ± 150 Mc, at which point the modulation would cause the minimum frequency of the resultant wave to decrease to zero.

Instead of a percentage, the amount of modulation is known as the modulation index, or *M*, which is

$$M = \frac{\Delta F}{f}$$

where again *F* is the center frequency and ΔF is the total deviation or frequency swing of *F*. The audio frequency of modulation is *f*.

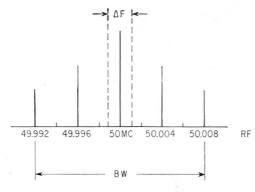

49.992   49.996   50MC   50.004   50.008   RF

BW

Fig. 2-9. Bandwidth is greater than deviation.

Knowing ΔF and f, M can be found, and, using M, the number of sidebands can be found directly. Table 2-2 shows the number of sideband pairs for several values of M.

TABLE 2-2. MODULATION INDEX (M) AND THE NUMBER OF SIDEBAND SETS (N)

M	N	M	N
0.01 ⎫		2.00	4
to ⎬ 1	1	3.00	6
0.40 ⎭		5.00	8
0.50	2	7.00	10
1.00	3		

For example, if ΔF is 2 kc (± 1 kc) and f is 4 kc, then

$$M = \tfrac{2}{4} = 0.5$$

And for $M = 0.5$ there are two sets of sidebands ($N = 2$), so where BW is bandwidth

$$BW = 2fN$$
$$BW = 16 \text{ kc}$$

Bandwidth and frequency deviation are *not* the same.

The bandwidth is greater than the deviation of the center frequency. Figure 2-9 is an example of the case above with a center frequency of 50 Mc. The deviation is 2 kc, but the total bandwidth is 16 kc.

Sideband and carrier amplitudes are given in Table 2-3. For a given modulation index the relative value of the center-frequency component and the sidebands can be found. If, for example, M is 0.5, the center frequency is 0.9385 times the unmodulated value, and the sidebands are 0.2423 (first set) and 0.0306 (second set). Beyond this second set there are other sidebands, but their amplitude is quite small and they are neglected.[1]

[1] John Thompson, "Radio Communication at Ultra High Frequency," p. 142, Methuen & Co., Ltd., London, 1950.

TABLE 2-3. MODULATION INDEX AND SIDEBAND AMPLITUDE

Modulation index	Center-frequency value	1st set of sidebands	2d set	3d set	4th set	5th set	6th set	7th set	8th set	9th set	10th set
0	1.000										
0.01	1.000	0.005									
0.05	0.9994	0.025									
0.1	0.9975	0.0499									
0.2	0.9900	0.0995									
0.5	0.9385	0.2423	0.0306								
1.0	0.7652	0.4401	0.1149	0.0196							
2.0	0.2239	0.5767	0.3528	0.1289	0.0341						
3.0	−0.2601	0.3391	0.4861	0.3091	0.1320	0.0430	0.0114				
4.0	−0.3971	−0.0661	0.3641	0.4302	0.2811	0.1321	0.0491	0.0152			
5.0	−0.1776	−0.3276	0.0466	0.3648	0.3912	0.2611	0.1310	0.0534	0.0184		
6.0	0.1506	−0.2767	−0.2429	0.1148	0.3576	0.3621	0.2458	0.1296	0.0565	0.0212	
7.0	0.3001	−0.0047	−0.3041	−0.1676	0.1578	0.3479	0.3392	0.2336	0.1280	0.0589	0.0235

Using Table 2-3 the amplitude of the center-frequency component may be examined. As M increases, this amplitude decreases until somewhat less than 2. Between 2 and 3 the center frequency disappears, or its amplitude goes to zero. This point is sometimes used to calibrate deviation-measuring equipment. Beyond this point the amplitude goes in a negative direction, which is actually only a change in phase.

This may be seen from Fig. 2-10, where in A the unmodulated center-frequency carrier is shown, as seen on an oscilloscope. Note the absence of any sidebands. In B the center frequency and two side-band pairs are shown for an M of 1.3. When M is increased to 2.4, the center-frequency component disappears, and only sidebands are present, as in C.

Below an M of 0.2 there is only one set of sidebands, exactly as in AM. If M is 0.2, ΔF is 1 kc, and f is 5 kc, there is one set of sidebands, the bandwidth is 10 kc, but the deviation of the center frequency is only a total of 1 kc.

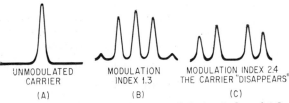

UNMODULATED CARRIER   MODULATION INDEX 1.3   MODULATION INDEX 2.4 THE CARRIER "DISAPPEARS"

(A)   (B)   (C)

FIG. 2-10. A is unmodulated carrier; B is a modulation index of 1.3; C is a modulation index of 2.4, where the carrier "disappears."

With a fixed f, the deviation (and bandwidth) increases with increasing M as in Fig. 2-11. The frequency separation between sidebands is constant and is equal to f, but as the number of sidebands and the bandwidth increase with the deviation going from A to D, the modulation index increases.

If ΔF (deviation) is kept fixed but f increases in frequency as in Fig. 2-12, the number of sidebands decreases as M decreases. The smaller number of sidebands allows greater separation between them for the same deviation. Here f, or the audio frequency, increases going from A to D, and the deviation is constant. Because of this the modulation index M decreases from A to D.

2-4. Phase Modulation

A carrier wave has a certain frequency, amplitude, and phase. Changing any *one* of these produces modulation; changing frequency (FM) or amplitude (AM) or phase (PM) are three methods of transmitting intelligence.

In Fig. 2-13 two rotating vectors are shown. Because they move at the same rate, they are of the same frequency. But because they start, and remain, 45° apart, the two waves are also 45° apart. Their *relative* phase is constant.

In Fig. 2-14, however, their relative phase varies in accordance with the audio signal. The average frequency is constant and the amplitude is constant, but the relative phase changes. An audio sine wave is used for modulation. In A, when the audio signal begins to build up,

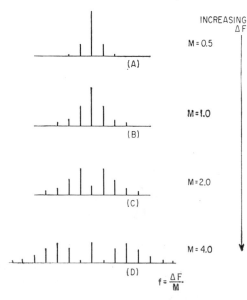

Fɪɢ. 2-11. Frequency spectrum where f is constant and ΔF is increasing.

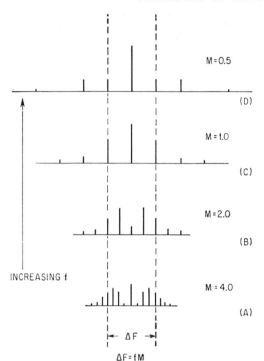

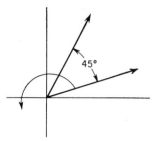

Fig. 2-13. Rotating vectors with constant phase difference.

Fig. 2-12. Frequency spectrum where ΔF is constant and f is increasing.

the differences between these waves is 45°. But as the audio signal increases in amplitude, the phase difference increases; in C this has increased to 60° for a maximum positive audio. As the modulating signal goes negative, the phase difference decreases to 30° for a negative maximum as in G.

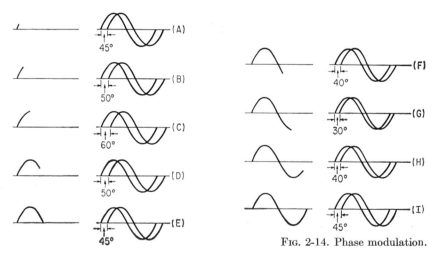

Fig. 2-14. Phase modulation.

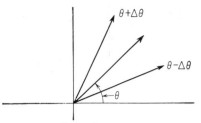

FIG. 2-15. Rotating-vector representation of phase modulation.

Thus if the phase angle is Θ for no modulation as in Fig. 2-15, the change in phase is ΔΘ and the phase changes from Θ + ΔΘ to Θ − ΔΘ. To represent the limits of the phase deviation or change, +ΔΘ is the upper limit and −ΔΘ is the lower limit.

The rotation of a vector represents the frequency of the radio wave; hence, the frequency of the carrier changes during modulation. PM can be considered as a form of FM.

The instantaneous phase is determined by the amplitude of the audio signal. The (equivalent) frequency depends upon the rate of change of this modulating signal. But this rate of change depends upon both the amplitude and the frequency of the audio signal.

As in Fig. 2-16 the rate of change of a sine wave is a cosine wave. Hence the FM resulting from PM is 90° out of phase with the phase deviation. From this, the frequency deviation ΔF is given by

$$\Delta F = \Delta\Theta\, f \cos \alpha$$

where ΔF = frequency deviation, cps
      $\Delta\Theta$ = maximum phase deviation
      f = audio frequency
      α = amplitude change of f

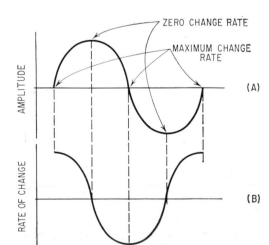

FIG. 2-16. Rate of phase change as a function of the audio signal.

As in Fig. 2-17, for example, if $f = 1,000$ cps, $\Delta\Theta = 20°$,

$$\Delta F = \frac{\pi}{9} \times 1,000$$

For zero audio-signal amplitude, where cosine of zero degrees is +1, then

$$\Delta F = 350 \text{ cps}$$

At maximum signal amplitude ($\alpha = 90°$, $\cos \alpha = 0$), the frequency deviation is zero.

Pure phase shift is a function of both the *amplitude* of the modulating signal and the frequency of this signal. If deemphasis or bass boost is added, by the use of an *RC* network, phase-shift modulation and pure frequency modulation are then the same. By using no emphasis PM is the same as preemphasized FM.

In PM the modulation index M, phase shift produced by the modulation, as measured in degrees is independent of the modulating frequency; in FM the modulation index is inversely proportional to the modulating frequency. If a fixed amplitude of signal is applied as modulation, the bandwidth of the PM signal would be proportional to the modulation frequency. In FM the bandwidth is not dependent upon the modulation frequency except for a very small modulation index.

In Fig. 2-18 both PM is shown in *A* and FM in *B* with the same

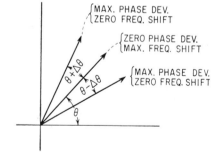

Fig. 2-17. Phase shift of rotating vector.

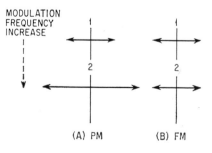

(A) PM   (B) FM

Fig. 2-18. FM-PM comparison.

bandwidth for a given modulation. With a constant amplitude of modulation the bandwidth of the PM increases with an increase in the modulating frequency, but the FM bandwidth remains constant. Thus PM ($A2$) has an increased bandwidth and FM ($B2$) has a constant bandwidth as the frequency of modulation alone increases.

Figure 2-19 illustrates the production of FM from PM. This is important, because most mobile FM transmitters produce FM by one of these methods, although some few do produce FM directly.   In A the bass boost (or deemphasis) *before* the phase modulator produces FM as the modulator output.   In B and C two simple networks are shown for this process.   In part D the situation is reversed, and the preemphasis network before the FM modulator produces a PM output.

2-5. FM and AM Compared

The two basic types of modulation (considering PM as equivalent FM) are AM and FM.   A comparison between these two, as a summary, is given below:

Conditions	FM	AM
With modulation the resultant RF........	1. Varies in frequency.	1. Varies in amplitude.
As the modulating *frequency* increases	2. The deviation rate increases.	2. The rate of the amplitude change increases.
As the modulating *amplitude* increases	3. The amount of deviation increases.	3. The amount of amplitude change increases.
	4. The power output remains fixed, and the resultant output is of constant amplitude.	4. The power output increases and the resultant output increases in amplitude.
The resultant modulated wave	5. Is a center frequency and a number of sidebands each separated by the audio frequency.	5. Is a center-frequency carrier and one set of sidebands each separated from the carrier by the audio frequency.
	6. The number of sidebands depends on the modulation index.	6. The number of sidebands is always two.
Signal-to-noise ratio...	7. Increases directly with deviation and inversely with the upper frequency limit of the audio; noise is amplitude-limited; FM noise interference depends on separation from the carrier.	7. Decreases with increased bandwidth.
Center frequency......	8. Varies in amplitude under modulation.	8. Is of constant amplitude under modulation.

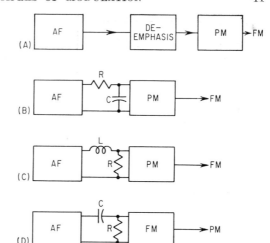

FIG. 2-19. PM to FM conversion.

2-6. Improving Communications

Where radio is used for commercial messages, as with mobile communications, the reliability of the system is vital to the user. A message which is garbled or missed entirely can be costly to a businessman or cause loss of life in emergency services.

Both noise and interference are problems in communications; they are significant factors in mobile radio where the transmitter power is low, as with vehicular equipment.

Noise. Both *impulse* and *fluctuation* noise will be found as undesired radio signals. Both of these are created by different types of electrical machinery. Impulse noise appears as a series of short pulses of RF energy usually below 150 Mc. Ignition systems are often producers of this form of noise from the spark gaps in the electrical system of the vehicle. Reducing these noises is an important part of an installation.

Fluctuation noise as produced by all types of electrical power devices, including motors, generators, power lines, and gas-filled rectifiers, appears as a broad spectrum rather than individual pulses. Frequencies below 30 Mc appear most affected by this type of noise, although gas-discharge noise extends to the UHF band.

Natural noise comes from lightning and other atmospheric disturbances including sun spots; it may appear either as impulse noise (lightning) or fluctuations (other sources).

Noise as above enters the communications system at the receiver; it may be induced in the antenna from a nearby source, or it may be received as a signal just as any other transmission is received. Some noise enters fixed stations through power lines.

Impulse noise, which appears as large changes in received signal

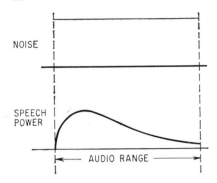

FIG. 2-20. Noise is constant across the audio band; speech peaks at the low-frequency end.

amplitude, is removed by the FM limiter, which is a clipper removing peaks above a fixed level. Fluctuation noise acts differently; spurious or undesired signals from these noise signals do travel through the receiver and appear at the detector output.

Not all noise originates outside the system; the random motion of electrons through conductors creates noise. This is largely contributed by current flow through resistors and the shot effect or random fluctuations of current through a tube. This receiver noise is a limiting factor in the sensitivity of radio receivers.

Preemphasis and Deemphasis. In a system of communication from transmitter to receiver the noise is roughly equally distributed throughout the audible range as shown in Fig. 2-20.

If the audio-signal amplitude was also equally distributed, the signal-to-noise (S/N) ratio would be the same for all frequencies. Human speech has a nonlinear distribution of power versus frequency. There is much more audio power in low frequencies than in the highs. But while the high frequencies have less power, they do contribute a great deal to the intelligibility of speech.

Most of the power contained in speech is between 300 and 3,000 cps. Thus the higher end of the audio spectrum has a poor S/N ratio; this can be seen from Fig. 2-20. Preemphasis, or the greater gain for higher frequencies, is applied during transmission. Deemphasis, or the reverse process, is used at the receiver to remove this extra-high-frequency audio gain. The result is an improved S/N ratio. Figure 2-21 is the graph of these curves. Preemphasis is constant from 50 to 500 cps and then rises toward the high-frequency end. This gain is 6 db per octave; deemphasis is just the reverse.

Preemphasis increases the transmission bandwidth, but because a relatively small amount of power is contained in the high-frequency end of the audio, this does not cause sidebands outside the desired limits.

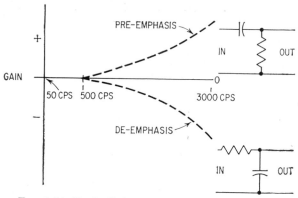

FIG. 2-21. Six-decibels-per-octave emphasis curves.

Noise Reduction in FM. FM noise reduction is most important in mobile communications and can be illustrated in part by Fig. 2-22. AM is shown in A, where the center frequency is F and the bandpass is from F_1 to F_2. Any noise in this band, regardless of frequency, can act as an AM sideband creating the effect of noise modulation. This rectangle shows that all noise signals of a fixed amplitude E will cause interference. The noise is equally distributed, in terms of frequency, through the passband.

But with FM the noise interference is a function of frequency. As the separation between the noise and the center frequency increases, the intensity of the interference increases. Where F is the carrier and Δf the separation from the carrier, a noise source at $F + 2\Delta f$ causes more interference than a noise source at $F + \Delta f$. This is shown in

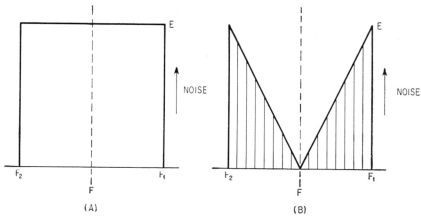

FIG. 2-22. Noise in the two cases; A is AM and B is FM.

B of Fig. 2-22 as a pair of triangles extending to the ends of the passband.   Only at the edges of the band is the FM noise equal to the AM noise.

Both AM and FM are shown in a comparison in Fig. 2-23.   With a center frequency of 50 Mc and a bandwidth of 10 kc the AM case is indicated with noise interference throughout the band.   But FM under the same conditions has the triangular distribution for less noise interference.   The FM deviation is equal to the AM passband in this example.

There are several ways to take advantage of this ability of FM to reduce noise.   One way is to increase the deviation as to ±20 kc as shown, but because this increases the bandwidth, this is not desirable for mobile communications.   Indeed the trend in communications is toward decreased bandwidth.

It is possible to reduce this noise markedly by frequency discrimination or preemphasis.   The gain versus frequency, or response of a flat amplifier, is taken as zero reference, which means all signals within this band of frequencies have equal gain.

But the FM noise triangle, as in Figs. 2-22 and 2-23, clearly shows that high-frequency noise causes more interference than low-frequency noise.   Preemphasis, the increased gain for the high-frequency signals, gives them an improved signal-to-noise ratio, and this makes the entire FM system appear to have even less noise interference than it would without preemphasis.   At the receiver deemphasis reduces this extra gain for the higher frequencies (in exactly the same relation), and the effective system is flat but with reduced noise interference.

This is summarized in Fig. 2-24, where *A* shows the normal FM noise triangle and *B* is the transmitter preemphasis curve.   Their combined effect is shown in part *C*, where the increased high-frequency gain

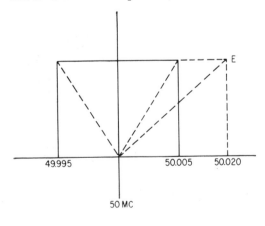

Fig. 2-23. Noise in FM decreases with increasing bandwidth.

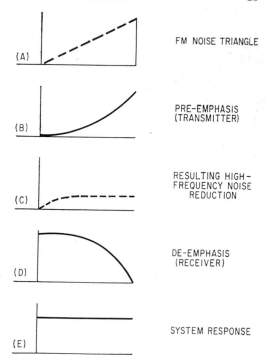

(A)   FM NOISE TRIANGLE

(B)   PRE-EMPHASIS
       (TRANSMITTER)

(C)   RESULTING HIGH-
       FREQUENCY NOISE
       REDUCTION

(D)   DE-EMPHASIS
       (RECEIVER)

(E)   SYSTEM RESPONSE

FIG. 2-24. Reduction in noise; A is FM noise triangle, B is transmitter preemphasis, C is the resulting high-frequency noise reduction, D is receiver deemphasis, and E is the resulting system response.

gives a stronger signal where the noise interference also is strongest, and the effective S/N ratio is shown. At the receiver a deemphasis curve, as in part D, is used to restore the frequency balance, so that the response is equal or flat.

Deemphasis and preemphasis are equal and opposite. The combined effect of B and D is then E, or flat system response. Because the upper end of frequencies has more noise interference and the combination of preemphasis and deemphasis most effectively improves the S/N ratio in this region, the net FM effect is as shown in Fig. 2-25.

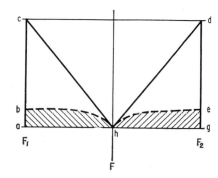

FIG. 2-25. FM and AM noise compared.

The AM noise is the area a, c, d, g; the FM noise without preemphasis is the sum of a, c, h and g, d, h; and the FM noise after preemphasis is the sum of a, b, h and g, e, h.

In Fig. 2-26 the FM noise characteristics are shown in another manner. Peak carrier-to-noise ratio is plotted as a function of signal-to-noise ratio. A reference line is shown for AM; two sets of curves are shown for FM, a modulation index of 4 and 1. For each modulation index the improvement for impulse noise (I) and fluctuation noise (F) is shown.

Until the FM carrier is of sufficient strength, FM is actually not as good as AM in noise reduction. But beyond this threshold of improvement (where the FM line crosses the AM line) FM is better than AM. For a modulation index of 1, impulse-noise improvement is about 6 db and fluctuation-noise improvement is about 5 db for the straight-line portion of the curve above the threshold. As the index increases to 4 (wideband FM), the impulse-noise improvement is about 18 db and fluctuation noise shows about 16-db improvement, again for the straight-line portion.

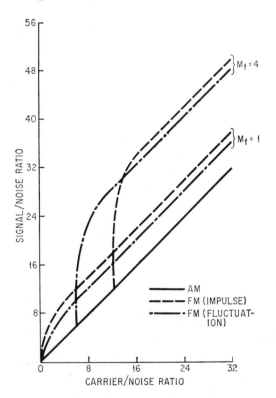

Fig. 2-26. FM impulse and fluctuation noise compared with AM.

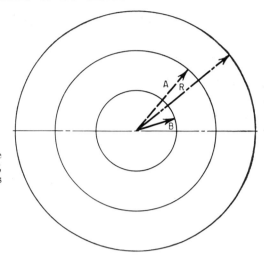

FIG. 2-27. Rotating interference vectors; A is the desired signal, B is the interference, and R is the resultant.

Interference Reduction. Signals which cause interference are classified as three types: *Cochannel* interference is another station on the same frequency. *Adjacent-channel* interference is, of course, created by a transmission on another channel whose frequency is close to the desired frequency but outside the band acceptance of the receiver. *Spurious responses* are signals which are on other frequencies than the desired channel but which the receiver cannot reject since they are partially within the passband of the receiver.

1. *Cochannel interference.* Assume that the desired signal A and the interfering signal B are both within the receiver passband. Both are, in Fig. 2-27, rotating vectors; hence, the resultant R has a frequency equal to the difference between the two. Since these vectors rotate at different frequencies, the resultant varies in length, or it is amplitude-modulated. The changing relation between these two also causes phase modulation of the resultant, and this is equivalent FM. Because this resulting signal is both AM and FM (PM), it causes interference in both types of receivers.

If B (Fig. 2-27) is AM, the interfering signal is modulated at the frequency of the AM modulation. If *both* carriers are AM, a very strong interference is created if the ratio in power is 100 to 1; at 1,000 to 1 the interference is still audible.

But with FM the modulation caused by interference, with the desired carrier unmodulated, *decreases* as the deviation of the unwanted carrier increases. If the desired carrier is frequency-modulated, the interference decreases as the deviation is increased. Actually, the interference vector cannot exceed an angle Θ where $\sin \Theta = B/A$; this is 30° where $2B = A$.

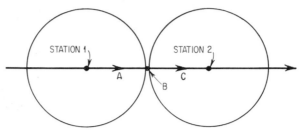

Fig. 2-28. Mobile radio in vehicle moving from A, in station-1 area, to C, in station-2 area. B is midway between 1 and 2.

The FM interference cannot be removed, but if the desired signal is at least twice as strong as the interfering station, the phase modulation is considerably less than the desired FM on the proper channel.   If the two stations are separated by 1 kc and their relative strength is as 2 is to 1, a frequency shift of only 500 cps will occur.

This property of FM is valuable in mobile radio.   Assume two stations of equal power on the same channel such as 1 and 2 in Fig. 2-28.   A radio receiver in a vehicle at A receives 1 twice as strong as 2, and 1 will be received without strong interference.   As the car moves to B, between the stations, 1 will be heard with 2 in the background. For a short time, exactly at B, there is a region of poor reception.   And as the car moves to C, station 2 will take over, or capture, the receiver. AM, under the same circumstances, would have submarginal reception all the way from A to C.

2. *Adjacent-channel interference.*   This is discussed in detail under FM receivers, but, in brief, this interference is lessened by sharp IF selectivity in the FM receiver and the characteristics of FM transmission where the stronger signal predominates.

3. *Spurious responses.*   These are related characteristics of the receiver including the local oscillator-image responses, and they are also discussed under FM receivers.

CHAPTER 3

FM TRANSMITTERS

3-1. Transmitter Block Diagram

FM is most often used in mobile communications; a phase-modulated crystal-controlled transmitter is used with one or more assigned frequencies.

While FM and AM are both used for mobile communications, the FM systems are more widely used because of their resistance to noise interference. Both of these are shown for comparison in block-diagram form in Fig. 3-1. A crystal-oscillator signal in the AM transmitter (A) is amplified and fed into the power-amplifier stage. Audio input is amplified in a second amplifier chain and fed into the RF power-amplifier stage as the modulating signal; output from this modulated stage is AM.

A block diagram of a typical FM transmitter is shown in B of Fig. 3-1. This general form of FM transmitter represents many different types. The crystal-controlled RF signal and the AF modulating signal are both fed into the modulator stage. Here the RF is frequency-modulated (or phase-modulated) by a small amount of equivalent frequency deviation. In the succeeding stages of amplifica-

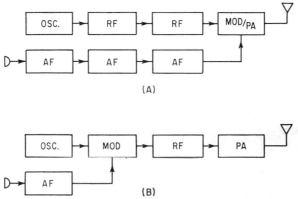

(A)

(B)

Fig. 3-1. AM transmitter (A) and FM (phase-modulated) transmitter (B).

49

FIG. 3-2. Motorcycle-
radio mounting.
(*General Electric.*)

FIG. 3-3. Front mounting in an automobile.   (*General Electric.*)

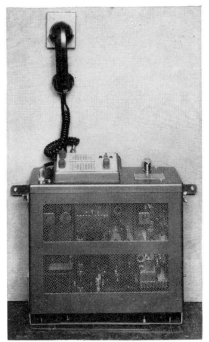

FIG. 3-4. Vehicle radio used as a base station. (*General Electric.*)

FIG. 3-5. Base station for the 144- to 174-Mc band; 250 watts. (*DuMont.*)

tion the modulated RF is frequency-multiplied. Each frequency multiplication *also* multiplies the deviation by the same amount. After several stages the proper carrier frequency has been reached with the desired frequency deviation. The final power amplifier increases the signal level and is coupled to the transmitting antenna.

All FM transmitters, whether they are for broadcast or communications, transmit an FM wave. This may be PM or FM, but the receiver cannot distinguish between them. There are two general methods of modulation: FM by direct or reactance-tube modulation and indirect FM (PM), which is a carrier phase-shift technique.

Two-way radios cover a broad range of radio equipment. By its very nature every transmitter is associated with a receiver; usually they are mounted together. Figure 3-2 illustrates a mobile unit in a motorcycle compartment. A front-mounted automobile unit is shown in Fig. 3-3. An a-c–fed power supply changes a mobile unit into a base station as shown in Fig. 3-4 and a high-powered base station is shown in Fig. 3-5.

A detailed block diagram of an FM transmitter is shown in *A* of

Fig. 3-6. Two crystals are shown for two-channel operation. If this transmitter was for the 450- to 470-Mc band, for example, a frequency multiplication of 36 could be used. There are two doublers and two triplers, and $2 \times 2 \times 3 \times 3$ is 36. Normal range for the original crystal would be 12.5 Mc (450 divided by 36) to 13.055 Mc (470 divided by 36). Two individual frequency assignments in this band could be used by choosing two crystals at these frequencies provided they were quite close so retuning would not be required.

Multiplication for a typical case is shown in *B*. With a crystal frequency of 13.050 Mc a deviation of 0.4 kc (400 cps) is required in the modulator stage. Each stage of multiplication increases both the deviation and carrier frequency by the same factor, and the final carrier is 469.800 Mc at a deviation of 14.4 kc.

Heterodyning, as used in receivers and some transmitters, does *not* change the deviation, although it changes the carrier frequency.[1] In *C* of Fig. 3-6 this same carrier is heterodyned with a 421.800-Mc oscillator, which produces a 48.000-Mc IF, but the deviation remains constant at 14.40 kc.

3-2. Modulation Systems

There are several different types of modulators for producing FM.

[1] R. Richardson, O. Eness, and R. Dronsuth, Experience with Single Sidehead Mobile Equipment, *Proc. IRE*, vol. 45, no. 67, pp. 823–829, June, 1957.

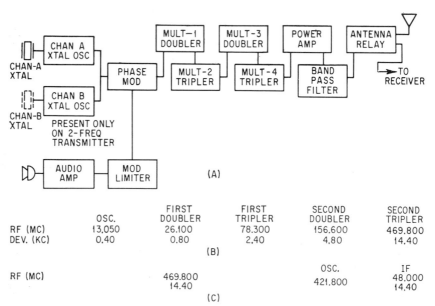

	OSC.	FIRST DOUBLER	FIRST TRIPLER	SECOND DOUBLER	SECOND TRIPLER
RF (MC)	13.050	26.100	78.300	156.600	469.800
DEV. (KC)	0.40	0.80	2.40	4.80	14.40

(B)

				OSC.	IF
RF (MC)		469.800		421.800	48.000
		14.40			14.40

(C)

FIG. 3-6. FM transmitter block diagram and frequency of various stages.

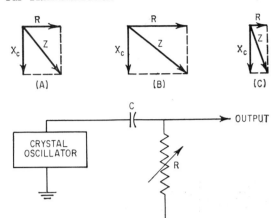

FIG. 3-7. Phase shift of a crystal-controlled signal.

The basic system for mobile communications is the phase-shift system. In a letter to the author Major Edwin H. Armstrong points out: "So far as I am aware, most communication systems, as distinguished from broadcasting, have always been phase shift systems."[1]

Other modulator types in addition to the single-tube phase shifter are reactance tubes, magnetic phase shifters, and balanced modulators.

Phase-shift Modulators. The modulator is the "heart" of the FM transmitter. A crystal provides the RF signal; this is the stable and accurate signal source required. In basic terms, as in Fig. 3-7, the crystal output is shifted in phase. The RF signal is applied to the RC network; R is variable, and there is a series circuit of the oscillator, R, and C. As R varies, the impedance of the network changes. If A is normal, B shows an increase in R, and C illustrates a decrease. If R can be varied in accordance with an audio signal, the RF output will be varied in phase; this is PM.

Replacing the resistor with a vacuum tube, as in Fig. 3-8, produces

[1] Private communication, Mar. 3, 1952.

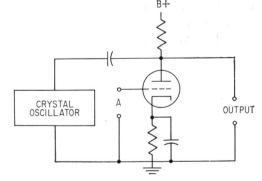

FIG. 3-8. Vacuum-tube phase shifter.

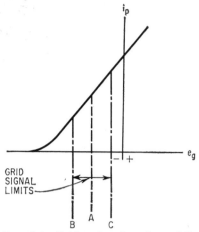

FIG. 3-9. Grid swing for phase-shift tube about operating point at A.

a more practical circuit. Plate resistance $(r_p = \Delta e_b/\Delta i_b)$ varies with grid voltage; if the grid voltage is the audio for modulation, the circuit output is phase-modulated. Cathode bias is used for the triode, which is a class-A amplifier. Figure 3-9 illustrates the bias and grid swing. As the grid becomes more positive, the phase angle of the output increases, since the plate resistance drops. When the grid becomes more negative than its operating point, the phase angle decreases, because the plate resistance rises.

Phase modulation is desired, but if there is a large change in plate resistance, the amplitude of the output will also change. Plate resistance is a function of grid voltage only over a restricted range; hence only a small change in phase, not greater than 25 to 30°, can be obtained without distortion. Even over this small range, however, the change in the output resistance (plate resistance) causes small amplitude variations; this can be overcome by using the drop across a cathode resistor.

In PM (as stated in Chap. 2) equivalent FM is proportional to the frequency of the audio modulating signal. Because, in FM, the frequency deviation is a function only of the audio-signal amplitude, a correction network is used. As mentioned in Chap. 2, audio correction is used to produce FM from a phase-modulator circuit.

Phase modulation in block-diagram form is shown in Fig. 3-10, and it depends for its action on both modulator interelectrode capacitance and stage gain. Figure 3-11 illustrates a modulator circuit showing the tube capacities. The input capacitance is a function of the grid-to-plate capacity (C_{GP}), the stage gain, the phase angle of the plate

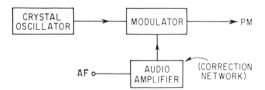

FIG. 3-10. Block diagram of a phase-shift transmitter modulator showing inputs.

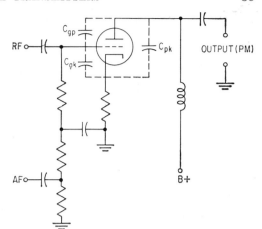

FIG. 3-11. Modulator stage for
phase shift.

load, and the grid-to-cathode capacity, C_{GK}.   When the plate load is
reactive, there is a resistive component to the input capacitance.

RF is applied to the grid, and the tube amplifies; the audio input
varies the gain of the stage and therefore the amplitude of the RF
output.   But some of the RF input is fed directly to the plate through
C_{GP}.   The vector sum of the two plate-signal voltages produces PM.

This may be seen from Fig. 3-12; normally an amplifier has a much
larger plate (a-c) voltage because of the stage gain than because of the
capacity feed-through.   This is shown in A of Fig. 3-12.   But the
gain of this stage is reduced, and these signals are made of equal amplitude as in B.   Because e_2 is amplified, it is almost 180° out of phase
with e_1, which is the same phase as the grid signal.

Output from this modulator is the resultant R of the vector addition
of e_1 and e_2.   In C the audio signal goes more positive, the gain is less,
e_2 is smaller, but e_1 is the same.   Hence their resultant shifts in phase

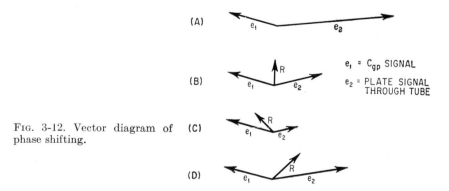

FIG. 3-12. Vector diagram of
phase shifting.

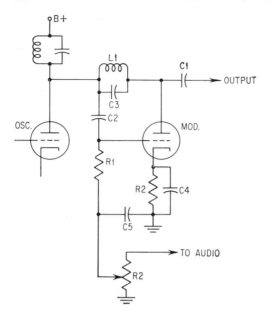

Fig. 3-13. Phase-shift modulator.

and amplitude. As in *D* the phase and amplitude change is in the other direction when the audio signal becomes more negative.

The RF input then is phase-modulated by the AF input. Amplitude variations are removed by later stages. A similar circuit is shown in Fig. 3-13. R_2 is the modulation control, since it changes the amount of audio applied to the grid.

Reactance-tube Phase Modulator. Broadcast FM transmitters, in some cases, use a reactance tube to vary the frequency of a self-excited oscillator for wide excursions of oscillator frequency. A reactance tube can also be used to vary a crystal-controlled RF carrier not by changing the oscillator frequency but, as in Fig. 3-14, by varying the output frequency of an amplifier. This amplifier follows the oscillator. Variations in the audio amplitude vary the reactance of the amplifier tank circuit; hence PM is produced.

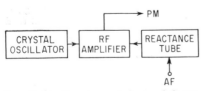

Fig. 3-14. Reactance-tube-modulator block diagram.

Reactance tubes, as in Fig. 3-15, can phase-shift an oscillator output. In some FM transmitters reactance tubes are used as modulators. In this circuit the tube is across the resonant tank circuit of the oscillator or amplifier as in Fig. 3-14. The tank-circuit voltage e causes a

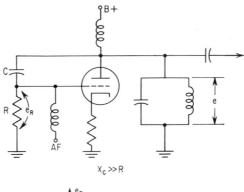

FIG. 3-15. Reactance-tube stage.

current i through the tube plate circuit. But, because X_c is much greater than R, in the tube grid current, a current i_1 flows in the RC-series network such that i_1 leads e by 90°. The drop across R caused by this current produces e_R. As a grid voltage e_R causes a plate current of i_2 in phase with the grid voltage e_R.

This current i_2 leads e, the tank-circuit voltage, and appears capacitive because it leads the voltage.

Audio voltage, applied to the grid, shifts the bias point and the amount of reactive output current from the tube to the tank circuit.

Magnetic Phase Modulator. The magnetic phase modulator is a delay line with the delay varied by a magnetic field controlled by a current flow. Figure 3-16 illustrates the use of a magnetic phase

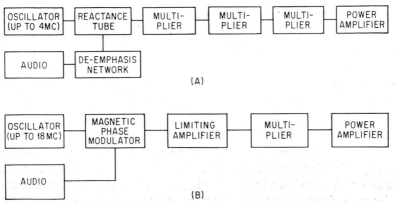

FIG. 3-16. Reactance-tube transmitter (A) compared with a magnetic-phase-modulator transmitter (B).

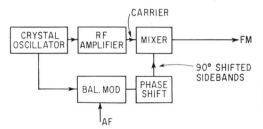

FIG. 3-17. Balanced-modulator block diagram.

modulator compared with the reactance-tube phase shifter.   Because the magnetic circuit operates at a higher frequency, fewer stages of multiplication are required.   No deemphasis network is required by the phase shifter.

Several different types have been tested in this application.

One model is designed for use in a low-band transmitter where the low operating frequency is multiplied to give 15-kc deviation in the 25- to 50-Mc band.   The other model is designed for use in a high-band transmitter where the low operating frequency is multiplied to give 15-kc deviation in the 144- to 174-Mc band.

Balanced Modulators.   The original Armstrong method for producing FM is illustrated in Fig. 3-17.   A crystal oscillator produces an RF signal, which is fed into the balanced modulator.   After the audio-correction network, an audio signal is also fed to this modulator, which has an output of two sidebands without a carrier component.   Push-pull input to the modulator tubes with paralleled plates for the output will remove the carrier.

A 90° phase shift is then introduced, and the shifted double sidebands are recombined with an amplified RF carrier.   The result is PM, or indirect FM.

At low levels of modulation both FM and AM have only one set of sidebands.   But in AM the sidebands are such that their resultant is either in phase or 180° out of phase with the carrier vector.   In PM the resultant of the sidebands is 90° out of phase with the carrier.

The balanced modulator produces two sidebands, which are phase-shifted and which, added to the unmodulated carrier, pass through the RF amplifier.   When these are added, in the mixer, PM results.

3-3. Crystal Oscillators

Crystal oscillators are used in two-way transmitters and receivers because of their inherent stability.   The growth of mobile communications would have been impeded without these accurate signal sources.

From a fundamental standpoint, an oscillator is a vacuum-tube device used to produce RF energy.   A transmitter is a low-powered oscillator followed by a number of stages of signal amplification.   Any ordinary oscillator may be considered to have four parts: These are the vacuum tube, its plate circuit, its grid circuit, and the feedback path. Included in either or both circuits is usually some sort of tuned circuit. An RF amplifier has an input grid circuit, a vacuum tube, and an output plate circuit. By introducing a method of feedback from the plate to the grid circuit, or from the plate to the cathode, sustained oscillations may be obtained. When this is done, a portion of the output signal is returned to the vacuum-tube input to become its signal. Various methods of feedback are used in basic oscillator circuits. Usually they use tuned tank circuits and a feedback path from plate to grid. The frequency of operation depends on the circuit constants. It is assumed in every case that the vacuum tube is capable of operating efficiently in the desired frequency region.

When an oscillator is first turned on, a small signal appears at the grid because of the initial surge of current through the tube. This causes the tuned circuit associated with the grid to set up an oscillatory current flow. A small signal on the grid produces a larger signal at the plate with any amplifier, and the feedback circuit provides a path for some of this energy from the plate circuit to return to the grid.

One of the conditions for oscillation is that this energy must be sent back to the grid in proper phase to maintain oscillations. The energy fed back must be in phase with the original energy in the grid circuit, and thus a larger signal is produced on the grid. This cycle is repeated with a larger signal on the grid producing a still larger signal in the plate circuit, which is again fed back to the grid circuit. This continues until the tube reaches its optimum operating condition, which is determined by the tube type, bias considerations, circuit constants, and amount of feedback. Once the tube has reached a stable state, it acts as an RF generator having a useful output.

Crystals for Oscillator Control. Quartz is one of the natural crystalline substances which, in small wafers, exhibits the piezoelectric effect. A voltage across the wafer causes it to oscillate at a fixed frequency determined by its dimensions. When a slice of quartz is fitted with electrodes on both faces, it appears as a high-Q low-loss resonant circuit. As shown in Fig. 3-18, this circuit has the effective

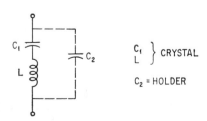

FIG. 3-18. Crystal equivalent circuit.

crystal L and C plus the crystal-holder capacity.   A high L/C ratio is obtained from the crystal resonant-circuit properties; a crystal is a series-resonant circuit.   The combined effect of C_1 and C_2 is to make the crystal a parallel circuit, as it is usually used for oscillator control.

A quartz crystal, as in Fig. 3-19, has three axes: X, Y, and Z.   A crystal cut is named for the axis to which it is perpendicular as the X, Y, or Z cut.   Many other cuts are available, but crystals for specific frequencies are available commercially; they may be obtained for any desired frequency.

Crystals, as with other mechanical vibrators such as tuning forks, have a fundamental frequency and harmonic frequencies.   Some crystals have outputs at various odd harmonics such as 3, 5, or 7. The range of crystal frequencies is as low as 25 kc and up to 100 Mc and higher.   In most mobile applications the crystal-oscillator frequency is multiplied.

Temperature control is used for highest accuracy and stability of the crystal frequency.   Figure 3-20 illustrates this variation in crystal frequency as a function of temperature. AB is a positive temperature coefficient; frequency increases and decreases directly with temperature.   In a negative temperature coefficient, as line CD, the frequency and temperature are inversely related.   For most accurate frequency control, heaters are used for crystals.

Oscillator Circuits.   There are many different types of crystal oscillators.   Those in this section apply, generally, to both transmitters and receivers.

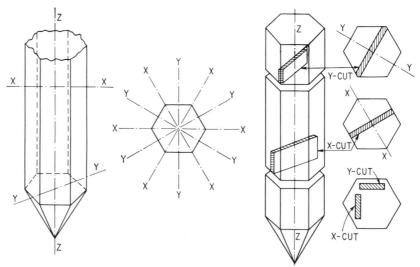

Fig. 3-19. Piezoelectric crystal axes.

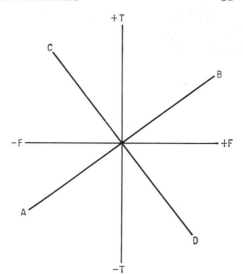

FIG. 3-20. Various cuts of a quartz crystal.

Some basic circuits are in Fig. 3-21; *A* is similar to a tuned-plate–tuned-grid oscillator with a resonant circuit on both grid and plate connections.

B is like the ultra-audion oscillator with feedback through the tube capacities. *C* is a common crystal oscillator with a pentode; a feedback capacitor is used because of the reduced tube capacities.

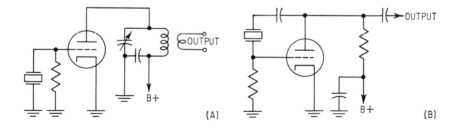

(A)

(B)

FIG. 3-21. Basic crystal oscillators.

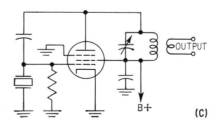

(C)

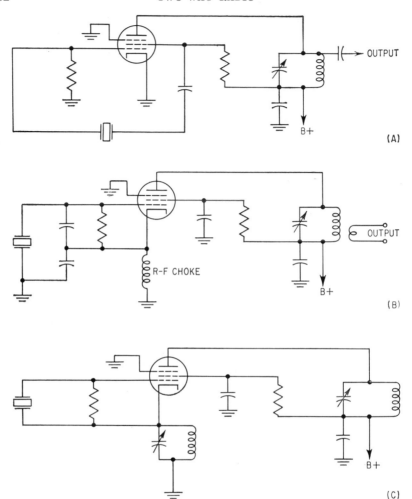

FIG. 3-22. Harmonic crystal oscillators where output is a harmonic of the crystal frequency.

Oscillators with a strong harmonic content are shown in Fig. 3-22; they provide a strong output, at the crystal fundamental, which is frequency-multiplied.   They are known as harmonic oscillators, since the output is a harmonic of the crystal frequency.

Crystals are not used at the desired circuit-output frequency in many circuits.   Harmonic oscillators and multipliers are used to obtain the necessary high frequency as for heterodyning in receivers.   All the circuits shown are for pentodes.   A triode is formed by the cathode, the control grid, and the screen grid acting as a plate.   This triode oscillates at the crystal frequency. But the output RF signal has a high harmonic content. The tube anode has a tuned-circuit output resonant to the desired harmonic frequency.

In A the crystal is tied between the screen and grid. By inserting the crystal between the cathode and grid, circuit B is made. This is less dependent upon the characteristics of the tube. C illustrates a variation with a tuned circuit in the cathode for greater harmonic output.

In Fig. 3-22 the circuit output in each case is tuned to a crystal harmonic; but it is possible to cause the crystal itself to resonate at an odd harmonic of its natural resonant frequency as in Fig. 3-23. Feedback at the desired output frequency is used; these circuits require

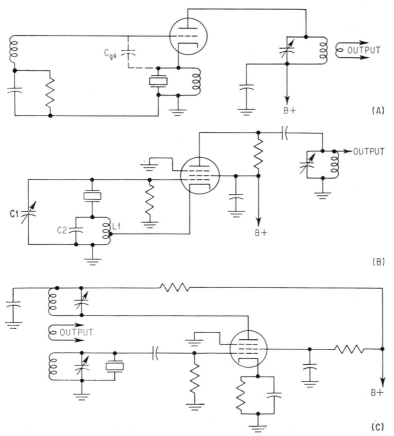

FIG. 3-23. Overtone crystal oscillators where crystal vibrates at a harmonic.

careful design, so that oscillation is caused by the crystal and not the frequency selection of the feedback. In *A* the crystal is in the cathode circuit. The crystal is *series*-resonant at the desired frequency as a harmonic generator. Both grid and plate circuits are resonant at the desired frequency.

A is a circuit where the crystal holder resonates with the inductance in the cathode circuit at the overtone frequency.

In *B* of Fig. 3-23 the circuit is a type of Hartley oscillator, but it is crystal-controlled; feedback is adjusted by the cathode tap. The circuit is very stable. In *C* there is regenerative feedback, by the inductive coupling between grid and plate. Operation is possible with very-high-order overtones.

When two or more frequencies are used for multichannel operation, they must be relatively close in frequency. A difference between these channels should not be greater than 0.4 to 0.5 per cent of the operating frequency. After multiplication any greater difference means the RF amplifiers (frequency multipliers) would not be able to cover both frequencies in the proper manner.

A selector switch is used, for two-channel operation with two oscillators, to close the cathode circuit of the desired oscillator. This switch permits the operator to use either preset channel.

3-4. The Audio Signal for Modulation

The crystal oscillator supplies the RF signal to the modulator; the AF signal is applied through an audio amplifier from the microphone.

Both carbon and magnetic microphones have been used for mobile radio. In some equipment a transistorized magnetic microphone is being used with a small amplifier built into the microphone case.[1] Carbon microphones, like those in ordinary telephone handsets as are found in the home, have a high sensitivity or a relatively large audio-signal output. Since the carbon microphone requires a d-c power source, the transistorized microphone can be used as a direct replacement by using this d-c source to power the transistor amplifier. A single transistor in a resistance-coupled amplifier provides sufficient gain. By using a dual transducer the single unit can function as both a microphone and speaker.

Audio Amplifier and Limiter. Between the audio-signal input from the microphone and the modulator are several stages of audio amplification. In Fig. 3-24, these are triode amplifiers with cathode bias.

The first two stages are audio-voltage amplifiers, operating class A,

[1] H. A. Johnson and Leo Rosenman, Transistorized Microphones for Vehicular Communications, *Trans. IRE*, *PGVC*-11, p. 3, July, 1958.

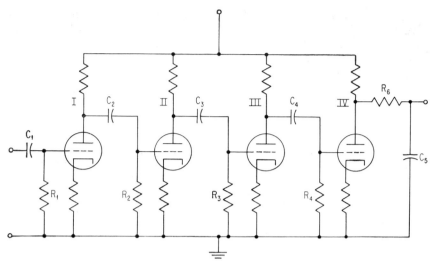

FIG. 3-24. Transmitter audio amplifier.

so there is always plate-current flow and no grid-current flow. Operation of these stages is shown in Fig. 3-25. *A* shows the grid voltage, which is always negative and never rises to zero. Plate current (*B*) is in phase with the grid voltage, and plate voltage (*C*) is 180° out of phase with both *A* and *B*.

In communications the understanding of message is most important, and limiting is used to assure that all audio signals are large enough but that none is so large that it would create sidebands outside the established limits.

The tubes III and IV of this chain of amplifiers are limiters.

Tubes III and IV are class-A amplifiers. But in stage III the plate voltage is reduced, which lowers the plate current, as in *D*, for a given grid voltage. In *E* the

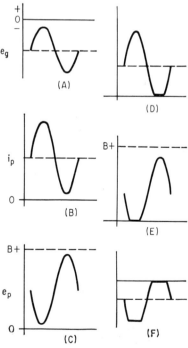

FIG. 3-25. Clipping action.

effect of this lowered plate voltage shows up as clipping of the negative alternation of the sine-wave signal.   Stage IV input F is the same phase as E, because E is the plate-voltage output of stage III and F is the grid input to IV through the RC coupling.   In F the grid bias is reduced, and clipping of the *other* peak of the sine wave occurs.   This double clipping is the result of the two-stage limiter action.   Larger-amplitude audio signals are limited in this way to prevent modulation outside the desired channel limits; small audio signals are not limited.

Because the maximum communication is desired, within the bandwidth limitations preemphasis is used as in Fig. 3-26.   The square corners resulting from limiting must be removed to prevent high-frequency sidebands outside the desired channel width. C_2, R_2, which couple stage I to II, have a preemphasis characteristic.   Because of the small capacity of C_2 the high-frequency audio signals have less attenuation than the low frequencies.   This preemphasis has a rising frequency-gain characteristic.

Before the audio is applied to the modulator stage, however, the signal is deemphasized with a falling gain characteristic which provides less gain for the high frequencies than for the low frequencies.   Because the "sharp edges" of the clipped or limited signals have high-frequency components, these are removed by the C_5 and R_6 deemphasis network.   This is permissible only because preemphasis was added in the second stage.

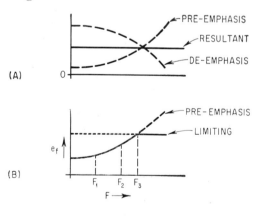

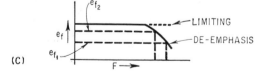

FIG. 3-26. Preemphasis and deemphasis.

This is a PM transmitter where the normal phase-modulated signal would receive deemphasis to make it ordinary FM. But PM without audio correction is, effectively, FM with preemphasis. The discussion above applies only to the limiting action.

3-5. Frequency Multiplication

Frequency multiplication in an FM transmitter is primarily used to multiply the frequency deviation produced by the modulator stage. The carrier frequency is also multiplied, but this desired center frequency could be obtained in fewer stages by using a higher crystal frequency.

As discussed earlier in this chapter, multiplication (doubling, for example) multiplies the center frequency and the deviation. A 13.050-Mc signal is multiplied by 36 to 469.800 Mc, while the deviation goes from 0.40 kc to 14.40 kc.

A multiplier is simply an RF amplifier whose output is a harmonic of the input. Figure 3-27 illustrates a basic circuit where C_1 couples the RF signal, F, to the grid of the amplifier. This signal drives the grid into the positive region, as shown, and current flow is across R_3, so as to make the grid negative with respect to ground. Capacitor C_1 charges and maintains this bias by discharging through R_3 during the time the tube is not conducting. This is grid-leak bias, or self-bias, because the amount of bias is a function of the signal strength. The stronger the grid drive, the greater the positive swing, which increases the grid current and hence the bias as in Fig. 3-28.

R_2, the cathode resistor, also adds to this bias, but its primary function is as a protective device. If the grid signal should fail, for any reason, the self-bias as in Fig. 3-27 would also fail, and the tube could be damaged by excessive plate current. But an increase in plate current will cause a greater drop across the cathode resistor, which will limit the flow of plate current and protect the tube.

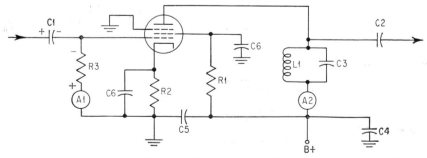

FIG. 3-27. Frequency doubler.

Output is taken from C_2 across the plate tank L_1 and C_3, which is tuned to a harmonic of the input frequency. R_1 is the screen dropping resistor, while C_6, C_5, and C_4 are low-impedance paths for RF, or bypass capacitors.

A class-C amplifier, as a multiplier, has a distorted output. That is, the input and output are not of the same waveshape. Output is a series of current pulses, and the input is a sine wave of voltage.

Any amplifier with a distorted output has harmonics of the input frequency present in the output. By tuning L_1 and C_3 to the desired harmonic (the second harmonic is shown) a multiplier results. Doublers or triplers are normally used because the amplitude of the harmonic decreases as the harmonic number increases.

In Fig. 3-28 four cycles of the input frequency are shown. As an amplifier there would be the same four pulses, at the same frequency in the output. But because the plate circuit is tuned to *twice* the input frequency (as a doubler), there are twice as many cycles in the output.

Any resonant circuit which is pulsed produces a series of sine waves because of the "flywheel" effect as in the circuit of Fig. 3-28. The first pulse charges C_3, which discharges through L_1. After C_3 has discharged and the current through L_1 stops, the magnetic field about L_1 collapses, which charges C_3 in the opposite sense, and the action repeats. This is how any tuned circuit responds to a current pulse, and if a series of pulses occurs at the resonant frequency, as it does in this case, a continuous sine-wave output appears across the output circuit.

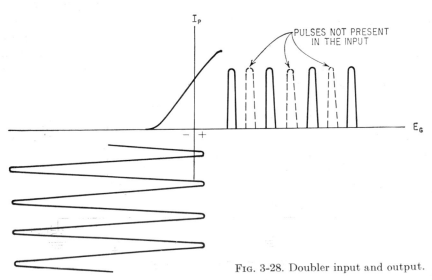

FIG. 3-28. Doubler input and output.

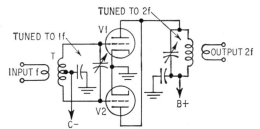

FIG. 3-29. Push-pull input, parallel-output stage.

Usually only doublers and triplers are used, although multiplication by other integers is possible. However, the power output rapidly drops off above the third harmonic.

A circuit, as in Fig. 3-29, is an effective doubler. The grids are in push-pull, but the plates are in parallel. Each grid conducts on alternate half-cycles (like a full-wave rectifier); hence the plate tank receives two pulses for each input cycle. This makes the plate circuit twice the frequency of the grid circuit, and it is tuned to this output frequency.

3-6. Neutralization

In a triode RF amplifier, as in Fig. 3-30 as an example, the capacity between the plate and grid causes feedback, which can make the stage an oscillator rather than an amplifier. This circuit could be a tuned-plate–tuned-grid oscillator. Feedback can be reduced by operating the stage as a grounded-grid amplifier, by using pentodes with less interelectrode capacity, or by neutralizing this interelectrode capacity.

In theory a multiplier does not require neutralization, since the output and input are not of the same frequency; however,

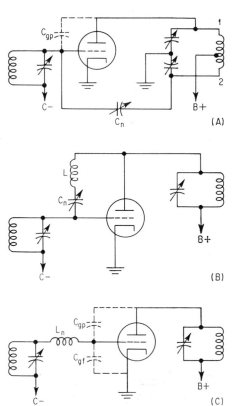

FIG. 3-30. Methods of neutralization.

in some cases, this feedback reduces the efficiency of the stage. But oscillation is prevented, as in A, and the tuned-plate–tuned-grid circuit changed to an amplifier (which may be a multiplier) by the addition of the neutralizing capacitor C_N. Because the plate coil is split by the B voltage, feed points 1 and 2 are 180° out of phase. There are two paths for feedback. One is through the grid-to-plate capacity, and the other is through the neutralizing capacitor. Since these signals are out of phase, they cancel, and oscillations are prevented.

In B of Fig. 3-30 the neutralizing capacitor and coil L are used which resonate together with grid-plate capacity at the desired frequency for neutralization. An added inductance, as in C, in the grid circuit will also prevent oscillations. Other methods include cathode degeneration to reduce undesired feedback.

Parasitic oscillations are present in some FM transmitter amplifiers. A portion of the circuit such as lead inductance or wiring capacity forms a resonant circuit; this undesired resonance causes spurious output signals at undesired frequencies. These oscillations are damped out by the use of series resistors, of low values, in the grid or plate leads.

3-7. Power Amplifiers

In AM the final power amplifiers are usually the stage which is modulated, and the amplifier must both amplify the RF power and preserve the modulation waveshape, but in FM amplitude distortion of the modulated signal does not affect the intelligence which is transmitted.

The operation of a class-C amplifier may be seen from Fig. 3-31. Because the bias is greater than cutoff, the plate current flows only during a small part of the input-signal cycle as in A. The flywheel effect produces the plate-voltage sine wave where the positive alternation is greater than the supply voltage.

Grid voltage is made up of the bias E_{cc} and the a-c signal e_c. Bias is greater than cutoff in a class-C amplifier, and plate current flows only during a short portion of the input cycle.

Plate current is in phase with grid voltage, but plate voltage, as shown, is 180° out of phase with the grid voltage. E_{bb} is the d-c plate voltage, and e_p is the a-c component. The flywheel effect of the plate tank circuit changes the pulses of plate current into the a-c sine-wave voltage.

The total space current, i_s as in C, is composed of the plate current, i_b in D, and the grid current, i_c as in E.

Power output depends upon several factors: For a given input signal greater bias means a higher efficiency and less power output. Less bias

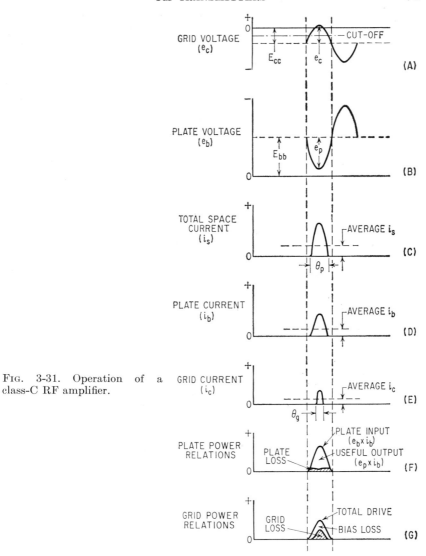

FIG. 3-31. Operation of a class-C RF amplifier.

means lower efficiency and greater power output. Power input to the plate circuit is the product of e_b, the total plate voltage as in B, and the plate current i_b as in D. Power output from the plate is the product of e_p and i_b. Grid power is shown in G. The ratio of output power to input power, or the efficiency, of a class-C amplifier is high. It is usually between 60 and 80 per cent.

Power-amplifier Circuits. By use of the grounded-grid circuit as in Fig. 3-32 a triode can be used as an RF amplifier without neutraliza-

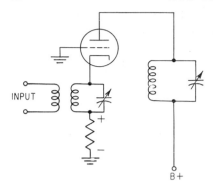

FIG. 3-32. Grounded-grid amplifier.

tion. Both the driver and the amplifier plate supply output power (the sum of cathode and plate RF voltage). This circuit permits triodes to amplify at higher frequencies, since the grid acts as a shield and the circuit requires no neutralization.

Increased power output is obtained by paralleled power amplifiers or by push-pull. Twice the drive is required, since there are two tubes; push-pull for neutralized triodes are shown in A of Fig. 3-33, while tetrodes are in B. In push-pull the voltage necessary for this purpose is available, since a grid is in phase with the plate of the other tube. Tetrode amplifiers do not require neutralization.

Input circuits from driver to power amplifier vary; in each case the impedance match and power transfer are important. Several circuits are shown in Fig. 3-34; because the input impedance of a class-C amplifier is not constant, these must be compromises.

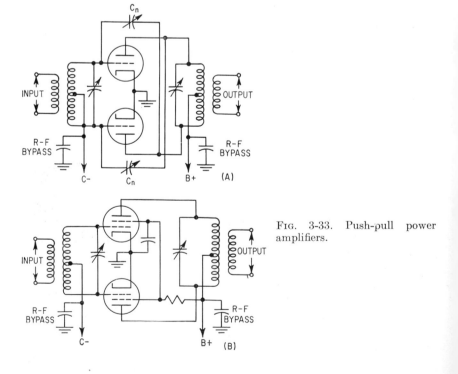

FIG. 3-33. Push-pull power amplifiers.

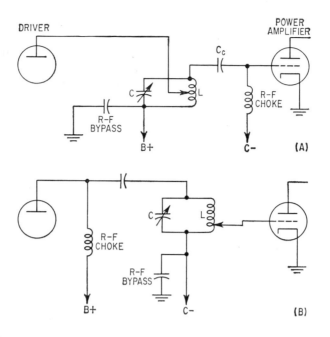

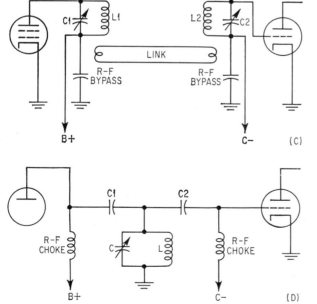

FIG. 3-34. Types of coupling between amplifier stages.

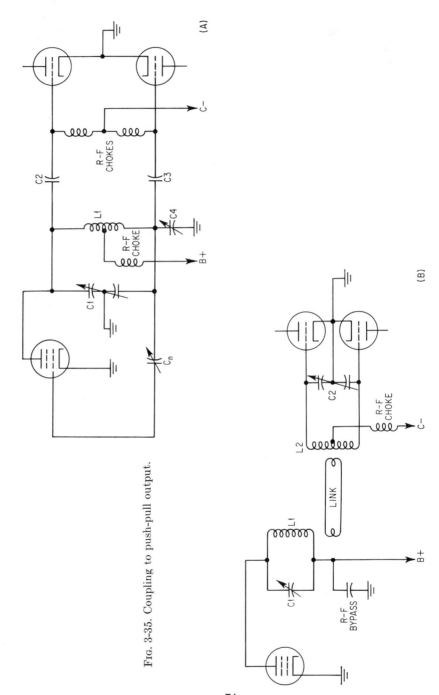

Fig. 3-35. Coupling to push-pull output.

In *A* the simplest circuit is shown; capacitive coupling to the grid is taken from the plate tank.   This feed point may be varied by use of a tap.   *B* illustrates a shunt-fed driver plate and is used for lower grid-input impedances.   The tank circuit is in common to both plate and grid.

Where, for any reason, the driver and final power amplifier are separated (as when they are on a different chassis), link coupling as in *C* permits the use of a low-impedance transmission line.   It is possible to isolate the tank circuit from both plate and grid by capacitors as in *D*.

Modifications for coupling to push-pull are shown in Fig. 3-35.   In *A* the out-of-phase voltages are developed in the driver plate and capacitively fed to the amplifier.   The power-amplifier grid tank is center-tapped in *B* to provide push-pull for the grids.   A split-stator tuning capacitor is used.

Output circuits are equally important for maximum transfer of energy to the antenna from the power amplifier; the circuit should prevent the coupling of frequencies other than the desired output.

A simple circuit, as in *A* of Fig. 3-36, uses a shunt-fed plate, so that there is a d-c ground for the tuning capacitor C_1.   When neutralization is required, a circuit such as *B*, with a split-stator capacitor and tapped coil, is used.   But because the tank circuit is, effectively, divided, a peak RF voltage of twice *E* can appear across each half; this requires

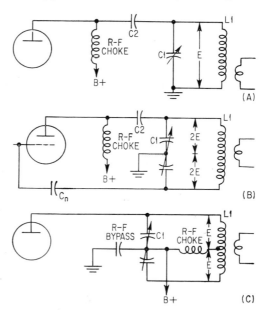

FIG. 3-36. Power-amplifier tank circuits.

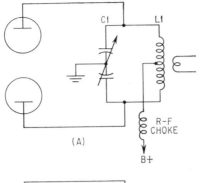

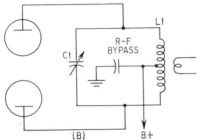

FIG. 3-37. Push-pull amplifier tank circuits.

a large capacitor with a high-voltage rating. In C the capacitor is at RF ground, which reduces the peak voltage in each half to E (total is $2E$); the RFC is tied between the split-stator capacitor and the coil tap. But care is required in tuning, for the capacitor is *not* at d-c ground.

Figure 3-37 illustrates push-pull plate tanks; A uses a split-stator capacitor with an RF ground, and B has a single tuning capacitor. The rotor in A is at ground potential, and plate voltage is fed through the center tap. The peak RF voltage, equal to twice the d-c plate voltage, is across each of the two parts of the tuning capacitor.

In B both rotor and stator are above ground, and an insulated shaft is required to prevent a shock hazard. An RF bypass provides a signal ground at the center-tap feed point.

Power amplifiers in transmitters are the final stages. A low-power transmitter can be converted into a unit of higher power by addition of an amplifier package. This equipment is a power amplifier with its own power supply. Suppose, for example, the present a-c–powered base station could produce 10 watts of output in the 25- to 50-Mc or 144- to 174-Mc band. By adding the power-amplifier package and using the 10 watts to drive the new amplifier the station would be increased to over 300 watts. For the 450- to 470-Mc band the output RF power would be less and the drive power somewhat more. In this way existing equipment can be used for greater coverage without replacing the transmitter with a completely new unit.

Another new technique is the variable-level power-output transmitter. In many cases the base station requires less than full power to communicate with a given vehicle. A substantial reduction in interference can be obtained by automatically reducing the station power, which is transmitted, for answering calls from nearby vehicles. For distant vehicles greater power is used. The transmitter power is changed in accord with the amplitude of the received signal as measured at the base station.

3-8. Antenna Feeding

Many transmitters have long transmission lines, in terms of operating wavelength. Different antenna lengths are also a tuning problem and require adjustment. A in Fig. 3-38 illustrates the use of a matching network; C_3 is a blocking capacitor. Antenna matches can be easily obtained with this circuit.

L_1, C_1, and C_2 are all in series and are resonant at the operating frequency. C_1 and C_2 form a voltage divider and are also, at the same time, a means of impedance matching. The output voltage, which is fed to the antenna, may be varied over a wide range. Then C_1 is adjusted to bring the entire circuit to resonance. This arrangement can match resistive and reactive antenna loads.

B illustrates a different network, but it also has two capacitors for adjustment. A voltage divider of these two in series permits matching to different loading conditions.

3-9. Complete Transmitters

The basic circuits, discussed in this chapter, are to be found in most FM transmitters. Two examples are given in this section, one for

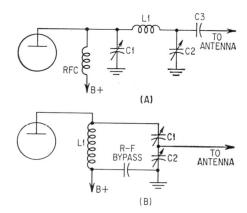

FIG. 3-38. Antenna feed circuits.

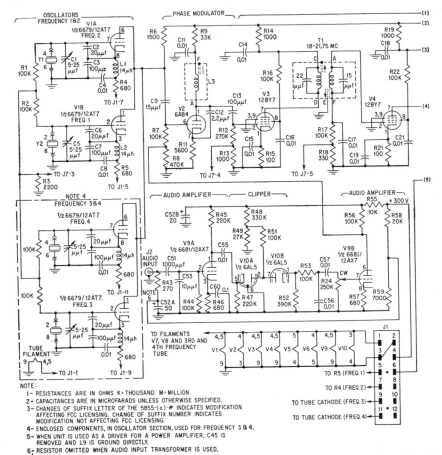

FIG. 3-39. DuMont 5855 transmitter, 144 to 174 Mc. (*DuMont.*)

the high band and one for the UHF band. These may be considered as typical. The low-band transmitter, which is not included, is quite similar to the high-band one in most circuit functions.

High-band Transmitters. The DuMont 5855 transmitter shown in Fig. 3-39 is designed for the transmission of phase-modulated signals in the 144- to 174-Mc mobile-communication band of frequencies. The transmitter is intended for use in base-station equipment and should be mounted in the upright base-station cabinet. It is representative of equipment for this band.

The transmitter circuits consist of the RF exciter, driver- and power-amplifier section, and the audio modulating section. The RF portion originates the carrier signal with a crystal-controlled oscillator; a phase-modulator stage modulates the phase of the RF crystal-oscil-

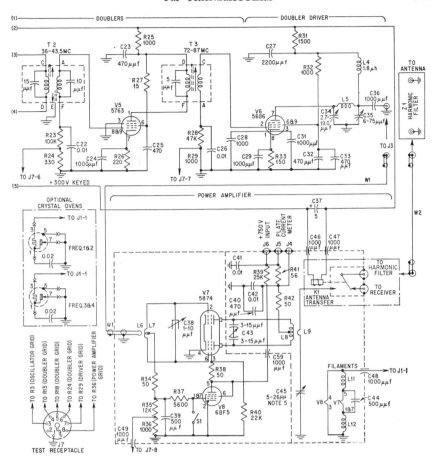

lator output; three multipliers raise the frequency to the output value; and the driver stage applies its signal to the final power amplifier. A low-pass harmonic filter is located in the antenna transmission line to attenuate spurious radiation above 174 Mc. The audio portion consists of two audio amplifiers and a limiter circuit to prevent excessive deviation.

In detail, the four crystal oscillators, using 6679/12AT7 tubes, are divided into two groups of two. Each pair of crystals has its own heater. A small variable capacitor is across each crystal for fine frequency adjustment. All four oscillators feed a common point to the phase modulator V_2, which is a 6AB4. The audio, after two stages of amplification and a dual limiter, or clipper, is applied to the modulator.

There are three doublers: The first two are 12BY7's, and the last is a 5763. Their frequency ranges are 18 to 21.75 Mc, 36 to 43.5 Mc, and 72 to 87 Mc, while the 5686 doubler driver covers the 144- to 174-Mc band.

A coaxial line W connects the V_6 output to the grid input of V_7, which is a 5874 double pentode operating in push-pull. V_8 regulates the screen voltage for the final power amplifier.

The antenna coaxial line passes through the harmonic filter and then, by the action of the antenna transfer relay, to the power-amplifier output transformer or to the receiver.

UHF Transmitter (Fig. 3-40). The basic difference between a UHF transmitter and those for other frequency bands lies in the UHF tuned circuits and tubes.

UHF amplifiers are different from those used for lower frequencies. The factors which limit the frequency of the ordinary type of RF amplifier are the construction of the tube and the external circuits which are used with the tube.

The tube-construction factors which limit the operating frequency of the usual oscillator are the interelectrode capacitances in the tube, the inductances of the leads, and the transit time.

At ordinary radio frequencies the interelectrode capacitances in a vacuum tube form reactances which are large enough not to cause any serious trouble. However, as frequencies increase, the reactance of these capacitances becomes small enough to affect materially the performance of a circuit.

The higher the frequency, or the larger the interelectrode capacitance, the higher the current flow through this capacitance. These higher currents cause power losses in the resistance in the tank circuit.

Another limiting factor within a tube is the inductance of the tube-element leads. They may represent a major portion of the inductance of the tuned circuit and limit the frequency by setting a minimum limit on the inductance. The cathode lead is common to both plate and grid circuits, feedback takes place through it, and this produces an additional loss of efficiency.

A third limitation imposed by tube construction is transit time, or the time required for electrons to travel from cathode to plate. At low frequency transit time is negligible, since it occupies only a comparatively small portion of the period of oscillation. But as the frequency becomes higher, transit time occupies an appreciable portion of this period and produces undesirable effects in tube operation. The effect of transit time is important in considering the input impedance of the tube. Some of the current that flows in the grid circuit is the current which charges the grid-to-plate capacitance. The voltage that produces this current is the vector sum of the input voltage (grid-to-cathode) and the output voltage across the plate load. At lower frequencies with a resistive load, these two voltages are 180° out of phase and add, algebraically, to determine the charging current; the current is 90° out of phase with the input voltage.

But at UHF, where transit time becomes an important factor, the plate current begins to lag the input voltage. This causes the plate voltage to be less than 180° out of phase with the input voltage and the voltage across the capacitor to lag the input voltage. Thus the charging current will no longer be 90° out of phase but will have an in-phase component, which means that power is consumed in the grid circuit. This is effectively the same as adding a high resistance in the input impedance; this resistance decreases as the frequency increases.

There are several ways to reduce the effect of interelectrode capacitances in vacuum tubes. One is to move the electrodes farther apart. This is not desirable, because it increases the transit time. Another method is to reduce the size of the tube and electrodes. This decreases the power-handling ability of the tube. Another method is to separate the leads and to bring them out of the envelope at the nearest point. This results in a slight decrease in the capacitances.

There are also several ways to reduce the inductances of the leads. Bringing out electrode leads through the envelope at the nearest point produces a slight decrease in the electrode capacitance in a tube. Another method is to make double connections, which makes two parallel inductances. This will reduce the lead inductance by a factor of two. Another method is to arrange the leads as extensions of external transmission lines.

The basic UHF tuned circuit is a quarter-wavelength transmission line with an effective short circuit at the load end. This line has an input impedance which is given by

$$Z_{in} = Z_o \tan \theta$$

where Z_o is the characteristic impedance of the line, and θ is the electrical length of the line. Hence, for a 90° line

$$Z_{in} = Z_o \tan 90$$

and since tan 90 is infinite (or very large), the Z_{in} is a high impedance or a parallel resonant circuit at the operating frequency.

The UHF tuned circuit has several limitations, just as a tube has certain limiting factors.

Radiation, which is a factor causing power loss, is due to incomplete

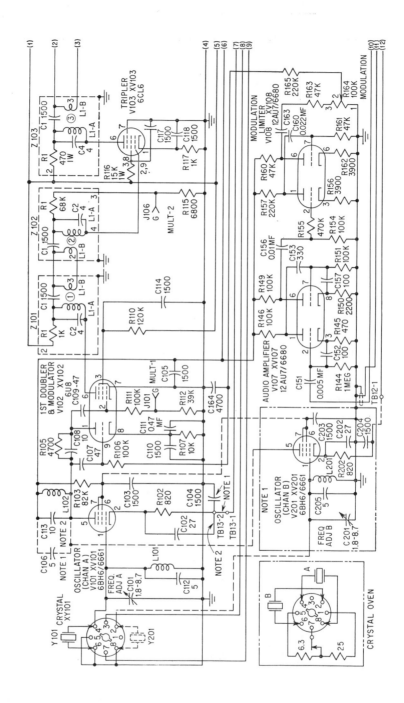

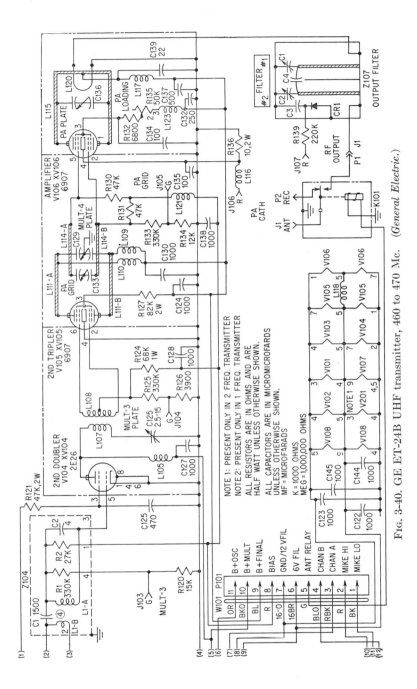

FIG. 3-40. GE ET-24B UHF transmitter, 460 to 470 Mc. (*General Electric.*)

83

cancellation of electromagnetic fields in the region around the circuit. When the frequency is low, and the spacing between two parallel conductors equals only a very small fraction of a half-wavelength, there is almost complete cancellation of fields in all directions. At higher frequencies, however, such spacing would represent a larger fraction of a half-wavelength. This means less cancellation. Where the spacing is a half-wavelength, the fields add in the direction of the two conductors. This causes the tuned circuit to radiate energy like an antenna. As the frequency increases, it is necessary to reduce the spacing between the parallel elements. However, there is a limit on how far it is possible to go in reducing the spacing.

Too close spacing, for example, causes arcing, which increases the RF resistance in the tank circuit. Another means of eliminating radiation is using concentric lines instead of open-wire lines. This eliminates radiation entirely, since the outer conductor acts like a shield.

With UHF frequencies it is necessary that the inductances and the capacitances in the tuned circuit be very small. The limit of capacitance is the sum of the interelectrode capacitances and the distributed capacitance of the leads. The limit of inductance is the lead inductance plus the inductance necessary to connect the tube electrodes externally. UHF amplifiers approach both these limits, the only capacitance in the tank circuit being a small trimmer capacitor for fine tuning adjustments, and the inductance being a short-circuited transmission line less than $\frac{1}{4}$ wavelength in length.

Skin effect causes a considerable increase in the resistance in a vacuum-tube circuit. This results in a lower Q and increased power losses. To prevent skin-effect losses conductors are made large in size, and since current flows only in the surface, they are in the form of tubes. They are often plated with silver, since it has a higher conductivity than copper.

Special types of parallel-plate transmission lines are conveniently used in transmitters designed for UHF citizens' band operation. The General Electric Company has done some early experimental work using flat parallel-plate transmission lines together with lighthouse tubes for citizens' band transmitting equipment. A crystal-controlled 25-Mc oscillator was used. This was followed by a frequency doubler, a frequency tripler, and a power amplifier which produces output at 150 Mc. These stages used ordinary tuned circuits and lumped constants. A 2C43 lighthouse tube is used as a final tripler which multiplies the 150-Mc output in order to produce the final frequency of 450 Mc using transmission lines. A second 2C43 is used as a power amplifier following the final tripler.   Both 2C43 and 2C39 lighthouse tubes were used for this early UHF transmitter.

While lighthouse tubes were successful, the 6907, first used in 1956, allowed less expensive UHF radio.   The 6907 is a double-tetrode designed for mobile and fixed-station use for frequencies up to 600 Mc. As a class-C amplifier in the 460- to 470-Mc band it is rated at 25 watts.

Figure 3-40 is a UHF transmitter (General Electric ET-24B).   The 13-Mc crystal frequency is multiplied 36 times.   This transmitter is for the 460- to 470-Mc citizens' band.   A 6907 is used both for the second tripler and the final power amplifier.   Transmission lines are used for the tuned circuits in these stages.   The tripler plate is a quarter-wave-length transmission-line resonant circuit with C_{129} as the tuning element.   Inductive coupling of this tank circuit to the power-amplifier grid circuit, which is also a transmission-line-tuned circuit, provides the grid input.   A similar circuit is used for the power-amplifier plate circuit.

CHAPTER 4

FM RECEIVERS

4-1. Introduction

Receivers have four significant characteristics: selectivity, sensitivity, fidelity, and stability.[1]

Selectivity is the measure of effectiveness in receiving the desired transmission to the exclusion of other stations which are on the air at other channels or different frequencies. Sensitivity is a measure of how small a signal a receiver can pick up and amplify to a level useful for communications. Fidelity is a measure of the faithfulness in reproducing the original audio signal. In commercial broadcast this feature is stressed; in communications fidelity is not important compared with the operator's ability to understand what is said at the transmitter. Stability is the measure of a receiver's ability to stay on the proper frequency for assigned channel reception.

A typical fixed-station receiver is illustrated in Fig. 4-1 showing the loudspeaker and the controls. Figure 4-2 shows a receiver (and transmitter) for mobile use. These receivers are double superheterodynes as shown in the typical block diagram of Fig. 4-3a, which is a high-band receiver, and Fig. 4-3b, which is a low-band schematic. Antenna input is from the antenna relay because of the common antenna. Tuned circuits before the RF amplifier discriminate against the undesired signals outside the receiver frequency band. The amplifier itself is not primarily used because of the gain of the stage. It helps reject unwanted signals and prevents radiation of the local oscillator signal, which would cause interference.

Fig. 4-1. Monitor receiver model MCA-353A for the 144- to 174-Mc band. (*DuMont.*)

[1] Minimum Standards for Land-mobile Communication FM or PM Receivers, *RS*-204 (rev. *TR*-119*A*), Electronic Industries Assoc., January, 1958.

Fig. 4-2. Receiver-transmitter for vehicle mounting; 144- to 174-Mc band. (*DuMont.*)

The first converter produces the high IF. There is little difference between the operation of the first local oscillator and transmitter oscillators. Multipliers are used to bring the crystal signal to the proper frequency. The local oscillator signal should have a strong fundamental output and very-low-amplitude harmonics to prevent harmonics from mixing to produce spurious outputs.

Automatic frequency control (AFC) is used in some receivers (Fig. 4-3a) to keep the receiver on exactly the same frequency as the transmitter to which it is tuned. Usually the discriminator voltage output is used to control the local oscillator. By the nature of its circuit the discriminator will have an output which is negative when the incoming signal is on one side of center frequency and which is positive when the incoming signal is on the other side of the center frequency. A reactance tube will have the amplitude of its plate current as a function of the d-c grid voltage derived from the discriminator. Any small change or drift in the transmitted signal or in the receiver local oscillator will cause the discriminator output to vary the inductive (or capacitive) current from the reactance tube. This will cause a small shift in the local oscillator and again lock the transmitter and receiver together.

Image frequencies are rejected by the RF amplifier and its tuned circuits. With a given local oscillator and an intermediate frequency there are two signal frequencies which will result in the IF. One signal is above the oscillator by the IF; the second is below the oscillator by the IF. This second is the image frequency, and the RF amplifier is tuned to the desired station signal, so that it reduces the level of the image frequency signal.

The second, or low, IF is of a lower frequency, and a crystal oscillator without multiplication is used. The exact frequency setting of this is most important to obtain the best receiver performance.

Advantages of the lower IF include greater ease in separating the adjacent and alternate channels because of the greater percentage of separation.

High selectivity is obtained by multiple tuned circuits. Between the plate of one tube and the grid of the next there may be as many as six or eight tuned circuits to help shape the IF response curve.

As the communications channels are narrowed and the channels are placed closer together, selectivity in the IF stages becomes increasingly important. Two techniques other than tuned LC circuits are useful. Crystal IF filters provide very sharp selectivity and can help reduce interference. Electromechanical filters use the principle of physical resonance of mechanical parts to produce steep-sided IF curves.

Limiter stages are used following the last IF amplifiers. In triple superheterodynes, three conversions and three IF amplifier strings are used. The limiter follows the last IF. The detector follows the limiters, and the detector produces the audio for the amplifiers.

The voltage and power audio amplifiers are quite conventional except for the noise-squelch features.

While an FM receiver has less noise on a station than an AM receiver, it is noisy between transmissions. A squelch circuit is used to mute the receiver when no voice is being received.

Mobile receivers are beginning to appear with transistor amplifiers and power supplies. But solid-state devices also have other applications. The Clevite Corporation, for example, has demonstrated a transistor radio and piezoelectric ceramic IF resonators known as Transfilters.[1] These are made in the form of small flat disks of ceramics which, because of their stability, overcome the need for periodic IF alignment.

Another new device is the semiconductor diode used as a low-noise amplifier. Point-contact diodes have long been used as mixers in microwave receivers. However, there is no amplification, but the new diodes can be used for amplification.

In an attempt to reduce the noise, which limits the signal that can be received, a new diode amplifier has been developed. It is called a Varactor, or parametric amplifier, which operates at normal room temperature.[2]

Any nonlinear device can be used as a mixer, and some new types of experimental silicon diodes have a capacitance which varies with the applied voltage. This variable capacitance has been used to tune RF circuits in receiver front ends. And, by the application of a pumping signal, the device can act as a converter with gain.

The block diagram of Fig. 4-3a is a double conversion system for

[1] Solid-state Tuned Circuits Improve IF Amplifier Reliability, *Electrical Design News*, p. 16, May, 1959.

[2] S. Bloom and K. K. N. Chang, Theory of Parametric Amplifiers Using Nonlinear Reactances, *RCA Rev.*, vol. 18, pp. 578–593, December, 1957.

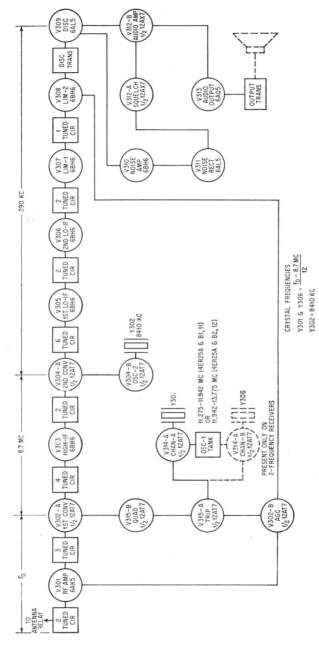

Fig. 4-3a. Receiver block diagram, 144- to 174-Mc band. (*General Electric.*)

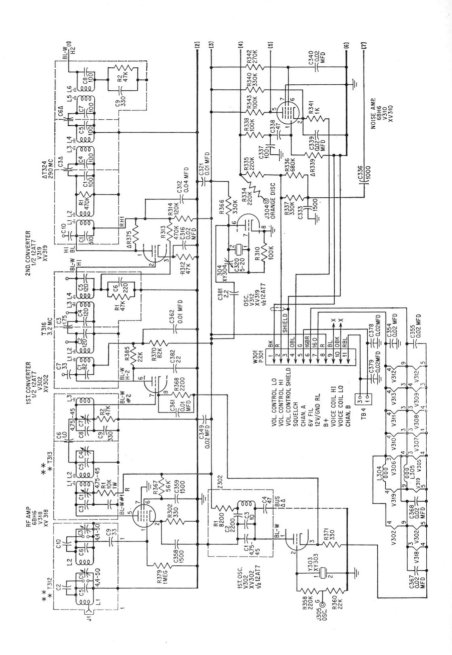

90

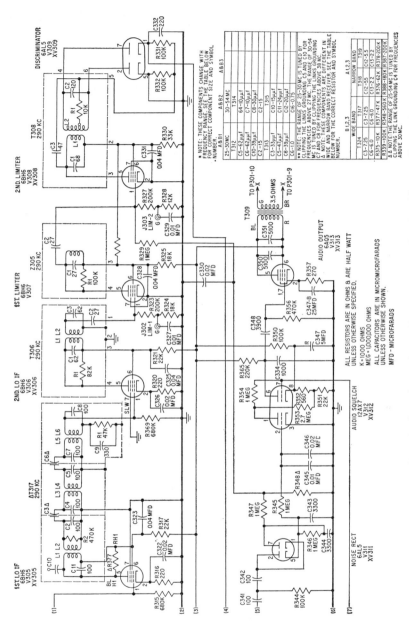

Fig. 4-3b. Simplified receiver schematic, 25- to 50-Mc band. (*General Electric*.)

91

operation in the 144- to 174-Mc band.   The high IF is 8.7 Mc and the low IF is 290 kc.   A multiplication of 12 increases the first local crystal oscillator to 8.7 Mc below the incoming signal which passes through the RF stage.   After the high-frequency IF stage a second crystal oscillator provides a signal for mixing to 290 kc, the low-frequency IF.

4-2. RF Amplifiers

There are three functions of the RF amplifier stage: The signal-to-noise ratio is increased, the local oscillator radiation from the receiver is reduced, and image-frequency rejection is increased.

Signal-to-noise ratio limits the smallest signal which can be received. Increasing the signal level in the RF stage is important, since it is the first receiver stage, and any noise here has a greater effect on the output than noise at any other point in the receiver.

Energy from the local oscillator can be radiated from the receiver antenna.   The RF stage reduces these undesired radiations, because the RF stage is tuned to a different frequency from that of the first local oscillator.

Receiver Noise.   Three sources of noise are tube noise, thermal noise, and random-fluctuation noise.

Tube noise is inherent in the vacuum tube itself; there are several sources.   Shot noise is created by the random changes in the total number of electrons emitted by the cathode.   This total number varies with time, and in effect there is an a-c component in the plate current due to this variation.   With no applied signal to the amplifier stage this shot effect, or shot noise, appears across the plate load as a small random noise.   It is important, because this noise is amplified through the succeeding stages.

Induced grid noise is a type of tube noise caused by the electron stream passing through the several grid structures of a pentode or a single grid in a triode.   As the electrons go through a grid, they cause an induced grid current which adds to the tube noise.

Current flow in a multigrid tube divides among the grids and creates noise.   This division is not constant, because as it changes the plate current varies.   As the different grid potentials change, the current distribution changes and creates noise.

Thermal and random-fluctuation noise are also significant.   Thermal noise occurs because of the electron motion in any conductor as the temperature is increased.   This electron motion acts like a small signal generator; as the temperature increases, the molecular motion becomes greater, and there is more thermal noise.   There is also noise created by the current flow through a conductor.   As with a vacuum-tube current, the current flow in any conductor has small random fluctuations which appear as noise.

All these factors are present in the first stage of radio receivers. An amplifier, of course, amplifies both the signal and the noise. Tube noises from all sources may be compared to the thermal noise in a resistance. Higher values of resistance have more thermal noise, and the equivalent noise figure for a tube increases with the number of electrodes. A triode, for example, has an ENR (equivalent noise resistance) of between 200 and 3,000 ohms; a remote cutoff pentode can have values from 2,500 to 14,000 ohms.

The effect of noise in the first stage is, as above, more important than in the following stages. This may be seen by an example:

Assume that the first RF stage has a noise voltage (total) of 5 μv and a signal of 10 μv with a stage gain of 10. Because the noise and signal are in a random-phase relation, their vector sum is taken, and this is 11.2 μv or a stage output of 112 μv. If the second stage has a noise voltage of 5 μv but the signal here is 112 μv, the vector sum is 112.1 μv and the stage output is 1,121.0 μv.

From this it can be seen that the effective noise in the receiver is determined largely by the first RF stage; if the stage gain exceeds 10, the noise is almost all from the first stage.

The signal-to-noise ratio (S/N) may be determined quite directly. An unmodulated signal source, of the correct frequency, is applied to the receiver. Power output, P_1, is measured. Next, the RF signal is modulated, with less than maximum deviation, and this power output, P_2, is measured, since P_2 is the power output due to the signal and the noise.

The S/N ratio is

$$\frac{P_2 - P_1}{P_1} = \frac{P_2}{P_1} - 1$$

where P_1 = noise power

P_2 = signal power plus noise power

$P_2 - P_1$ = signal power

The S/N ratio is not constant. When the received signal is higher than the squelch-sensitivity level, the S/N ratio is high. When the signal is lower than this level, the ratio is low.

In theory a receiver which was perfect would add no noise to the signal which is received. The noise figure is a measure, in decibels, of the noise added by the actual receiver. Typical noise figures vary from 10 db or higher in the UHF band to about 3 db in the low band. A perfect receiver would have a 0-db noise figure. While the noise figure does not depend on the receiver bandwidth, it is more difficult to obtain a low noise figure with a wideband receiver because of the greater amount of noise.

RF Amplifier Circuits. RF amplifiers usually operate class A. Choice of a tube type depends upon a number of factors.

High gain is desirable to produce an improved S/N ratio, since less noise will be added by succeeding stages. Transformer coupling is used for the RF stage input, since the transmission-line impedance is low and the grid-input impedance is high. The transformer provides a voltage step-up, and since the transformer generates no noise, the greater the voltage step-up, the better the S/N ratio.

In order to have a high step-up ratio, tubes with low input conductance are desirable. Input conductance is the RC network, in which the grid appears to be across the tuned transformer output. It decreases with the square of the rise in operating frequency and also is a function of the input capacity and the transconductance of the tube. Hence a tube with a low transconductance (low gain) is required for greatest voltage step-up in the input transformer.

The two factors are in conflict: high gain for less noise added in the following stages and low gain for greatest voltage step-up and low stage noise. Because of this a compromise design value is used.

Input is through a transformer, as above, for impedance matching and voltage step-up. A balanced two-wire line is tied to a split-transformer input with the center tap grounded as in A of Fig. 4-4. A coaxial line, which is unbalanced, has an input transformer as in B, where the center conductor is tied to the high side and the lower end of the transformer is grounded. Noise voltages in the balanced line are equal in the two conductors and are canceled out in the input where they are out of phase. In the coaxial line the outer conductor acts to shield the signal voltage from noise pickup.

Input circuits can be of several types, as shown in Fig. 4-5 for coaxial lines. A illustrates a tapped coil which acts as an autotransformer. As the feed point is moved up toward the top of the coil, the impedance at the tapped point increases. Direct current is blocked from the transmission line by the series capacitor. In B and C the variable capacitors provide adjustments for impedance matching.

When both the primary and the secondary of a transformer are tuned, as in a bandpass IF, the action of the transformer depends on the coefficient of coupling K between the primary and the secondary. Figure 4-6 is a circuit

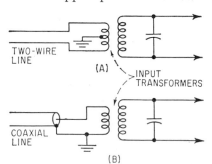

FIG. 4-4. Antenna input transformers.

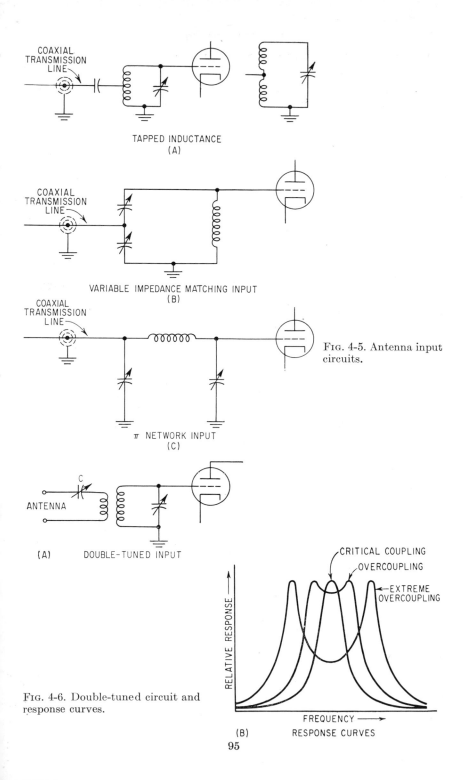

TAPPED INDUCTANCE
(A)

VARIABLE IMPEDANCE MATCHING INPUT
(B)

COAXIAL
TRANSMISSION
LINE

π NETWORK INPUT
(C)

FIG. 4-5. Antenna input circuits.

ANTENNA

(A)   DOUBLE-TUNED INPUT

CRITICAL COUPLING
OVERCOUPLING
EXTREME
OVERCOUPLING

RELATIVE RESPONSE

FREQUENCY

(B)   RESPONSE CURVES

FIG. 4-6. Double-tuned circuit and response curves.

with a tuned primary and tuned secondary transformer. The curves showing the response due to the primary and secondary current for three values of coupling are in *B*. When the coefficient of coupling is small, less than *K*, the secondary current is low, and the response curve is sharply peaked.

But as the coefficient of coupling is increased, the response curve changes and becomes broader. This is because of the reduction in the primary current at resonance and the increase in current at frequencies which are just off resonance. At the same time, the secondary-current peak becomes larger and, at the same time, broader. This continues until the resistance, which is coupled from the secondary into the primary, is equal to the primary resistance.

This point is *critical coupling*, as shown. This causes the secondary current to rise to the maximum value.

The primary-current curve now has two peaks. This humplike curve occurs because it is larger below and above resonance than it is at resonance. At coupling greater than critical, the double peaks of primary current become more pronounced, and they have greater separation. The secondary current also begins to show double peaks. The peaks of primary current are decreased, but the peaks of secondary current are about the same as for critical coupling.

The double humps of these response curves result from the coupled impedance. Total primary impedance includes the impedance of the primary plus the impedance coupled to the primary from the secondary. Thus the effective primary resistance at resonance increases, which results in a reduction in primary current. At frequencies below resonance the impedance of the primary alone is capacitive, but the reflected impedance is inductive. Because of this the effective series impedance is decreased, and the current becomes maximum at a frequency below resonance and above resonance where primary impedance is inductive and the coupled impedance is capacitive. Current is greatest, since the total reactance is less.

Current flow in the secondary is a function of the secondary impedance and the voltage induced in the secondary, which has the characteristics of the primary-current curve. This means that the secondary-current curve is the result of the shape of the primary-current curve and the shape of the resonance curve of the secondary when each is considered separately. The secondary-current curve is more peaked than primary-current curve.

The value of *M*, or mutual coupling, in conventional receiver circuits is equal to, or just slightly greater than, the critical value. The sides of the curve fall off more rapidly than with a single tuned circuit, and the curve has a flatter top, which makes the discrimination effect between the passband and other frequencies much better than could be obtained with a single tuned circuit. Such a circuit has good selectivity and is more useful for bandpass circuits.

The selectivity curve depends upon the degree of coupling between primary and secondary, but it also depends on the Q and resonant frequency of the primary and the Q and resonant frequency of the secondary. Critical coupling causes the greatest amount of current flow in the secondary and also the greatest voltage output. The shape of this curve and the amount of the current in the secondary depend on the primary and secondary being tuned to the same resonant frequency and the Q of each circuit. The greater the Q, the greater the selectivity.

The Q of the primary or the secondary is a function of several factors and may be expressed as

$$Q = \frac{X_L}{R}$$

The coefficient of coupling K, for critical coupling, is given by

$$K_c = \frac{1}{Q}$$

where $Q = \sqrt{Q_p Q_s}$.

But the value of Q which is used is greater than that needed for critical coupling by a factor of 1.5.

Bandwidth is a function of both K and the resonant frequency f. Thus

$$BW = Kf$$

When the Q's of the primary and the secondary are equal, the response curves are symmetrical with respect to a mean frequency. However, when the primary and secondary are tuned to frequencies which differ slightly, the effect is as if the coefficient of couplings were increased and the two circuits were tuned to the same frequency.

The RF input circuit feeds the amplifier tube as in Fig. 4-7. A common circuit is the grid-input grounded-cathode pentode in A. A triode in this circuit requires neutralization to prevent oscillation; pentodes can be used, as shown, but their noise figure is higher than that of triodes.

In the grounded-grid circuit B the input is to the cathode, and the grid acts as a shield between cathode and plate. Voltage gain is less than the grounded-cathode circuit.

The input impedance is low; hence a large voltage step-up cannot be used. For this reason the noise performance is poor. Triodes can be used as grounded-grid amplifiers without the need for neutralization.

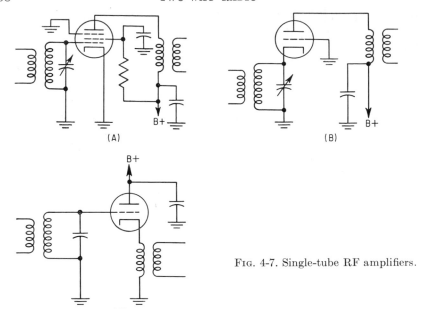

(A)   (B)

Fig. 4-7. Single-tube RF amplifiers.

(C)

The grounded plate or the cathode follower C has the input to the grid and the output from the cathode. The plate is at RF ground. This type of amplifier does not require neutralization either, and a triode may also be used. Input impedance is higher than in the grounded-cathode circuit in A, and a voltage step-up can be used. But the tube always has a voltage gain of less than one. Because the cathode current is high and the voltage is low, the impedance of the output is low. This sometimes creates problems for the matching to the mixer stage.

Improved reception at base stations is made possible by the use of a new RF amplifier, the 7077 ceramic tube which amplifies at frequencies beyond the UHF region. This, in effect, increases the sensitivity of the base-station receiver and allows it to pick up weak transmissions from mobile units operating at extreme ranges. This tube and its packaged amplifier can also be used in the mobile radio, thus extending two-way communications. Gain from this tube, when used in the base station, provides a range increase equivalent to an increase of four times in the power of the mobile transmitter. Thus with a large number of mobile units a single amplifier placed ahead of the base-station receiver increases the range of each of the mobile units without any change in the mobile equipment.

This amplifier, produced by General Electric, also serves as an antenna-matching unit, which allows the use of four receivers from a single high-gain antenna. The 7077 ceramic tube is ½ in. long and ½ in. wide; it was originally designed for use as an RF amplifier at frequencies up to 1,200 Mc. At 450 Mc it is rated at 5.5-db noise figure with 14.5-db gain.

All the RF amplifiers discussed above may be used in push-pull; the grounded-grid circuit in Fig. 4-8 is an example. Compared with single-tube amplifiers the input voltage must be twice the value, the input impedance is four times as great, and the effective tube capacity is one-half normal. The grounded-grid circuit as illustrated has a low input impedance, as does the same single-tube circuit.

Two RF tubes can be used in series as well as in push-pull. The cascade grounded-grid circuit is illustrated in A of Fig. 4-9. This does not need neutralization and, in part, makes up for the low gain in a single stage, since the total gain is the product of the two. One

FIG. 4-8. Push-pull RF amplifiers.

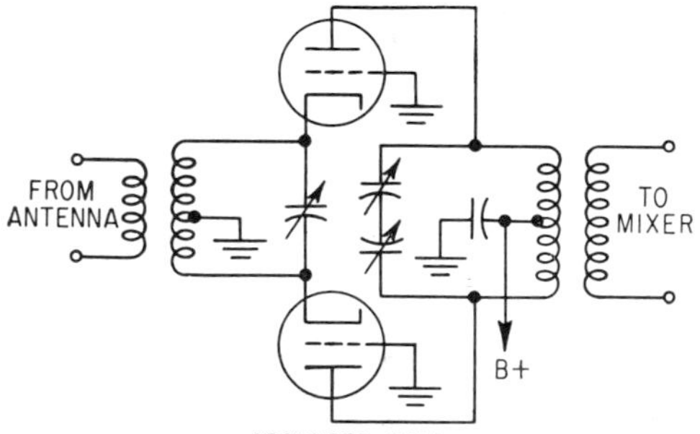

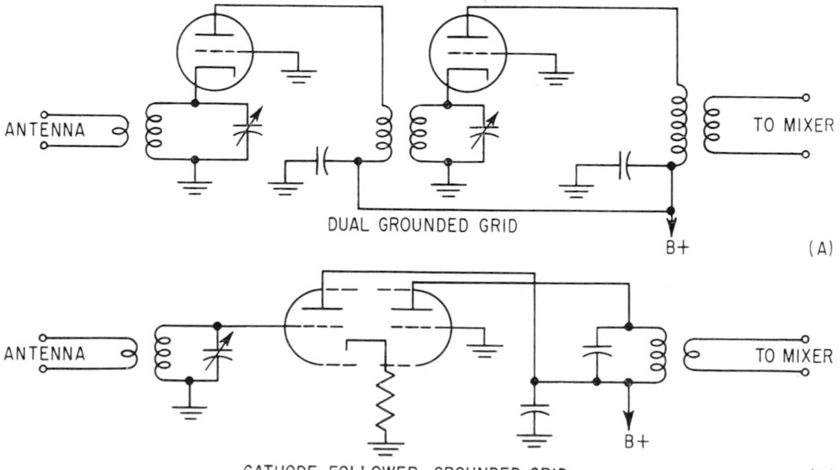

GROUNDED GRID

DUAL GROUNDED GRID

(A)

CATHODE FOLLOWER–GROUNDED GRID

(B)

FIG. 4-9. Cascade RF amplifiers.

of the other possibilities is the cathode-coupled circuit in *B*. A common cathode resistor couples the two amplifiers. Input to the first grid causes cathode current and a cathode signal voltage. This cathode voltage is the input to the second stage, whose plate provides the output. Other cascade amplifiers include the grounded-cathode neutralized triode driving a grounded-grid amplifier; it provides a good noise figure.

4-3. Frequency Conversion

Frequency conversion heterodynes (mixes) the RF signal and a local oscillator signal to produce the IF. Usually a separate oscillator stage and a mixer stage are used. In some low-frequency applications these may be combined in a single converter stage.

Mixers. The mixer tube receives the RF-modulated signal input and the local oscillator signal; the mixer output is the first IF. The local oscillator signal is much stronger than the modulated RF signal. Nonlinear mixer operation is necessary to produce the IF and may be obtained in several ways. Figure 4-10 illustrates the mixer-tube operation. The local oscillator, or unmodulated signal, is mixed, or

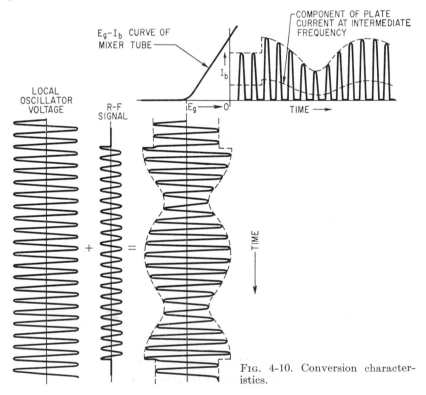

Fig. 4-10. Conversion characteristics.

heterodyned, with the received signal and results in the IF with the same modulation characteristics as the original received signal. In the block diagram of the receiver, Fig. 4-3a, the crystal signal is multiplied 12 times, so it will be of the proper frequency to mix and produce the high IF.

Many different frequencies are present in the mixer output; where f_0 is the oscillator signal after multiplication, f_1 is the RF input, and f_2 is the IF, the components of the output are $f_0 + f_1, f_0 - f_1, f_0, f_1$, and f_2, as well as others. Because the output is tuned to the IF, this output has the greatest amplitude.

Conversion gain is the IF amplitude divided by the RF amplitude. It depends upon the size of the oscillator signal, the tube transconductance, the plate load, and other factors.

Spurious mixer responses are possible because of signals other than the desired RF passing through the RF stages and local oscillator harmonics coming from the local oscillator. Local oscillator pulling or frequency shifting is caused by coupling between the RF signal and the local oscillator. Isolation between these controls this pulling.

Oscillator radiation is to be avoided, since this would be a source of interference for other receivers. One of the functions of the stages of RF amplification is to prevent the local oscillator signal from appearing at the antenna.

Mixers can be diodes, triodes, or pentodes. In Fig. 4-11 a pentode tube appears as an amplifier. The input is tuned to the RF signal, but the output is resonant at the IF frequency. A high conversion gain can be obtained, and use of the pentode reduces the coupling of the input and output signals.

The oscillator signal and the RF signal from the preceding stages both are applied to the mixer grid, but in special mixer tubes (pentagrid converters) two different grids are used. One, the signal grid, or grid 3, has screen grids on both sides. The other, grid 1, is used for the oscillator signal.

Oscillators. In two-way radio the local oscillators all provide

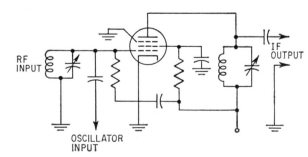

FIG. 4-11. Converter, or mixer, stage.

RF INPUT

IF OUTPUT

OSCILLATOR INPUT

crystal-controlled signals.[1] This is required by the need for stable oscillators. Crystal oscillators for this purpose are described in Chap. 3. As in the receiver block diagram, frequency multiplication brings this local oscillator signal up to the proper frequency for mixing.

Converters. A converter stage is a single tube operating as an oscillator mixer. A pentagrid converter is shown in Fig. 4-12. The cathode, grid 1, and the screen (acting as a plate) form the crystal-oscillator triode. Electrons from the cathode to the actual plate are modulated by this local oscillator signal. RF from the amplifier stages is applied to the shielded control grid and the output is tuned to the IF frequency.

4-4. IF Amplifiers

Both RF and IF amplifiers operate at radio frequencies, but the RF amplifiers are before frequency conversion, and IF amplifiers are after the conversion and hence operate at lower frequencies.

Pentode amplifiers, because of their low grid-to-plate capacity, provide the highest gain with the least tendency to break into self-oscillation.

The heart of a modern mobile receiver is the IF amplifier, as in Fig. 4-13, which provides most of the selectivity and a large part of the gain. Three characteristics of IF stages are frequency, gain, and selectivity.

Gain. Gain is most easily obtained at lower frequencies; the lower the IF, the higher must be the crystal-oscillator frequency, through the multiplier chain, but temperature-controlled crystals provide adequate stability.

The choice of frequency depends upon several factors. Spurious responses from other signals affect the choice of the IF frequency. One of the most important is image response.

[1] A. G. Manke, Crystal Oscillators in Communication Receivers, *IRE, PGVC*-7, p. 10, December, 1957.

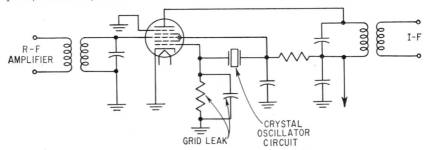

FIG. 4-12. Single-tube oscillator and mixer.

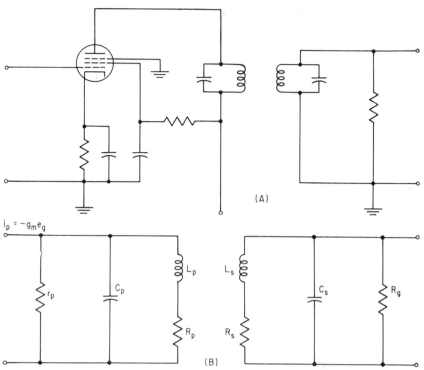

FIG. 4-13. Double-tuned IF amplifier.

A local oscillator can produce the desired IF from two different signals. The proper channel, to which the receiver is tuned, is one signal and the other is the image signal. Let the desired channel be 165.060 Mc with a local oscillator (first crystal oscillator) at 156.360 Mc, resulting after a multiplication of 12 from a 13.03-Mc crystal. The difference will be 8.700 Mc, which is this particular IF. But another transmitter, also in the 144- to 174-Mc band, operating on 147.660 Mc, will also beat with 156.360 Mc to produce the same 8.7-Mc IF.

Selectivity. Single-frequency amplification occurs because of the parallel resonant circuits at the input and output. These parallel circuits discriminate against all other frequencies by developing maximum voltage at their resonant frequency and minimum voltage at other frequencies. This ability of an amplifier to select one frequency and reject others is called *selectivity*.

Selectivity in an amplifier is greatest when high-Q-tuned circuits are used. A high-Q-tuned circuit is produced by using powdered-iron cores in the transformers.

The RF tuning must be at least selective enough to attenuate image signals, for they will not be removed by any degree of IF selectivity. However, the choice of the IF is important, because the lower the value of this frequency, the greater will be the image interference. Raising the IF gives greater separation of these image responses.

A transmitter operating on 8.7 Mc, the IF in this discussion, could cause interference, but here again this would be removed by the RF-tuned circuits.

A basic part of the problem of the increased use of mobile radio is adjacent-channel operation, which requires a receiver of high selectivity. It is not possible to obtain this degree of selectivity in the RF stages alone, of even modern receivers, and the IF-tuned circuits provide the selectivity. Figure 4-13 illustrates the double-tuned IF amplifier. The primary circuit has output capacitance and wiring capacitance which are, in total, C_p. The coil resistance is R_p, and the inductance is L_p. Secondary elements are L_s and R_s, as in the primary, the total capacitance C_s, and the grid resistance R_g.

The equivalent circuit (B in Fig. 4-13) in the constant-current form has a plate current of

$$i_p = -g_m e_0$$

The theoretical response which is desired is shown in A of Fig. 4-14. All signals in the desired 30-kc band are amplified equally, and there is no amplification outside the desired channel. An actual IF-tuned circuit has a response more like that in B of Fig. 4-14, since all tuned circuits have sloping sides; the difference is in the degree of slope. The important characteristics of a response curve are shown. A flat top to the response means all signals in the passband are amplified equally. Unequal amplification results in signal distortion. Steep sides relate to how fast the response drops off at the edges of the band. A 30-kc channel is assumed here, and because the sides of the curve cannot drop off vertically, the position where they cross the channel

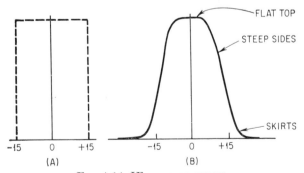

FIG. 4-14. IF response curves.

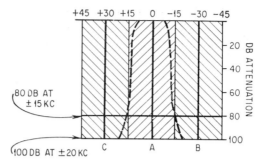

Fig. 4-15. Adjacent-channel response.

limits is important. The skirts, or ends, of the curve extend into adjacent channels, and these should be as small as possible. Other bandwidths have curves with similar characteristics.

Adjacent-channel Interference. These factors may be seen in terms of numbers in Fig. 4-15. A is the center frequency of the channel ± 15 kc wide. B and C are the center frequencies of the adjacent channels. The response of the desired circuit is shown as the dashed line. Acceptable commercial limits for this curve are 80 db down at the adjacent-channel limits and 100 db down at 20 kc away from the center frequency. This is an approach to the ultimate as in A of Fig. 4-14. At the channel edges the power ratio is 1 to 10^7, or if the power at the center frequency is 1 watt, the power at this ± 15-kc point is 0.000 000 1 watt, or 0.1 microwatt. The ± 20 kc signals are as 1 watt is to 0.000 000 001 watt, or 0.001 microwatt.

Second IF. After a second conversion the low IF is produced. Advantages of this 290-kc amplifier, as a typical example, may be seen from Table 4-1, where A is the desired channel, B and D are adjacent, and C and E are alternate channels. Again with a 30-kc channel this 30 kc is 0.018 per cent of the RF, 0.34 per cent of the high IF, but at the low IF this is 10.4 per cent, which means greater ease in separating the adjacent and alternate channels because of the greater percentage of separation.

TABLE 4-1. RF AND IF RELATIONSHIP

Channel	RF	High IF	Low IF
C	164.970	8.640	0.230
B	165.000	8.670	0.260
A	165.030	8.700	0.290
D	165.060	8.730	0.320
E	165.090	8.760	0.350

High selectivity is obtained by multiple tuned circuits.   Between
the plate of one tube and the grid of the next there may be as many as
six or eight tuned circuits to help shape the IF response curve.

In some receivers, as in *B* of Fig. 4-16, triple conversion is used for
greater selectivity.   Crystal *Y* frequency is multiplied 36 times to
heterodyne with the RF signal to produce the first IF at 48 Mc in the
first converter.   The second crystal is at 44.8 Mc and mixes in the
second converter, resulting in the second IF of 3.2 Mc.   A low IF of

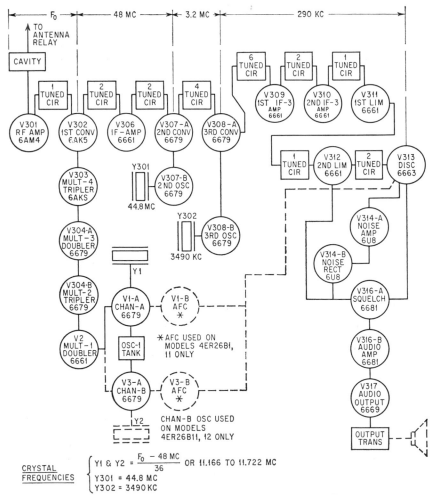

F_{IG}. 4-16. UHF-receiver block diagram.   (*General Electric.*)

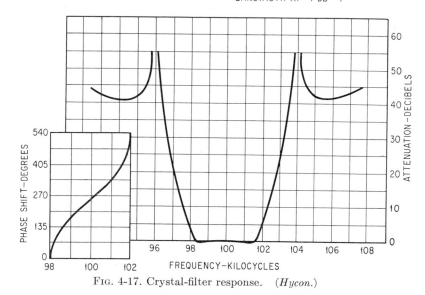

BANDWIDTH 0.6 TO 10%   MEDIUM SELECTIVITY: $\dfrac{\text{BANDWIDTH AT 40 DB}}{\text{BANDWIDTH AT 4 DB}} = \dfrac{1.8}{1}$

FIG. 4-17. Crystal-filter response. (*Hycon.*)

290 kc is the result of the third crystal, Y_{302}, at 3.49 Mc heterodyning with the 3.2 Mc in the third converter.

As the communications channels are narrowed and placed close together, selectivity in the IF stages becomes increasingly important. Two techniques other than tuned LC circuits are useful. Crystal filters, as in Fig. 4-17, provide very sharp selectivity and can help reduce interference. This is an example of the selectivity of a crystal filter. The center frequency here is 100 kc, but any other desired frequency can be obtained. This response is flat for about 4 kc and cuts off above and below 4 kc for a total of 8 kc. Other channel widths can be designed for specific purposes. This example is used only to show the possibilities in this crystal filter.[1]

An electromechanical filter is another device for improving IF selectivity. This is a mechanical resonant circuit, driven by the plate and received by the grid. It has been used in military equipment, and its application to two-way radio has been the subject of experimental radios. Figure 4-18 illustrates two possible circuits: *A* shows plate driving with the magnetic driver fed in shunt. *B* shows the electromechanical filter used with transistors.

[1] See also Daniel Elders and Emanuel Gikow, Ceramic IF Filters Match Transistors, *Electronics*, p. 59, Apr. 25, 1958.

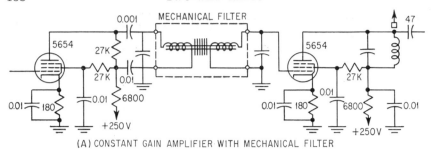

(A) CONSTANT GAIN AMPLIFIER WITH MECHANICAL FILTER

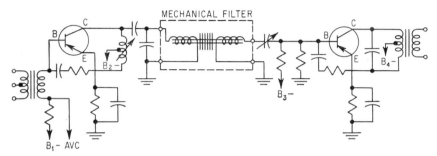

(B) USE OF A MECHANICAL FILTER IN CONJUNCTION WITH TRANSISTORIZED IF AMPLIFIERS

FIG. 4-18. Mechanical-filter circuits. (*Collins Radio.*)

Examples of the bandpass are shown in Fig. 4-19. A 12.6-kc bandwidth is shown in A; B shows a 25-kc bandwidth. These are examples of the possibilities.

4-5. Limiters

A limiter is an IF stage designed to produce an output signal of a certain level. Any further increase in the signal input level does not increase the output. In the ideal limiter, as shown in Fig. 4-20A, the amplitude variations in the input are removed. Modulation of the RF signal is a change in phase or frequency; hence this clipping does not cause distortion.

There are several types of limiting which result in peak clipping of the amplitude variations in the FM signal.

Grid limiting can be illustrated by Fig. 4-20B. The desired clipping, or limiting, action will remove the peaks of the input signal and hence take away the undesired amplitude variations. Bias for this tube is developed by the cathode current through the cathode resistor. If this voltage drop is 5 volts, the grid-to-cathode voltage difference will bias the tube by this amount.

Input voltage, applied to the grid, is shown in C; the peak positive

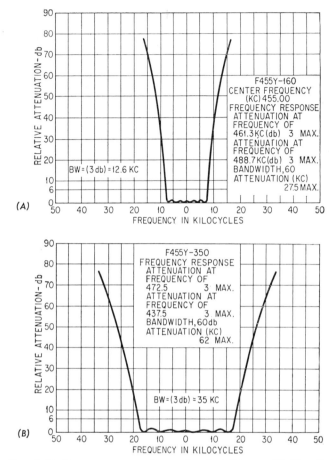

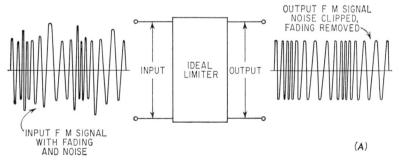

FIG. 4-19. Response curves for mechanical filters. *(Collins Radio.)*

FIG. 4-20. Limiters: *(A)* ideal limiter.

109

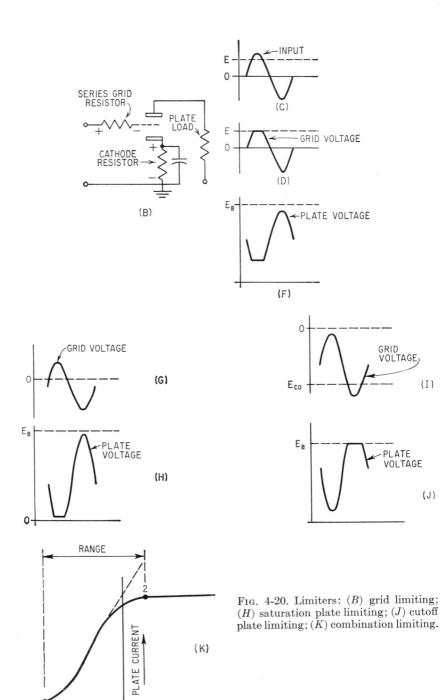

FIG. 4-20. Limiters: (B) grid limiting; (H) saturation plate limiting; (J) cutoff plate limiting; (K) combination limiting.

110

input voltage exceeds E. When the input signal starts from zero and increases in a positive direction (C), the grid-signal voltage increases (D) while the plate current increases and the plate voltage decreases, as in F. When the input signal is slightly greater than E, current will flow from cathode to grid and through the grid resistor, developing a voltage across this resistor. Any further increase in the signal voltage will increase the grid current and voltage across the series grid resistor; hence the grid voltage is limited to E. The plate voltage, in turn, does not drop below the value determined by the plate current, and the plate voltage is clipped or limited on its negative swing.

It is possible to limit, in much the same fashion, without a series grid resistor. This may be seen from Fig. 4-20G. If the grid signal is large enough and the operating point is correct, plate saturation will occur, which will limit the negative portion of the plate voltage swing. A large value of plate load resistance and a low value of plate supply voltage are required. As the grid signal drives the grid positive, the plate current increases, but there is a limit to the plate current equal to E_b/R_1, where E_b is the supply voltage and R_1 is the load resistance. Actually, because there is a small plate-to-cathode resistance during saturation, the plate current is somewhat less than the limiting value. During the negative-going portion of the grid signal, the plate current decreases and the plate voltage rises. In a stage with a resistive load, the plate voltage can rise as high as E_b. Thus, as shown in H of Fig. 4-20, saturation limiting will also clip the negative portion of the plate voltage output.

A third type of limiting is the cutoff action of the plate current as illustrated in Fig. 4-20. In I the grid voltage swing is between a value less than zero and a value beyond cutoff. Going first in the positive direction, the grid voltage causes an increasing plate current with a corresponding decrease in plate voltage as in J. During the negative-going alternation of the grid voltage, the grid exceeds E_{co}, which is the value necessary to cut off the plate current. The plate voltage rises to E_b, when the plate current ceases, and the result is a limiting of the positive alternation of the plate voltage.

By overdriving, an amplifier clipping of both alternations is possible by use of both saturation and cutoff limiting. All the amplitude variations are removed by such a circuit, and the output has a constant amplitude.

Limiting is effective in removing some of the AM noise provided that the signal input is large enough to permit the clipping action.

Bias for the limiter stage is small, and the d-c supply for the screen and plate is lower than normal. Thus when a positive-going grid signal exceeds point 2 on the curve of Fig. 4-20K, there is no amplification; the tube is at saturation. In the opposite sense the signal can swing in the negative direction to point 1, after which the tube is cut off. To obtain the proper limiting action the grid signal input to the stage must swing beyond the range from point 1 to point 2.

For proper limiting action the signal input must be sufficiently large; otherwise the stage operates as an IF amplifier without clipping.

A limiter stage is shown in Fig. 4-21. Self-bias (grid bias) is used rather than the cathode bias in regular IF amplifiers. Both the input and output tuned circuits are resonant to the IF. Grid rectification, caused when the grid goes positive in relation to the cathode, causes a current flow through the grid resistor, making the grid negative. This charges the capacitor C to the maximum (peak) of the a-c grid voltage.

Grid rectification provides bias for the stage, and it also clips the positive peaks of the input signal. A steady bias is developed by this RC network. Impulse noise or short-term variations are removed by this action.

Cascade Limiters. Both fading, which is a long-term change, and impulse noise, which is a short-term change, are removed by two limiters in series or cascade (Fig. 4-22). Transformer coupling (A) provides greater gain for the second stage whenever this is required by a small input signal. The circuit in greatest use is the RC coupling as in B, and it has less gain than transformer coupling. C illustrates impedance coupling, which has a gain between A and B.

The action of a cascade limiter may be seen from Fig. 4-23. In A the first-stage grid voltage is shown with positive clipping due to grid rectification. Plate voltage is 180° out of phase with the grid voltage, and this plate voltage is the grid voltage of the following stage. This is B. Clipping results in the alternate cycle being limited; hence both peaks are clipped, one by each stage. This is the grid action only and assumes a small input signal. A large signal is clipped by both grid and plate in each stage.

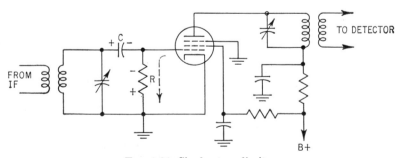

FIG. 4-21. Single-stage limiter.

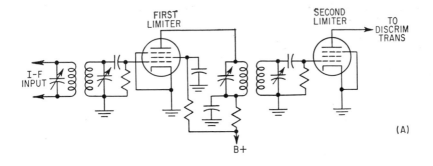

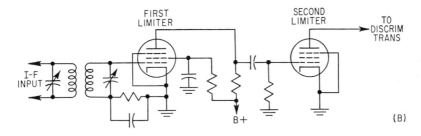

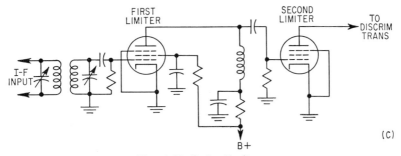

Fig. 4-22. Series limiters.

Fig. 4-23. Clipping or limiting action.

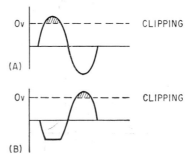

4-6. Detectors

A tuned circuit as in Fig. 4-24 can be used to change FM into AM for detection when tuned to one side of the IF frequency.   For AM where f_0 is the IF, the resonant circuit is tuned to this, and the diode detector operates as an AM demodulator.   But, when FM is received, the IF is f_1, and the detector appears detuned.   The FM signal swings over the range from $f_1 - \Delta f$ to $f_1 + \Delta f$, and the changes in frequency appear to the diode as changes in amplitude.   Variations of the IF signal when an FM signal is received are changed into AM variations by the resonant circuit.

This detuned, or slope, detector illustrates the principle of the FM detector.

Figure 4-25 illustrates the Travis discriminator, which is effectively two slope detectors, one tuned above and one tuned below the center frequency. A shows the circuit, and B indicates the separate response of each circuit taken alone.   If the low IF is 290 kc, I is tuned to 275 kc (15 kc below), and II is tuned to 305 kc (15 kc above). B shows the response of each circuit taken alone.   But by connecting the two load resistors in opposition, output I is positive and output II is negative.

At 290 kc the two outputs are equal.   Going from 290 kc toward 275 kc the positive output (I) increases and the negative output (II) decreases.   The resultant output is positive.   Going from 290 kc toward 305 kc the situation reverses, and the resulting output is negative.

C is B redrawn to indicate the proper polarity, and D is a drawing of only that part of the combined output which is used for detection.

Figure 4-26A is the single-tuned (Foster-Seeley) discriminator.

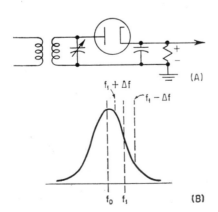

Fig. 4-24. Slope detection.

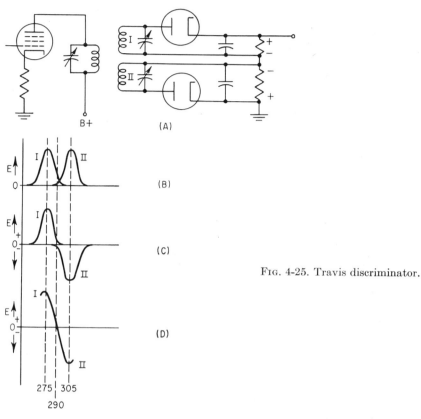

FIG. 4-25. Travis discriminator.

Operation of the detection process may be seen from Figs. 4-27B and 4-27C.

The two coils L_1 and L_2 are the primary and the secondary, respectively, of the IF transformers. The secondary coil is tuned to the correct frequency. Tubes V_1 and V_2 are diode detector tubes. The filters R_2C_2 and R_3C_3 serve the same purpose as the filters in the diode detector; that is, they remove the RF component from the circuit. R_2 and R_3 are the diode loads, and C_2 and C_3 are RF bypasses.

The presence of R_1 and its connection to the primary at the top and to the secondary at the center furnishes an unusual feature in the discriminator circuit. Since it is connected across the primary, the primary-voltage resistor appears across it at all times. The connection to each diode from this causes the primary voltage (E_p) to appear at the plates of the diode with the same phase shift in each case. This voltage causes currents to flow in the opposite directions in the resistors R_2 and R_3, resulting in zero output from received carrier only. There-

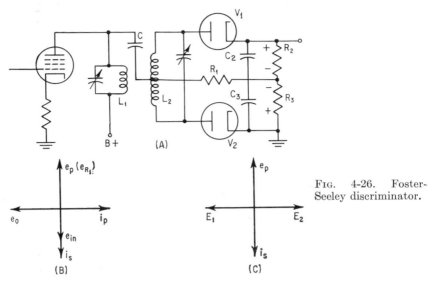

FIG. 4-26. Foster-Seeley discriminator.

fore, the discriminator is not affected when the amplitude of the applied voltage changes.

The discriminator circuit is fed by two signals from the preceding limiter stage. One signal is inductively coupled by the transformer; the second signal is capacitively coupled, and it is the same as the a-c plate voltage of the limiter.

L_1 is the limiter plate coil, and it is the primary of the discriminator transformer. The primary current i_p lags the primary voltage e_p by 90°, as in B of Fig. 4-26. As the primary current changes, it induces a voltage, e_{in} in the secondary. This e_{in} lags the primary current by 90° and the primary voltage by 180°. Because of the induced secondary voltage there is a secondary current i_s which is in phase with e_{in} if the signal frequency is that of the resonant circuit.

The secondary of a tuned transformer is a *series*-resonant circuit. Hence, when the signal frequency is higher than the circuit-resonant frequency, the circuit is inductive, and the current lags the voltage. And if the signal frequency is below resonance, the circuit is capacitive, and the current leads the voltage.

Output voltage from the secondary, as a series circuit, appears across the tuning capacitor; hence this e_o, or output voltage, lags the secondary current i_s by 90°. The significant relationships are shown in C of Fig. 4-26. Primary voltage e_p appears across R; hence it is applied to both diodes equally. The secondary voltage e_o appears to the two diodes with two components which are 180° out of phase. These are shown as E_1 and E_2 in the drawing, and they are out of phase because the two plates of the capacitor must have opposite charges. And e_p is applied to both diodes in the same phase.

The action may be seen in the following steps: Resonance is at the IF. At resonance E_1 and E_2, the voltages from the secondary, are equal, and the diodes conduct equally. The total output is zero as in Fig. 4-27A.

Above resonance the secondary is inductive (series circuit above resonance), E_1 exceeds E_2, and the resulting output is positive as in B.

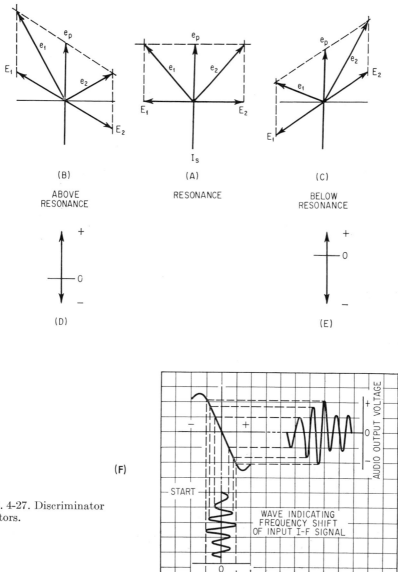

FIG. 4-27. Discriminator vectors.

Below resonance the secondary is capacitive (series circuit below resonance) and E_2 exceeds E_1; the resulting output is negative as in C.

4-7. Squelch Systems

While an FM receiver has less noise on a station than an AM receiver, it is noisy between transmissions. A noise-squelch circuit is used to mute the receiver when no signal is being received. A method for doing this is shown in Fig. 4-28A. The grid voltage from the limiter stage is fed to the squelch tube, whose cathode bias resistor is common with the audio-voltage-amplifier cathode. With no signal through the receiver, the limiter grid has no bias, and this causes the squelch tube to conduct heavily. This current, through the common cathode resistor, is sufficient to cut off the audio amplifier, so that there is no audio output and no noise amplification when the signal is absent.

When a signal is received, the limiter negative-grid potential cuts the squelch tube off and permits normal audio amplification. While this circuit works well enough for strong received signals, a more complex arrangement is required for smaller signals.

Limiter Squelch-voltage Source. The circuit in Fig. 4-28A used the limiter as the control-voltage source. Limiter-derived voltage can be used in other ways for noise squelch; Fig. 4-28B illustrates another method. R_1 is a voltage divider to the B voltage, and this voltage

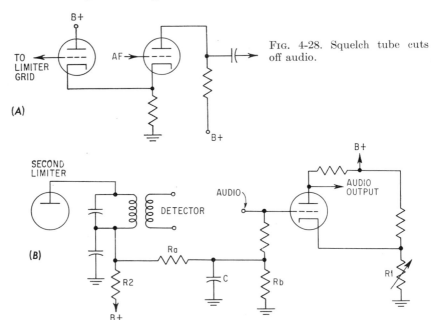

Fig. 4-28. Squelch tube cuts off audio.

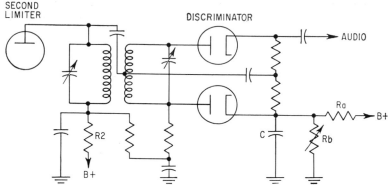

FIG. 4-29. Limiter controls diode conduction.

drop, applied to the cathode, can be adjusted to cut the audio amplifier off with no signal input to the limiter. A received signal applied to the limiter changes the limiter plate voltage; this change is fed to the amplifier grid through the R_a, R_b network. The amplifier then conducts and provides an audio output. Figure 4-29 shows the limiter plate voltage applied to the discriminator diodes; through R_a and R_b a positive voltage is applied to the cathodes of the diodes. Only when the limiter has an applied signal can the diodes conduct in the normal manner.

Discriminator Squelch-voltage Source. Discriminator voltage can also be used for noise squelch as in Fig. 4-30. Audio from the top of R_3 is applied to the amplifier grid. At the junction of R_3 and R_4 there is a negative voltage when a signal is being received. This negative

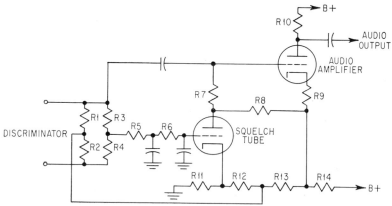

FIG. 4-30. Discriminator as a squelch source.

potential allows the audio tube to amplify by preventing current through the squelch tube. In the absence of a received signal, the squelch tube conducts, which lowers its plate voltage; this cuts off the audio amplifier through R_7. B voltage through the divider R_{14}, R_{13}, R_{12}, and R_{11} is applied to the junction of R_1 and R_2. This positive voltage permits the squelch tube to conduct when no signal is being received.

Noise-rectifier Squelch. A system using a noise amplifier and rectifier is shown in Fig. 4-31. Audio from the detector is applied to the voltage-amplifier tube. Noise voltage only is placed on the noise-amplifier grid by a small-value series capacitor. These noise voltages are rectified by the diode, and the resulting positive potential e_1 keeps the squelch tube conducting, which cuts off the audio amplifier by a negative grid voltage e_2. When a signal is received, the limiter-grid negative voltage e_3 overcomes the positive voltage on the squelch tube. This cuts off the squelch tube, which removes the grid bias on the audio amplifier and permits an audio output.

Figure 4-32 illustrates another noise-rectifier system; without a received signal there is a small amount of noise from the discriminator. This small noise voltage is fed to the noise amplifier, and the output is rectified by one section of the noise rectifier. The negative voltage of C_6 is applied to the grid of the first limiter through R_5. This reduces its gain. Positive peaks are rectified by the other half of the tube. The positive voltage through C_5 is applied to the grid of the squelch tube through R_6. The squelch tube conducts and cuts off the audio amplifier by a negative grid voltage.

A modification of this circuit applies the negative voltage from the first limiter grid to the squelch amplifier through a resistor network. A diode, connected across one resistor, keeps the rectified audio signal

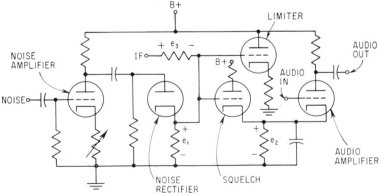

FIG. 4-31. Limiter grid voltage opens audio amplifier.

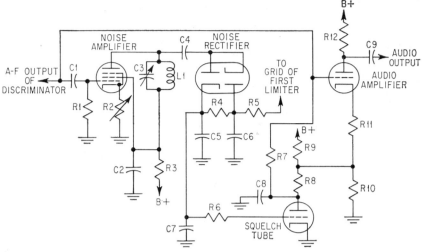

FIG. 4-32. Noise amplifier cuts off audio amplifier through squelch.

in the limiter grid circuit from the squelch tube. Higher-frequency audio, from the discriminator, is taken by a high-pass filter to a rectifier and also supplied to the squelch grid. With no signal present, a positive voltage results from the noise diodes with no signal operating the squelch tube and cutting off the audio amplifier. With a signal, the negative voltage from the first limiter grid cancels this voltage, and the audio amplifier can conduct. This squelch circuit can operate on very weak signals.

The amplifier circuit above requires a steady value of supply voltage. In portable battery-operated equipment a different circuit may be used. The circuit in Fig. 4-33 is dependent on the abrupt starting

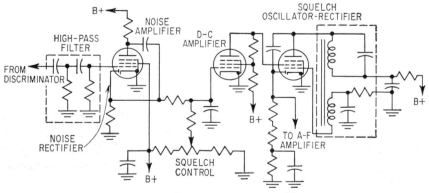

FIG. 4-33. Squelch-oscillator rectifier.

FIG. 4-34. Control head showing controls. (*General Electric.*)

characteristic of a pentode oscillator. A noise amplifier and rectifier are fed with noise from the discriminator. The rectified noise voltage is applied to a d-c amplifier with an adjustable squelch control. Only the high frequencies are applied to the noise rectifier. The high-pass filter provides a high impedance to any audio voltages. With no signal the rectified negative voltage at the grid of the d-c amplifier is sufficient to cut off the tube. The resulting high value of screen voltage starts the squelch-oscillator-rectifier tube oscillating. The output is fed to a second rectifier; it is rectified and results in a high negative voltage. When fed to the grid of the first audio tube, it cuts the tube off and prevents noise in the output.

When a signal is received, voltage is removed from the rectifier and the noise amplifier. Conduction of the d-c amplifier lowers the screen voltage and stops oscillation. The audio amplifier passes the audio signal, since the rectified voltage output from the oscillator diode stops.

Figure 4-34 illustrates the squelch and volume controls on a mobile-radio control head.

Tone Squelch. An important addition to noise squelch is a second, and a parallel, system of tone squelch.[1] As in Fig. 4-35 the receiver is equipped with a second squelch circuit, which responds to the audio tone only. This is in addition to the noise squelch. When the transmitted carrier is continuously modulated by this tone, the receiver's tone-squelch circuit allows the audio amplifiers to operate, and this permits the message to be heard. Other transmissions on the same channel which are not tone-modulated will *not* be heard by the operator.

Figure 4-36 illustrates the tone-squelch circuit added to the receiver. The received tone signal is amplified by the selective amplifier, rectified, and then applied to the existing d-c amplifier. This amplifier and the limiters provide for protection, so that only the desired tone

[1] J. Najork, *Electronic Technician*, Double Barreled Squelch in Two-way Radios, p. 31A, February, 1958.

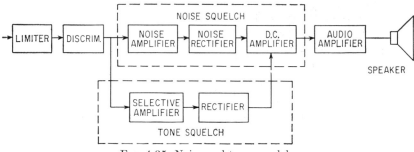

FIG. 4-35. Noise and tone squelch.

signal transmitted at the proper level will operate the tone-squelch circuit.

Tone squelch can be added to present mobile and base stations now in use, or it can be factory-installed on new radio equipment. Monitoring of the operating frequency, to determine if it is clear of other signals before transmitting, is possible with this system.

Using this system of tone squelch the audio tone is transmitted together with the audio signal, and it continues during the signal transmission. But it is also necessary for the operator to be able to listen for other possible calls on the same frequency before transmitting his reply, to avoid interference. This requires a method for opening, or disabling, the tone squelch at the receiver. With the tone squelch removed, the operator can listen for other calls before transmitting.

When the microphone is removed from the hook switch, the tone squelch is opened but the noise squelch remains in operation.

Modulation of the transmitter is by means of a circuit which converts the selective-amplifier circuit used for the receive function into a stable tone generator or oscillator. A silicon diode is connected across the transmitter crystal.

As the voltage across the diode changes, it can be made to look like a small variable capacitor. The audio-tone signal across the diode varies this capacity and frequency modulates the transmitted signal. The frequency deviation of the tone modulation is kept at a very low value (± 1 kc for wideband and $\pm \frac{3}{4}$ kc for narrow band). Frequency shift at the crystal is small and is equal to the desired swing divided by the crystal multiplication factor. Tone deviation is small, since the tone signal is transmitted at all times, and the sound volume of the tone should be as small as possible, so it will not interfere with the message. Also, all other receivers on the channel without tone squelch will also hear the tone.

Tone squelch of this design reduces the tone interference through

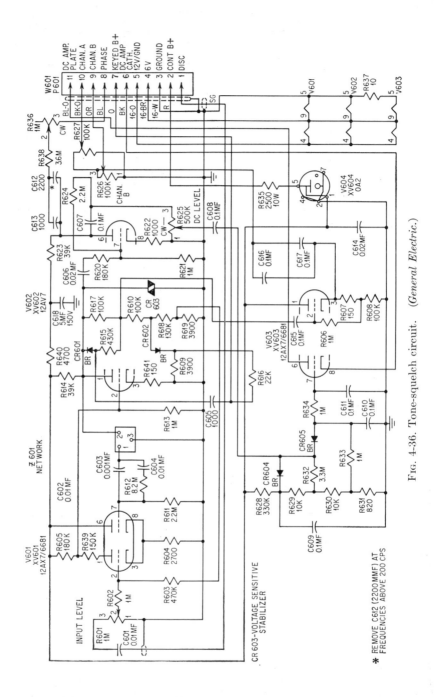

Fig. 4-36. Tone-squelch circuit. (General Electric.)

use of low-frequency audio tones ranging in five steps from 100 to 254 cycles. These are below the normal receiver audio-frequency response. The squelch circuit also has a phasing control to adjust a voltage to permit canceling out almost all of the remaining tone. This phasing circuit, with the small low-frequency gain of the receiver's audio circuit, reduces the tone at least 30 db.

Three combinations of tone-squelch operation are possible in a communications system. These are:

1. Mobile-receiver protection only. The vehicle operators hear only their own tone-coded transmitters. Base stations hear all stations on the channel. This is useful, for example, in taxi systems where constant radio chatter can annoy both drivers and customers.

2. Base-station-receiver protection only. Base station hears only his own tone-coded mobiles. Mobiles hear all stations on the channel. This is useful in systems where dispatcher has other duties and constant signals not intended for him are annoying.

3. Complete two-way protection. Base and mobile stations hear only their own tone-coded transmitters.

In considering various forms of tone-squelch protection it should be recognized that no tone squelch gives a two-way-radio user sole use of a channel. The use of tone squelch eliminates the nuisance of listening to other transmitters on the same channel, but that is all it can do, because the receiver is still captured by the strongest carrier. Interference and skip signals will still be present. The tone-squelch user will not hear them, but he must still contend with them whenever he uses his system.

Squelch Sensitivity. Squelch sensitivity is a measure of the minimum input voltage for the proper suppression of the receiver's internal noise. If there is no transmitted signal being received, a loud hissing sound may be heard; this is generated by the noise voltages in the receiver. A received signal is amplitude-modulated by this noise. The amount of modulation is a function of the amplitude of the noise voltage.

If there is no AGC, the AM noise may be considered as a constant value as shown in Fig. 4-37. In *A* the signal level is such that limiting

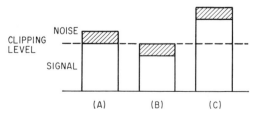

Fig. 4-37. Noise and signal clipping.

action removes all the noise. But if the signal level is reduced to a sufficient degree, all the noise will be passed, and none will be removed by limiting. This is shown in B. If the signal level is decreased even further, there will be no decrease in noise level. By increasing the signal level above noise clipping, as in C, there will be no decrease in noise as compared with A. The level of input voltage which permits noise clipping (A) is the effective squelch sensitivity of the receiver. This is the *lowest* input signal which will overcome the internal noise of the receiver. In many receivers this is also the minimum input signal which will produce a satisfactory audio output.

Squelch circuits (as discussed earlier in this chapter) cut off the audio in the absence of a received signal; hence no noise hiss is heard.

4-8. Audio Amplifiers

Audio amplifiers are conventional in mobile radio, and straightforward circuits are used. The squelch circuits are used to mute the audio amplifier when no transmission is being received. (See Sec. 4-7 above.)

RC networks for deemphasis are used, where necessary, between the detector and the audio amplifier.

Since only small amounts of audio power are required, a single-tube output stage is usually sufficient. In special applications where higher audio power is needed for public-address systems, an additional audio amplifier is used.

4-9. Split-channel Operation

The FCC has established more narrow bands for mobile two-way radio. Using 60-kc channels, as in A of Fig. 4-38, the center frequencies, or the assigned frequencies, are 60 kc apart. Each channel has a deviation (total) of 30 kc in an authorized band of 40 kc. A separation of 20 kc between the channel edges is provided.

"Necessary bandwidth," according to the FCC, is " . . . the width of the frequency band which is necessary in the overall system, including both transmitter and receiver, for the proper reproduction of the desired information and does not necessarily indicate the interfering characteristics of an emission."

A formula is given by the FCC which permits you to calculate the necessary bandwidth from the desired audio-frequency band and the desired carrier deviation. This formula is stated as

$$BW = 2M + 2DK$$
$$K = 1 \text{ for commercial telephony}$$
$$D = \tfrac{1}{2} \text{ maximum total deviation}$$
$$M = \text{maximum modulation frequency}$$

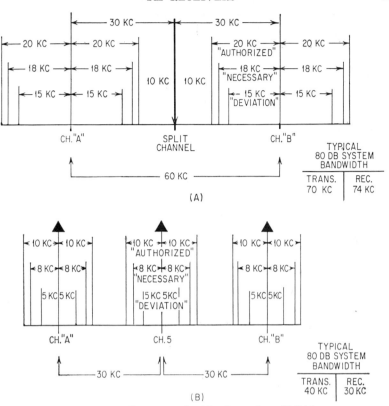

Fig. 4-38. Narrow and wide channels. (*RCA.*)

From this, it can be determined that the necessary bandwidth for the existing 60-kc channel allocations in the high band is 36 kc and for the proposed split-channel, or narrow, band it would be 16 kc on the basis of 3 kc maximum modulating frequency.

"Authorized bandwidth" is greater than "necessary bandwidth." Since it is recognized that the transmitter will occupy more than the necessary bandwidth in out-of-band radiation, it allows for frequency drift and high-frequency modulation components. The FCC defines the authorized bandwidth as " . . . the maximum width of the band of frequencies as specified in the authorization to be occupied by an emission."   For the present wideband assignment, this is 40 kc.

Authorized bandwidth for the proposed narrow band will be 20 kc. In order to allow adequate protection between adjacent channels, an additional 20 kc was provided as a guard band and for the proposed split channels will be 10 kc.

The bandwidth which is occupied by a transmitter, according to the

FCC, is " . . . the region in which 99% of the radiated power of the transmitter will appear and usually extends out to include any discrete frequency on which 0.25% of the radiated power appears."

The new more narrow, or split, channels are shown in *B* of Fig. 4-38. This shows the channels in which the reassignment of channels will be made at 30-kc intervals. Note that the guard channel is now half of what was previously allowed. Therefore, attenuation between channels will have to be more rapid with relation to frequency.

FCC Docket 11253, originally dated January 12, 1955, became effective on October 15, 1956. The four most important requirements of this docket are as follows:

1. It requires existing licensees to conform to the split-channel standards within 7 years. This means that anyone who now has a mobile communication system operating with equipment which is adequate for 60-kc allocation either will have to buy new equipment meeting the new standards at the end of 7 years or will have to modify his existing equipment to meet the new allocation standards at that time.

2. It requires new licensees to conform after 2 years (i.e., November 1, 1958). This means that anyone now obtaining a license to operate a mobile communication system does so with the knowledge that he should either buy equipment now designed to perform within the new standards or equipment which can be modified to conform to the new standards. Any nonconforming equipment licensed before this date will not have to conform until October 31, 1963.

3. It permits the mixture of existing systems having the present 60-kc allocations with new systems having 30-kc allocations. However, such intermixed allocations will be made subject to a review by the FCC, in cooperation with users and frequency-coordination groups, of the existing allocations in the area of interest.

4. It establishes new technical standards to provide adequate interference limits as related to emission characteristics and systems stability.

For a necessary bandwidth of 19 kc the stability required is 0.001 per cent, and for a necessary bandwidth of 17.5 kc it is 0.0005 per cent.

After an industry-wide study of the problem the following recommendations were made:

1. Split-channel operation would become feasible.
2. Improvement of over-all systems selectivity would be required.
3. Careful assignment of frequencies would be necessary.
4. Definite considerations of physical separation of systems would be necessary.

5. Users to be encouraged to use antenna farms for receivers and transmitters.

6. A higher degree of user cooperation and toleration would be necessary.

7. A recommendation for more rigid maintenance standards.

In summary: Split channels will mean wider use of two-way radio by providing more available channels. It also means that best possible use of the channels will require careful maintenance of the new standards.

4-10. Transistors and Mobile Receivers

Because of their low current drain transistors will play a significant part in receivers for mobile and portable use. Bell Telephone has demonstrated the possibilities inherent in this type of receiver using diffused-base transistors.[1]

The performance of the experimental transistorized receiver is comparable to vacuum-tube equipment in the 150-Mc frequency range. This is possible because of the low noise figure of the diffused-base transistor and because of its ability to provide useful gain at 150 Mc. The real advantage of the transistorized receiver is the long battery life possible because of the low power drain. In portable communication equipment, this is important, since the receiver must be tuned to the channel at all times to monitor the channel and it operates on nearly a 100 per cent duty cycle.

Transistor receivers will be used in systems with vacuum-tube receivers; hence their operation must be compatible. This experimental receiver works in the 152- to 174-Mc band. It has a drain of 130 milliwatts (0.130 watt). In the block diagram, Fig. 4-39, there are 11 transistors in the RF and IF stages.

[1] W. J. Giguere, A Transistorized 150 Mc FM Receiver, *Proc. IRE*, p. 693, April, 1958.

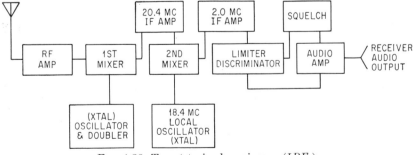

Fig. 4-39. Transistorized receiver. (*IRE*.)

The high-frequency portions illustrated in Fig. 4-40 are of special interest, since one important obstacle to mobile radio receivers has been the operation of transistors in this region.

The RF amplifier has two stages in cascade for an over-all gain of 22 db at 150 Mc.[1] Other transistors, such as the 2N700, amplify well into the UHF region;[2] other transistors which operate beyond 300 Mc include: Philco 2N499 (320 Mc); Texas Instruments 2N1143 (480 Mc); 2N1142 (600 Mc); and 2N1141 (750 Mc).

The tuner is made up of three stages of RF amplification: a crystal-controlled oscillator, a frequency doubler, and a mixer.   RF selectivity is obtained by a single-tuned antenna circuit and two capacitance-

[1] See also C. H. Knowles and E. A. Temple, Diffused Base Transistors, *Electronic Design*, p. 12, July 9, 1958.

[2] C. H. Knowles, New Transistor Design: The Mesa, *Electronic Industries*, p. 55, August, 1958.

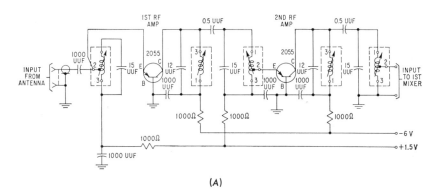

(A)

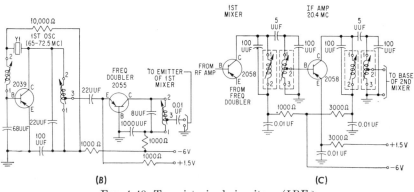

(B)   (C)

Fig. 4-40. Transistorized circuits.   (*IRE.*)

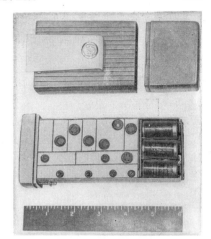

FIG. 4-41. All-transistor receiver. (*RCA Communication Products Dept.*)

coupled double-tuned interstage coils. RF amplification is provided by two diffused-base transistors in the circuit shown in *A*.

The noise figure is about 10 db, and this is better than many designs of tube equipment.

B illustrates the first local oscillator, which covers from 65 Mc to 72.5 Mc for stability with available crystals. The frequency is doubled by overdriving an amplifier stage following the oscillator and tuning its output to twice the oscillator frequency. The frequency doubler provides adequate drive to the first mixer. Frequency stability is ±0.001 per cent for an 80°C temperature change.

The 20.4-Mc IF in *C* is used to permit image rejection by the RF stage by attenuating the low-frequency image response. A 70-db attenuation is provided.

Remaining stages are the second oscillator at 18.4 Mc, the second mixer and 2.0-Mc IF, the detector, squelch, and the audio amplifier, which uses General Electric 4JD1A42 transistors.

The squelch circuit disables the audio amplifier in the absence of received carrier by removing the bias from the audio stages.

The loss in receiver sensitivity with the squelch control is less than 5 db.

An example of the use of transistors may be seen in Fig. 4-41. This RCA unit is the Personalfone, and it can be used in any existing 50- or 150-Mc-band radio system.[1] The specifications of the low-band

[1] J. R. Neubauer, A New Arm for Vehicular Communication, *Trans. IRE*, *PGVC*-11, p. 34, July, 1958.

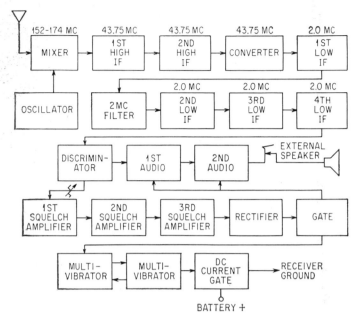

Fig. 4-42. Transistor receiver schematic.

receiver include a sensitivity of about 1 to 2 μv (at 20 db noise quieting), a selectivity which is 60 db down at 60 kc, an audio output of 6 milliwatts, a battery life of 150 hr minimum, and a noise-operated squelch which opens at 8 db of noise quieting. The receiver block diagram is shown in Fig. 4-42.

In addition to transistors, other semiconductor devices such as parametric amplifiers with special diodes have demonstrated remarkable low-noise RF amplification. Only their present cost prevents their use in two-way receivers.

CHAPTER 5

AM TRANSMITTERS AND RECEIVERS

5-1. Introduction

AM is widely used for general industrial use, low-power industrial radio (LPI), as well as ground-to-air and ground communications in aviation. LPI service is designed for short-range communications, as within a manufacturing-plant yard, at a large shopping center, on a golf course, or in a lumber yard. A typical unit is shown in Fig. 5-1. This is a self-contained unit with its controls and antenna. Any business may be licensed for this service (if it meets the citizenship requirements), power is limited to 3 watts input to the final RF stage, and assigned frequencies are shared.[1]

5-2. AM Transmitters

While FM (or PM) is, at present, the most widely used system for mobile radio, more radio communications are carried on by AM than by FM. One reason is the long-range qualities of AM. The second, and most compelling, reason is the advances being made in various types of AM, for AM is not dead and new techniques such as single

FIG. 5-1. Industrial mobile-phone (IMP) AM radio. (*Kaar Engineering.*)

[1] LPI has been absorbed by the new Business Radio Service, which can use AM or FM, as of Aug. 1, 1958. See page 15.

sideband promise to make AM a serious competitor for FM in mobile radio.

While most mobile transmitters are, at present, phase-modulated (changed to FM in the transmitter), AM is also used.

An AM transmitter is shown in Fig. 5-2; the greatest difference between this and an FM transmitter is in the modulation process. A crystal oscillator is the RF signal source. Because there is no need for frequency multiplication to increase the deviation as needed by FM, the oscillator can be of higher frequency. For low-band operation the crystal can be the final RF frequency; for high-band work a frequency multiplier can be used. The driver amplifier and the final power amplifier are like those in an FM transmitter. All stages are class C except where the modulation process requires a linear final amplifier, which is then class B (push-pull) or class A.

The audio chain is of greater power output than required by an equivalent FM transmitter, since in AM all of the sideband power is supplied by the audio-frequency chain. In FM the total RF output is of constant amplitude under modulation (see the AM and FM comparison), but in AM the total RF output varies in amplitude, and the additional power, over and above the unmodulated RF output, is provided by the final audio stage. Because the RF stages are class A (or class B push-pull), more d-c power is required by an AM transmitter than for an FM transmitter with the same total power output.

AM has one set of sidebands under all conditions of modulation, and the amplitude of the audio signal determines the power in these sidebands. Modulation can be accomplished in a number of ways; two methods are shown in Fig. 5-3. Where F is the unmodulated RF output, and f is the AF, the modulation process produces F, $(F + f)$, and $(F - f)$. This is the same as the result of heterodyning F and f.

In A of Fig. 5-3 the audio signal, coupled through T, changes the plate voltage of the RF final amplifier. The d-c supply for the AF stage is E_1 and a higher voltage, E_2, is used for the RF plate d-c supply. The plate supply of the final RF stage is the d-c voltage E_2 and the

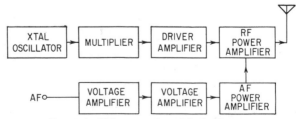

Fig. 5-2. AM-transmitter block diagram.

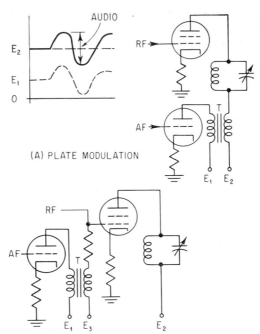

(A) PLATE MODULATION

FIG. 5-3. Modulation methods for AM.

(B) GRID MODULATION

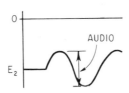

AF across the secondary of T, as shown. Variations in the audio voltage change the instantaneous voltage on the RF plate and produce the amplitude variations in the resulting RF output. For 100 per cent modulation, using the circuit A, the audio signal must have one-half the power of the unmodulated RF output.

Grid modulation is another way to produce AM, as shown in B. Here the audio voltage is in series with the d-c grid bias E_3. Again the variations in the audio change the effective bias at an audio rate, and the output from the RF amplifier varies in amplitude. Much less audio power is required, but the RF amplifier is only 25 per cent as efficient as an unmodulated class-C amplifier.

AM transmitters require a form of amplitude limiting to prevent overmodulation and an audio filter to limit the highest audio frequency to remain in the prescribed bandwidth.

A partial schematic of an AM transmitter is shown in Fig. 5-4. A crystal oscillator feeds a buffer amplifier (which could be followed by other RF amplifiers) and the final RF power amplifier shown. Push-pull beam power amplifiers are illustrated; this is a plate-modulated final amplifier. The modulator amplifies the audio power and varies the d-c plate voltage of the final RF power amplifier.

Typical AM transmitters in low-power industrial service have a lower power output than most two-way transmitters; hence they are smaller. Figure 5-5 is a block diagram of a transmitter-receiver showing the audio portions which are common to the receiver and transmitter. The block diagram is redrawn in Fig. 5-6.

The IMP (industrial mobile phone) is a small transmitter-receiver suitable for vehicle or desk use. Operating controls are (1) receiver volume control and on-off switch; (2) receiver squelch control; (3) paging switch, whereby, without transmitting, the audio system may be also used for public-address purposes by plugging in an external speaker; (4) press-to-talk switch on microphone. The power supply is a three-purpose unit, and it can be converted from 6- to 12-volt operation by reversing the power plug, or to 117-volt a-c operation by using the a-c cord.

Audio from the microphone has a voltage amplifier stage V_{8A} (which performs the same function in receiving) and a power amplifier, V_9, which modulates V_{12}, the RF final. In receiving this audio power amplifier is the audio-output stage.

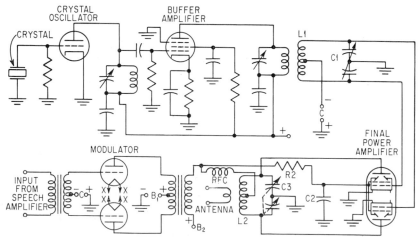

FIG. 5-4. Simplified schematic, AM transmitter.

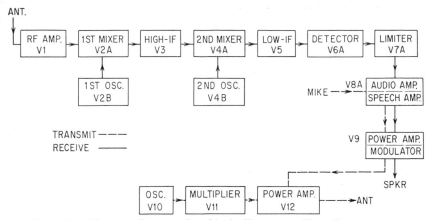

FIG. 5-5. AM transmitter-receiver block diagram. (*Kaar Engineering.*)

The transmitter is a standard crystal-controlled unit, using multiplier stages, and is Heising-modulated by the receiver audio section. The RF portion consists of a crystal one-eighth or one-twelfth of the operating frequency (19.32125 Mc for 154.57 Mc), a 6CB6 oscillator-multiplier, 6AK6 multiplier, and a 6J6 push-pull RF power-amplifier-doubler. Link coupling with capacitive loading feeds the antenna. The microphone-button current is derived from cathode current of the 6AQ5 audio-output stage. Audio from the carbon microphone feeds the receiver volume control, and is amplified by one section of the 12AX7. This audio is coupled to the 6AQ5 output stage, which modulates the 6J6.

Keying is by the microphone press-to-talk switch, which actuates

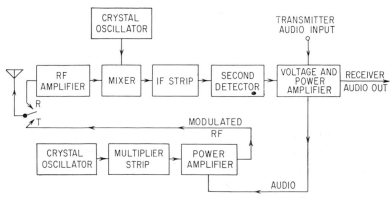

FIG. 5-6. Transmit-receive signal flow (simplified diagram).

the keying relay. This relay, in the process of switching the antenna circuit, passes +B voltage through these same contacts. RF voltages are isolated by choke coils, and the passage of direct current tends to burn the contacts clean.

In the *page* position, multiplier and power amplifiers are biased off, and audio power is delivered to the external speaker plug.

5-3. AM Receivers

The AM receiver can be quite similar to the FM receiver. But it is possible to reduce the system complexity through the use of the audio-output stage of the receiver as the transmitter modulator, as in Fig. 5-6. This overcomes the objection to several stages of audio for the modulation requirements, since these stages are already in the equipment as part of the receiver.

In *receive* position the voltage and power audio amplifiers take the audio from the detector and feed it to the speaker. But in the *transmit* position the microphone input is fed to the voltage amplifier and then to the audio power amplifier, which now acts as the modulator stage. In some cases, the power level of the audio power amplifier is raised during transmit.

The receiver in Figs. 5-5 and 5-6 uses double conversion with a high IF of 10.7 Mc and a low IF of 1,500 kc. Most of the RF circuits are similar to those in an FM receiver except for the oscillator. A crystal-oscillator tripler (overtone oscillator) as in Fig. 5-7 is used for the first converter local oscillator.

A single pentagrid converter is the second oscillator and mixer. The detector, or mixer, is quite similar to detectors used in AM broadcast receivers.

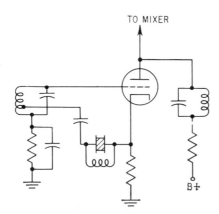

FIG. 5-7. Crystal oscillator.

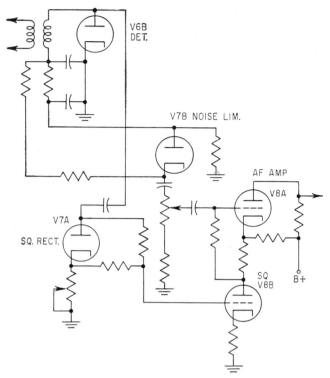

Fig. 5-8. Noise-limiter circuit.

But, because noise is a problem with low-power radio, squelch and noise-limiter circuits are used as in Fig. 5-8. As with an FM receiver the squelch operates to cut off V_{8B} by the squelch rectifier during the periods when no signal is being received. V_{8A} then cannot pass the audio, and the receiver speaker is quiet.

During the received signal, tube V_{8B} conducts, which allows V_{8A} to amplify the audio, and the output is heard from the speaker.

V_{7B} operates as a noise limiter to clip the peaks of the noise bursts, which are of greater amplitude than the normal audio.

In other respects the receiver resembles the FM receiver.

5-4. Transceivers

In a sense all mobile two-way radios are transceivers for they both transmit and receive. However, the use of the word *transceiver* is usually reserved for units which use tube sharing, or dual functions.

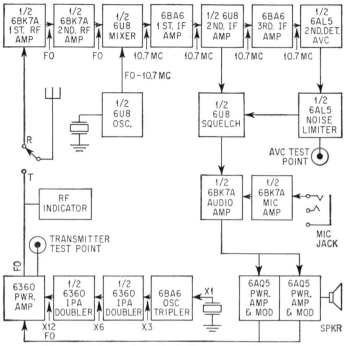

FIG. 5-9. Transceiver block diagram.   (*Aerotron.*)

Figure 5-9 illustrates a low-power transceiver.

The fundamental frequency of the transmitter crystal is between 9 and 15 Mc.   A type-6BA6 tube operates as a harmonic oscillator with its plate circuit tuned to the third harmonic of the crystal, for the transmitter.   The oscillator output feeds the first grid of a type-6360 twin-tetrode tube with the two sections operating in cascade. Each section operates as a frequency doubler.   A type-6360 tube is used as a push-pull RF final.   The output of the final amplifier is link-coupled, through the antenna relay, to the antenna.   A pilot lamp, link-coupled to the output tank circuit, serves as an output and modulation indicator.   In the audio stages, one half of a type-6BK7A twin-triode tube is used as a grounded-grid microphone amplifier. This feeds the second half of the same tube, which operates as a voltage amplifier driving the grids of the modulator.   Two type-6AQ5 pentode tubes in parallel serve as the modulator.

In the receiver a type-6BK7A tube is used as an RF cascade-connected amplifier.   This is followed by a type-6U8 tube, with its triode section connected as the mixer.   The pentode section of this tube operates as a crystal-controlled harmonic oscillator with the plate circuit tuned to the fourth harmonic of the crystal.

Three stages of amplification follow the mixer at 10.7 Mc as the IF. The first and third stages utilize type-6BA6 tubes. The second stage utilizes a type-6U8 tube's pentode section. The triode section of this 6U8 is used as an audio-squelch stage. The demodulator stage uses one half of a type-6AL5 dual-diode tube. The other half of the 6AL5 acts as series limiter. One half of a type-6BK7A tube, the same as is used in the transmitter modulator, operates as a receiver audio-voltage amplifier feeding the grids of two type-6AQ5 tubes in parallel. These are the same tubes used as the transmitter modulator. For reception they are transformer-coupled to the receiver's loudspeaker and headset jack.

Figure 5-10 shows how the operating level of the 6AQ5 tubes is raised during the transmitting period to provide maximum audio power for modulation. When the push-to-talk button on the microphone is depressed, the low resistance of the relay coil is across the 1,000-ohm cathode resistor of the 6AQ5 tubes. This reduces the bias and increases the output-power capabilities of the tubes. In receiving position the cathode resistor is in the circuit, and this bias reduces the tube gain.

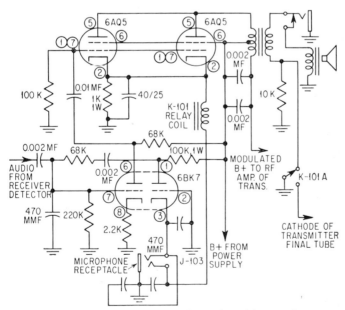

Fig. 5-10. Power-output schematic. (*Aerotron.*)

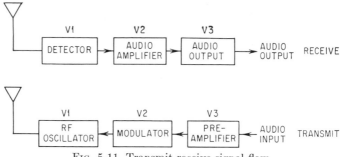

FIG. 5-11. Transmit-receive signal flow.

While many AM units have tube sharing between the transmitter and receiver, a transceiver has many of the tubes shared.   Figure 5-11, for example, has three tubes; all the tubes have dual functions.   This is a form of radio for the citizens' band; it is also shown in Fig. 5-12.

Radio systems for mobile communications can obtain a great reduction in complexity.   An extreme case of simplicity in a transceiver for class-B citizens' radio on 465 Mc is illustrated above and used as an example.   Three tubes are used; each serves a dual purpose as controlled by the transmit-receive (push-to-talk) switch; the schematic diagram is shown in Fig. 5-13.

This transceiver operates as a superregenerative receiver, and amplitude-modulated power oscillator for transmitting, at a frequency

FIG. 5-12. Vocaline transceiver.   (*Vocaline Co.*)

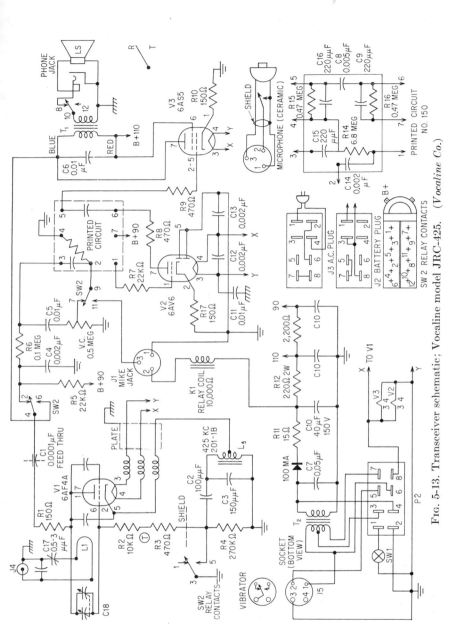

FIG. 5-13. Transceiver schematic; Vocaline model JRC-425. (*Vocaline Co.*)

of 465.0 Mc.   A special wideband receiver circuit is used, so that when both stations are operating within the frequency limits set by the FCC, no receiver-tuning adjustment is necessary.   When the transmitter circuit is calibrated properly, the receiver circuit is automatically set for proper operation.

The functions of the tubes are:

Number	Type	Transmit	Receive
V_1(6AF4A)	UHF triode	Modulated RF oscil-lator	Superregenerative detector
V_2(6AV6)	Duodiode triode	Preamplifier for microphone input	Audio-voltage amplifier
V_3(6AS5)	Beam-power amplifier	Power amplifier and modulator	Audio power amplifier and output

Transmit: The push-to-talk switch is pressed, which places SW_2 in the down position.   Audio from the microphone is across 1 (ground) and 3 of the microphone jack.   Grid 1 of V_2 has this audio applied through C_{15} and across R_{14} to ground.   Pins 1 and 2 of this jack energize the relay coil K_1 for the switching between the transmitter and receiver.

Through C_8 this amplified audio is applied to the grid (2-5) of V_3, the 6AS5 beam-power amplifier-modulator.   The speaker (or earphone) is disconnected from T_1; the primary is in series with the audio signal going through R_1 to the plate of V_1.

RF power is generated by the self-excited oscillator V_1, a 6AF4A. The cathode of V_1 goes to ground through the lower part of L_5 (both ends of this inductance are grounded—the bottom directly and the top through C_2 and the switch).   A transmission-line tuned circuit is between the grid and plate.   This is effectively a quarter-wavelength short-circuited line, which is a parallel resonant circuit.[1]

Capacity loading shortens the physical length of this transmission line.   The capacity below C_1 acts as a short-circuit termination for RF because of the low reactance. C_{18} provides a method of frequency adjustment, or tuning, for the required 465-Mc operation.   When this capacity is varied, the effective electrical length of the transmission line is changed, which alters the oscillator frequency.

Feedback for this oscillator, an equivalent Colpitts circuit, is through the voltage divider of the interelectrode capacitance.

[1] A. Lytel, "UHF Practices and Principles," p. 224, John Francis Rider, Publisher, Inc., New York, 1953.

Audio modulation varies the plate voltage of the oscillator; the output RF is coupled to the antenna and provided with tuning (C_{17}) to match different antenna characteristics.

Receive: When pressure is removed from the push-to-talk switch, the transceiver is in *receive* position. The oscillator now acts as a regenerative detector. Regenerative, or positive, feedback is a powerful technique (with certain drawbacks), and signal gains of 1 million or more are common. Modulated RF is fed from grid to plate to grid in a closed cycle, while the RF is amplified each time. This would result in oscillation except for L_5 and C_3. Because this tank is resonant at 425 kc, in this case (other frequencies *above* the audio range could be used), the tube amplifies. Signal feedback continues, but this 425-kc tank controls the operation by swinging the tube on and off at the 425-kc rate. Because it is on for short periods, the RF gain builds up, but *before* sustained self-oscillation occurs, the 425-kc quench signal brings the tube back again to a low-gain condition, not actually to *off*.

Plate voltage, for V_1, is applied through R_5 in this condition. Audio from the V_1 detector plate is filtered (for RF) by C_4, R_6, and C_{15}. From the volume control, the audio is coupled to the grid of V_2 by C_{14}. R_{14} is the grid leak to ground. This is shown in Fig. 5-14, which is rearranged from the complete schematic diagram. C_8 couples the audio from the V_2 plate to the V_3 grid; R_{15} is the V_3 grid return. T_1 is the output transformer to the speaker or headphones.

The power-supply source can be either 6 (or 12) volts d-c or 115 volts a-c. A vibrator is used on direct current, and the 115 volts a-c is applied directly to the T_2 secondary.

5-5. Other Modulation Systems

Mobile communications have the problem of conserving spectrum space. Because of the expanding use of mobile radio, there is just not

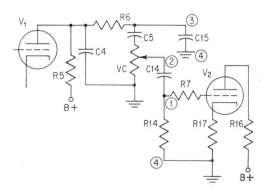

Fig. 5-14. Audio-frequency section of the transceiver, V_1 and V_2.

enough room for all the transmitters in the frequency spectrum. This has been recognized for several years, and the trend has been toward more narrow-band systems.

Broadcast FM has 150-kc channels, and mobile has gone from 120-kc channels all the way down to 30-kc channels with further decreases in prospect.

Decreasing the FM bandwidth is accomplished by decreasing the deviation, which carries with it a decrease in signal-to-noise ratio. But there are other limitations more serious than this. When the modulation index (M) is decreased to 0.4, or less, there is only a single set of sidebands.

Now assuming $M = 0.4$ there are two sidebands, and if 3 kc is the highest audio frequency, then ΔF is 1.2 kc, by the relation $\Delta F = fM$. But where N is the number of sideband pairs, the bandwidth is $2fN$, or 6 kc.

Thus, as in Fig. 5-15, there is little difference between FM and AM except for the freedom from certain noise, but this advantage decreases as the deviation goes down. This example shows equal bandwidths, and the sidebands are always the audio frequency away from the carrier.

But FM has other advantages over ordinary AM, the smaller total transmitter power among others. However while FM has advantages, a reexamination of AM is significant for two reasons: FM is losing some of its inherent attractiveness as more narrow bandwidths are required, and AM is having a renaissance in forms other than conventional AM. Amplitude modulation never has, in the conventional form, made greatest use of the total transmitted RF power, but this is not inherent in AM; rather it is a result of the techniques which have been used.

Recent advances in techniques have provided methods of other AM transmissions than the ordinary conventional type.[1] The center-

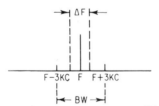

(A) FM CASE

M = 0.4
f = 3KC
ΔF = 1.2KC
BW = 6KC
N = 1

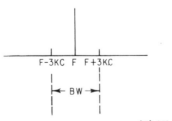

(B) AM CASE

FIG. 5-15. FM-AM bandwidth.

[1] W. L. Firestone and H. Magnuski, Application of Single Sideband for Mobile Communication, *Trans. IRE, PGVC*-11, p. 48, July, 1958.

frequency component, or carrier, of an AM transmission carries no intelligence at all, as shown in Chap. 2.   It is only a convenient device to produce the sidebands.   This can be shown theoretically; experimentally a highly selective receiver can be tuned to receive a single sideband of a standard AM transmission with full understanding of the audio modulation.

Telephone companies have, for many years, taken and used audio to modulate an RF carrier of about 30 to 40 kc.   As a part of this modulation process (AM) the center-frequency component is removed, and only the sidebands are sent by wire.   In this case the elimination of the carrier (center-frequency component) reduces the amount of power which must be sent through various parts of the system, but the intelligence is not impaired in any way.

Long-range communications also have used carrier suppression plus the elimination of one sideband.   Equipment for this purpose has been large and complex.   However, it is now feasible to remove either sideband by phasing or filtering.   Most systems now use variations of sideband filters rather like the vestigial sideband transmission of broadcast-television signals.

The following terms will be used in this discussion with the abbreviations indicated:

DSB—Double sideband with suppressed carrier

SAM—Synchronous (AM) detection

SSB—Single sideband with suppressed carrier

AM—Standard double sideband with full carrier

NBFM—Narrow-band FM

PM—Phase modulation

CW—Continuous wave

5-6. Double-sideband Suppressed Carrier (DSBSC)

A balanced modulator, as in Fig. 5-16, is an example of the type of circuit used to produce DSB.   The audio is fed in push-pull (180° apart), and the RF is fed in parallel.   RF, which is the center-fre-

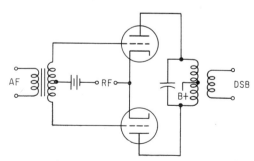

FIG. 5-16. Balanced modulator, DSB.

(A)   AUDIO MODULATION

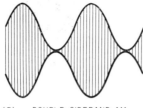

(B)   DOUBLE SIDEBAND AM

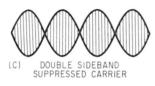

(C)   DOUBLE SIDEBAND
       SUPPRESSED CARRIER

(D)   SINGLE SIDEBAND
       SUPPRESSED CARRIER

FIG. 5-17. Modulation wave-
forms.

quency component, or carrier, does not appear as an output, because it is balanced out in the output transformer by equal and opposite currents. Sidebands are not balanced out, and both appear as the output.

Figure 5-17 shows an audio-modulating signal in *A*, AM in *B*, and DSB in *C*. This sideband without a carrier signal can be received with a communications receiver, but each of the modulating signals will appear as *twice* their original frequency when rectified by a diode detector, for example.

This transmission requires the same bandwidth as AM with a carrier, but carrier interference, such as beat notes, will be absent.

If a carrier (unmodulated RF) is reinserted at the receiver, the detected signal will be in all respects like a normal AM signal. But the reinserted carrier must be in the same phase and of *exactly* the same frequency as the original suppressed carrier. This is a most difficult problem with zero carrier transmission, so, in many cases, a small portion (less than 5 per cent) of the carrier is transmitted to allow the reinserted carrier to be locked in with the original phase and frequency.

This oscillator requirement in ordinary DSB reception is difficult to meet, but there are techniques, as in the following sections, which overcome this problem.

5-7. Single Sideband with Suppressed Carrier (SSB)

Since both sidebands contain identical information, it seems, except for fading and special cases discussed below, that either sideband *alone* could furnish the required reception. This is SSB (with suppressed carrier), and here the reinserted carrier at the receiver need be only of the correct frequency. The waveshape of SSB is shown in *D* of Fig. 5-17, where it appears as a single frequency which is the beat note (sum or difference) between the transmitter suppressed carrier and the modulating note.

Detection of SSB requires a local oscillator in the receiver of exactly (to within several cycles per second) the original RF carrier frequency.

The heterodyning of the receiver carrier signal and the single sideband will beat notes of the original modulating frequencies. The receiver oscillator signal must be larger than the SSB signal.

Advantages of SSB are, apparently, an increase in transmitter effectiveness assuming a fixed peak power. It can be shown that SSB gives a 9-db gain in signal-power improvement over ordinary AM. There are many examples of this improvement in the literature.

But the 9-db figure assumes sine-wave modulation, equal peak power for both transmitters, and a full carrier (center-frequency component) for the AM case. With these assumptions the average SSB power is indeed 9 db higher than the sidebands of the AM case.

However, the waveshape of the modulation is important. In mobile communications, for example, the modulation is not a pure sine wave. In measurements of peak deviation an audio-signal generator which does produce reasonably pure sine waves is always used with the caution that an actual voice transmission is the only real modulation check, because voice is a complex wave and *not* a sine wave.

If a square wave is used for comparison, AM has a marked advantage over SSB with a fixed peak power of transmission. A perfect square wave, theoretically, cannot be transmitted by SSB without infinite peak power and infinite bandwidth.

Also the RF envelope for SSB bears little or no relationship to the modulating waveshape. In both AM and DSM there is a direct relationship between the modulating waveshape and the RF envelope. Any flat-top modulating signal where the rise time is small compared to the duration will produce high peak voltages in SSB; hence audio clipping and filtering, which can increase the average transmitted power in AM or DSB by at least 10 db, cannot be used by SSB.

There are two general methods for generating an SSB signal, the filter method and the phasing method. The filter method has been used for years by telephone companies for wire and radio transmission. A block diagram is shown in Fig. 5-18. Audio is fed to the first balanced modulator with the first oscillator or translating frequency source. Two normal AM sidebands appear (DSB), and one is filtered out by the first filter. For HF, VHF, or UHF it becomes difficult to

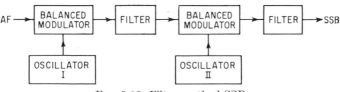

Fig. 5-18. Filter-method SSB.

obtain filters to reject one sideband[1] completely, and the same procedure is followed several times.   Two such translator-filter combinations are shown; more are quite common.

Only linear amplification can be used; frequency changing requires the heterodyne technique; frequency multiplication is not possible.

Phasing is shown in Fig. 5-19.   While this is simpler than the filter method, it is also more critical in adjustment and operation. Two balanced modulators are used.   Both the AF and the RF are split into two parts 90° apart.   The outputs (DSB) from both modulators are then added, so that one sideband is canceled out and the other is of increased amplitude.   The carrier center frequency is not present.   This SSB is fed to a linear power amplifier and then to the antenna.   This system can produce either sideband by a simple switch of the AF leads to the modulators.   Another advantage of this phasing method over the filter method is that the desired output frequency may be obtained directly without a translation oscillator-mixer.

In summary, the three modulation processes are shown in Fig. 5-20 in their most simplified form.

[1] D. K. Weaver, A Third Method of Generation and Detection of Single Sideband Signals, *Proc. IRE*, vol. 44, no. 12, p. 1703, December, 1956.

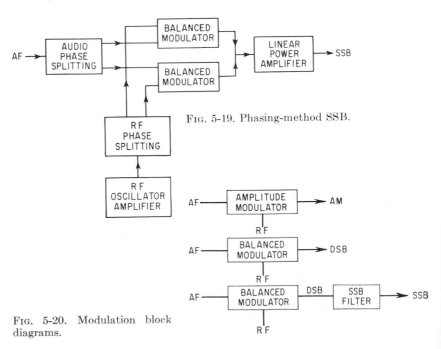

FIG. 5-19. Phasing-method SSB.

FIG. 5-20. Modulation block diagrams.

5-8. Synchronous AM Detection (SAM)

SAM[1,2] is a development which has promise of improving AM reception. Basic design includes reception by use of a synchronous oscillator and two detectors, an I and a Q channel. The I channel has intelligence from *both* sidebands; the Q channel has an audio null. Either or both sidebands can be used. The local oscillator is phase-locked on the demodulated sideband; hence the system is completely independent of any carrier. A transmitter producing AM, SSB, or DSB can be received.

The SAM receiver is compatible[3] with many other types of communication now in use as shown in Fig. 5-21.

A basic block diagram is illustrated in Fig. 5-22. The incoming signal is mixed with the coherent local oscillator, and audio is produced directly. This audio signal is amplified and filtered to any desired

[1] John P. Costas, Synchronous Communications, *Proc. IRE*, December, 1956.

[2] John P. Costas, AM versus SSB, *CQ*, January, 1957.

[3] George J. Kelley, Selection of Search Modulation for Voice Communications, *Electronics*, p. 56, Mar. 28, 1958.

Modulation Methods

Receivers	AM	SSB	DSBSC	FM
AM	✓	✓[1]		
SSB	✓	✓	✓	
DSBSC	✓	✓	✓	
FM				✓
SAM	✓	✓	✓	✓

[1] Modified full-carrier SSB.

Fig. 5-21. Compatibility diagram.

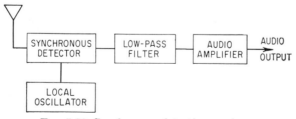

Fig. 5-22. Synchronous-detection receiver.

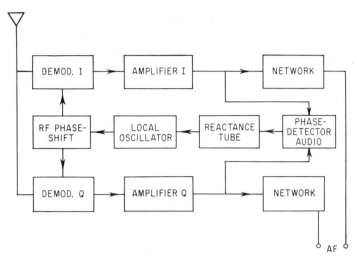

Fig. 5-23. Synchronous-detection block diagram.

bandwidth. Figure 5-23 is a more complete block diagram. Assume that the local oscillator is the same as the carrier component of the AM transmission. Detector I will have an audio signal, but because of the 90° phase difference in the oscillator signal, the Q channel will have no output.

When the local oscillator drifts so that there is a phase shift of a few degrees, an audio output will appear in the Q channel, but the I channel is only slightly affected. The Q-channel audio, which is proportional to the local oscillator phase shift (for small phase errors), has a phase the same as the I channel for one direction of oscillator drift and an opposite phase for oscillator shift in the other direction. Because of this, I and Q signals provide a d-c output voltage from the audio-phase detector, which controls the local oscillator phase and locks it in place.

This phase-control information is obtained entirely from the sideband demodulation and does *not* depend, in any way, upon the carrier component of the transmitted RF. Reception is the same with or without a carrier center-frequency component in the transmission. If this carrier is received, it is ignored; if it is not received, the reception is unchanged. Because of this, suppressed-carrier transmission can be received.

Phase control stops when no modulation is received, but the local oscillator establishes phase-lock almost instantaneously with modulation. Experimental SAM receivers have provided phase locking at signal-to-noise levels which render reception impossible.

All these AM possibilities (DSB, SSB, SAM) have been demonstrated for mobile use.

CHAPTER 6

ANTENNAS

6-1. Introduction

With the growth of two-way radio, greater use is being made of antenna designs which improve the system performance and also reduce interference. Particularly is this important in the bands where maximum performance is required because of the increasing interference problems of channel crowding and the concentration of base stations in some areas.

While there have been many improvements made in both transmitting and receiving equipment to help meet the problem, the antenna is a vital part of the two-way system. Antennas must keep up with the new development and be used where they meet the requirements of individual stations.

In two-way radio, most of the improvement in system performance through use of antennas is limited to the base, or fixed, stations, since only nondirective antennas are used for vehicles.

Directive antennas can be used to improve the system coverage where the service area is not circular or where the base station is not located in the center of the area and to reduce the interference between stations in the same area as well as to reduce noise interference from directional sources.

The complete antenna system, for any transmitter, is composed of the radiator, its mounting, or support, and the transmission-line feeder.

6-2. Transmission Lines

Transmission lines are an important part of a radio system; a line is for the sole purpose of transferring energy between the transmitter or receiver and the antenna radiator. A match between the line and its load is measured by the voltage standing-wave ratio (VSWR). This is defined as

$$\text{VSWR} = \frac{Z_o}{R} \; (R < Z_o)$$

153

where R is the load and Z_o is the characteristic impedance of the line. If R is greater than Z_o the fraction is inverted as

$$\text{VSWR} = \frac{R}{Z_o} \ (R > Z_o)$$

Both of the above assume a resistive load; since Z_o is a pure resistance, any complex impedance load creates a mismatch.

A rise in VSWR above unity causes two problems: Any resonances of standing waves can cause arc-over in the transmission line, and it also increases the losses. The effect of the power loss as the VSWR increases is shown in Fig. 6-1. The VSWR is also decreased by the attenuation of the line; this is indicated in Fig. 6-2.

No transmission line operates with a perfect match, and, as shown in Fig. 6-1, a mismatch with a VSWR of 1.55 or smaller has less than a 10 per cent increase in power loss.

Coaxial transmission lines are used for most fixed stations and all mobile stations. Solid dielectric cables are used for mobile installations and low-power fixed stations. Table 6-1 lists the characteristics of five different cables for this application including the attenuation, in decibels per 100 ft at both 160 Mc and 450 Mc.

Because of the losses of solid dielectric cable, lines with insulating spacers or beads are used for high-powered transmitters. These lines are also pressurized with dry gas. This excludes moisture, which in turn prevents changes in the characteristic impedance with their resulting losses. Pressurization also helps detect small breaks or loose connections in a line.

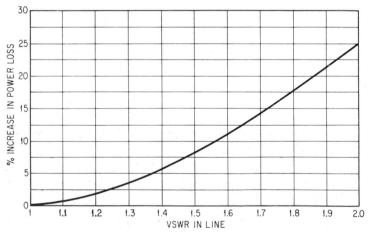

Fig. 6-1. VSWR versus power loss.

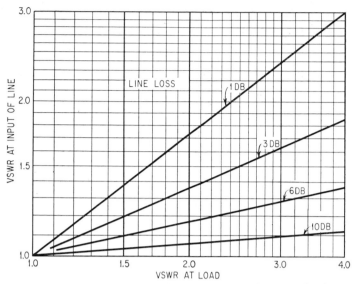

FIG. 6-2. Effect of line attenuation on antenna VSWR at line input.

TABLE 6-1. TRANSMISSION-LINE CABLES

Army-Navy type number	O.D. over jacket (armor), in.	Weight, lb/ft	Imped-ance, ohms	Velocity, per cent	Capaci-tance, μμf/ft	Dielectric constant of insulation	Attenuation, db/100 ft at frequency	
							160 Mc	460 Mc
RG-58/U	0.195	0.029	53.5	66	28.5	2.29	7.6	20.0
RG-8/U	0.405	0.12	52	66	29.5	2.29	2.75	2.10
RG-11/U	0.405	0.096	75	66	20.5	2.29	3.2	8.2
RG-87A/U	0.425	0.176	50	70.7	29.5	2.0	3.0	7.6
RG-17/U	0.870	0.49	52	66	29.5	2.29	1.20	2.40

If the inner conductor was of constant diameter, the insulating beads would cause reflections because of the abrupt changes in characteristic impedance. To prevent this the center conductor is undercut, as in Fig. 6-3. The combined effect of the undercuts and the spacer insula-

FIG. 6-3. Undercut bead in-sulators.

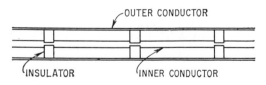

tors is to provide a constant impedance along the entire line. A line with this type of undercut insulation and peg insulators is illustrated in Fig. 6-4.

A typical semiflexible line is shown in Fig. 6-5; the diameter is 0.375 in., the impedance is 50 ohms, and the velocity of propagation is about 84 per cent (the wavelength in the line is 84 per cent of the free-space wavelength). Ceramic insulators are used, and the line has a power rating of 650 watts at 175 Mc.

The flexible air-dielectric cable, illustrated in Fig. 6-6, is a low-loss line with a spiral polyethylene strip wound around the copper-tubing inner conductor. This spiral is, in turn, covered with strips of polyethylene and polystyrene. The corrugated-steel tubing is copperclad; the line has a velocity of 91.6 per cent, an impedance of 50 ohms, and an average VSWR of 1.08 up to 3,000 Mc.

A rigid line of 1.625-in. outside diameter which can take 5 kw is shown in Fig. 6-7. Teflon[1] insulator supports are used; since these are pegs rather than disks, the dielectric losses are less. The attenuation at 450 Mc is less than 5 db per 100 ft. A special connector, as shown, is used to join the inner conductors when two sections are bolted together.

[1] Du Pont.

FIG. 6-4. Undercut dielectric insulators.   (*Andrew Corp.*)

FIG. 6-5. Semiflexible coaxial line, Andrew type 83A.   (*Andrew Corp.*)

FIG. 6-6. Construction of Heliax line.   (*Andrew Corp.*)

FIG. 6-7. UHF transmission line, 1⅝ in. in diameter. (*Andrew Corp.*)

6-3. Vertical Antennas

Mobile-radio service uses vertical polarization, while FM radio and television broadcasting use horizontal polarization.

Mobile communication requires an antenna which can be conveniently mounted on an automobile. Vertical whips, as in Fig. 6-8, are easily supported and have a circular radiation pattern. Any simple horizontal antenna has a bidirectional pattern. Mobile communication usually requires a circular radiation pattern for base stations and always requires a circular radiation pattern for radios in vehicles.

Antennas mounted on vehicles are usually of the vertical-whip type. Base loading, shown in Fig. 6-9, is used to decrease the physical length

FIG. 6-8. Vehicle antenna ASP126. (*Antenna Specialists.*)

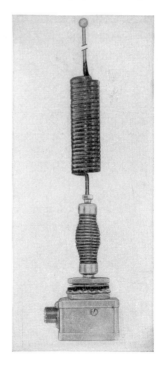

FIG. 6-9. Spring mounting and loading coil ASP-74. (*Antenna Specialists.*)

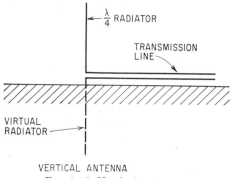

FIG. 6-10. Vertical antenna.

of the antenna. A circular horizontal pattern permits reception and transmission from any direction. Base-station antennas are also of vertical polarization, but they may be more complex to provide directive patterns.

Vertical antennas for mobile radio differ from other vertical antennas as, for example, the transmitting antennas for AM broadcasting. Figure 6-10 illustrates a transmission-line feed to an AM-station antenna. One wire of the line goes to the radiating element, while the second is tied to ground. The effect is that of a center-fed dipole with the ground reflection acting as a virtual antenna. This provides vertical polarization and a circular radiation pattern.

Since mobile antennas are not directly on the ground, like those above, some type of simulated ground is required at the antenna-fed point for end-fed antennas. Figure 6-11A shows an elevated vertical antenna with a ground plane. Some center-fed antennas, as in Fig. 6-11B, are used in several different forms; these do not require ground planes.

Ground-plane antennas are essentially vertical quarter-wavelength radiators in the center of an artificial ground plane as in Fig. 6-12. This plane should be a conductor surface at least one-quarter wavelength in radius, but because this would be heavy, with a large ice and wind loading, four grounded wires have been successfully used.

Although a ground plane will usually be heavier than a coaxial antenna of the same size, the ground-plane antenna has advantages not

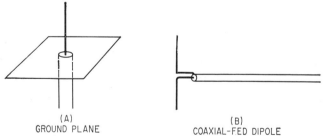

FIG. 6-11. Two vertical antenna types: (A) is a ground plane; (B) is a coaxial-fed dipole.

obtained with the coaxial antenna. The radiator is at d-c ground potential and provides protection against lightning; it is well shielded, so that changes in height or length of line have very little effect on the vertical pattern; and the ground plane lowers the vertical angle of maximum radiation to the horizon, where energy is desired.

A coaxial antenna is a radiator, as in Fig. 6-13, designed to connect to a coaxial line. An effective quarter-wavelength whip is used in *A*, fed by the inner conductor of the transmission line; a quarter-wavelength skirt over the outside

FIG. 6-12. Vertical ground-plane antenna GP-150. (*Scala Radio.*)

of the support may be used to terminate the outer conductor of the transmission line. The matching section (*B*) is also used to provide an impedance match between the radiator and the coaxial line fed. *B* is shown with a ground plane of four radials tied to the outer conductor of the coaxial feed.

C and *D* are also vertical radiators with ground planes and matching

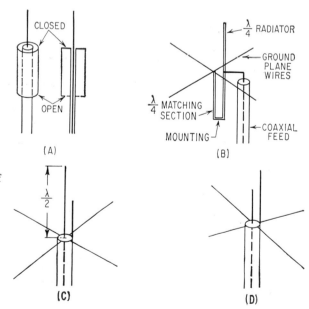

FIG. 6-13. Types of vertical antennas.

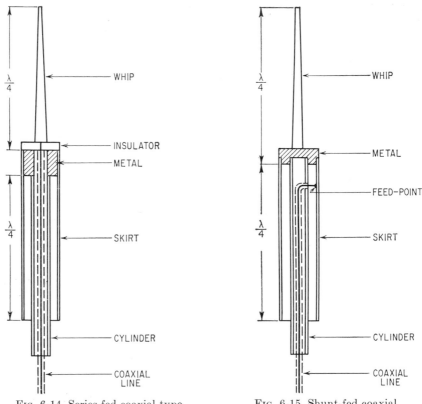

FIG. 6-14. Series-fed coaxial type.   FIG. 6-15. Shunt-fed coaxial.

sections; the effective length of the radiator is that part above the matching section.

Figure 6-14 shows vertical coaxial antennas each with a quarter-wavelength whip and a skirt of the same length. This is series-fed, and Fig. 6-15 is shunt-fed.

6-4. Vehicle Antennas

Whip antennas are usually used for vehicles, and they may be mounted on the top of the car where the roof acts as a ground plane. New top-mounted whips with loading replace the older bumper-mounted antennas, which are difficult to tune. Some roof-top whips for the 25- to 50-Mc band, for example, are only 21 in. long, and they replace bumper antennas up to 96 in. long.

Antennas for use in vehicles are vertical, usually a quarter-wave-length long or shorter. A typical vertical-whip antenna for roof-top use is shown in Fig. 6-16. Spring mounting may be used to prevent damage, and coil loading, as in Fig. 6-17, can be used to make the antenna physically shorter.

The vertical antenna presents a complex impedance at its base, or feed point. The impedance is a pure resistance at a quarter-wavelength; the value of this resistance is about 35 ohms. To use an antenna less than a quarter-wavelength long, it is necessary to cancel the capacitive reactance at the feed point or to cancel the reactance at the point on the line near the antenna, so that only the resistive component of the impedance is left. This resistive value is required to permit a simple matching between the antenna and transmitter.

This may be done in a number of ways. One method is to insert an inductance in series with the antenna at its base as in Fig. 6-17. The inductance has a value that makes its reactance equal and opposite to the reactance of the antenna. The loading coil may be placed at any point in the antenna. Raising the coil allows the portions of the antenna which carry large currents to be the straight portions of the antenna, which increases the radiation efficiency. Another method of feeding an antenna shorter than a quarter-wavelength uses a stub which may be either shorted or open. A shorted transmission-line stub, less than a quarter-wavelength long, has an inductive reactance.

FIG. 6-16. Whip antenna for 144-to 174-Mc band. (*Model ASPA-10, Antenna Specialists.*)

FIG. 6-17. Loading coil for 25- to 50-Mc band. (*Model ASP-63, Antenna Specialists.*)

A shorted line between a quarter- and half-wavelength long has a capacitive reactance.   A stub of the correct length is connected so that it cancels the reactance of the transmission line.   The total reactance is reduced to zero.   From the stub, in the direction of the antenna, there is a pure resistive impedance which is equal to the characteristic impedance of the transmission line, and the short antenna is matched to the coaxial cable.

At frequencies above about 120 Mc, antennas electrically longer than a quarter-wavelength are used.   A $\frac{3}{4}$-wavelength antenna has the impedance characteristics of the quarter-wavelength antenna, but the vertical angle of maximum radiation is higher.   The antenna with a quarter-wavelength stub and a half-wavelength antenna is useful. The stub section provides a match to the half-wavelength antenna. The coaxial antenna is useful at the same frequencies.

It is used where a roof-top antenna is not possible, and this type has a quarter-wavelength rod and a quarter-wavelength skirt.   This rod forms the upper half and the tube the lower half of the radiator.

The standard low-band communications antenna uses a spring base and has a whip ranging from 5 to 8 ft in length.

A vertical antenna less than about 4.5 ft long may be mounted on the cowl or on the fender, and the communications antenna may be a disguised antenna as for unmarked police cars.   The standard ordinary transmitting whip could indicate the identity of the vehicle, so that antennas such as in Fig. 6-18 are used.   They resemble standard receiving antennas.   For transmitting service, the telescopic antennas cannot be used, because of the RF resistance in the joints and the possibility of detuning the antenna by transmitting with the rod partly telescoped.   RF currents passing through the joints can cause arcing.   The disguised antenna, as in Fig. 6-18, is solid rod.

Lead-ins on these antennas are stub-matched in order to compensate for short length.   A special lead-in must be built for each antenna and is cut and matched for each operating frequency.

Mounting procedure for this type of antenna is similar to that for the regular car-radio antennas, and it looks exactly like an ordinary antenna.

FIG. 6-18. Nontelescoping transmitting antenna which appears as an ordinary automobile antenna. (*Model ASP-85, Antenna Specialists.*)

FIG. 6-19. Vehicle antenna with gain. (*Andrew Corp.*)

At frequencies above 100 Mc the roof-top antenna is often used because of its superior electrical characteristics; the conducting surface of the roof-top provides a ground-plane surface.

Mobile units are required to communicate with fixed stations usually almost at ground level. Because of this it is important to radiate most of the power at small angles above the horizon. A circular horizontal pattern is also desired, so that the direction of travel of the vehicle does not change the communication path. This type of horizontal pattern is best obtained with a roof-top antenna at frequencies above 100 Mc. The roof of the vehicle is a large part of a wavelength, and, in effect, it acts as a good ground-plane system.

For the 450- to 470-Mc a new antenna is the whip shown in Fig. 6-19.

This antenna effectively multiplies mobile transmitter power by 1.5 without adding to cost of mobile unit or increasing battery drain. The inductive-tuned $\frac{9}{16}$ wave radiator has 1.3 db measured gain.

A portable ground-plane antenna is shown in Fig. 6-20; this is used for civil defense and all other types of temporary installations. This model (ASP-92) is available in two ranges, 120 to 176 Mc and 450 to 470 Mc. It is designed for quick mounting.

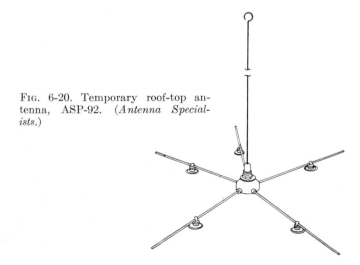

FIG. 6-20. Temporary roof-top antenna, ASP-92. (*Antenna Specialists.*)

Another temporary antenna is the automobile-gutter mounting shown in Fig. 6-21. By means of the special clamp it may be snapped into place on the rain gutter of an automobile for emergency or temporary use. This antenna with the lead-in through the open window permits rapid system setup for short-term use.

6-5. Base-station Antenna Types

Directive antennas such as the corner reflector (Fig. 6-22) or the parabolic section (Fig. 6-23) are used for specialized applications such as remote control of a base station. These directive antennas also have applications to use for base-station communications to mobile units.

Since vertical polarization is used, the fundamental radiator is the vertical type

FIG. 6-21. Automobile-gutter clamp-on, ASP-157. (*Antenna Specialists.*)

FIG. 6-22. Corner reflector for 140 to 170 Mc. (*Scala Radio.*)

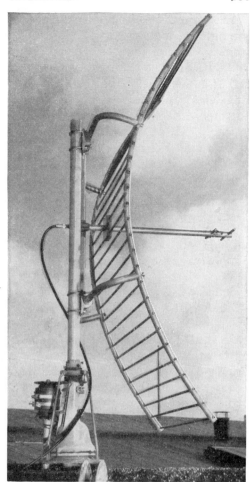

Fig. 6-23. Parabolic section for use from 350 to 1,000 Mc. (Dipole shown horizontal.) (*Scala radio.*)

discussed in Sec. 6-3.   There are also other methods for feeding other vertical antennas.

Some matching methods are compared in Fig. 6-24, where all of these are dipoles.   Feeding systems vary for mechanical reasons and to provide a proper impedance match for maximum transfer of energy.

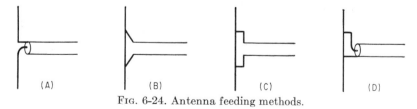

(A)   (B)   (C)   (D)

Fig. 6-24. Antenna feeding methods.

In *A*, direct feed is used from a coaxial line; the center impedance of the antenna matches the 72 ohms of the transmission line.   Feeding from a 300-ohm line (or higher impedance), a delta match (*B*) or *T* match (*C*) can be used.

The gamma match, as in *D*, is used to match a 52-ohm line to half-wavelength radiator.   Gamma-match coaxial dipoles are available for communications use.

In Fig. 6-25, *A* shows a single vertical dipole which matches a 52-ohm coaxial line; the pattern is nondirectional as with all single vertical dipoles.   Twin dipoles, both fed in the same phase, produce a figure-8 horizontal pattern; the gain over a single dipole is 3.6 db.   Two sets of twin dipoles (mounted at right angles) produce a cloverleaf pattern with a sharper vertical angle.   The vertical stacking, as in *B*, produces a cloverleaf with a more restricted vertical angle.   Antennas of this same general type are available as quarter-wavelength ground-plane antennas.

Vertical dipoles have been used to develop specialized antenna systems.

Folded Unipoles.   A popular and effective vertical antenna with a ground plane is the unipole as shown in Fig. 6-26.   This antenna has a gain equal to a free-space dipole; the polarization is vertical, and the horizontal pattern is circular.   The four ground-plane arms are at ground potential, because of the support tube which connects the coaxial feed to the radiator.   Because the radiating element is also grounded at the junction of the horizontal arms, the installation is

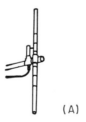

(A)

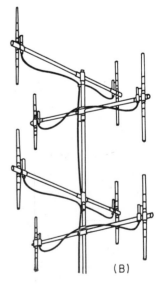

(B)

FIG. 6-25. Coaxial vertical antennas.

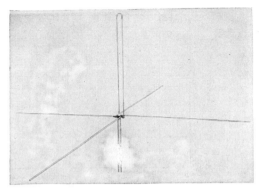

Fig. 6-26. Single unipole. (*Andrew Corp.*)

protected against lightning. This d-c path to ground also drains off any static charge which might gather on the radiator; this grounding of the radiator also improves the signal-to-noise ratio.

Unipole antennas are made in several models. Characteristics of two models of the folded unipole are indicated in Table 6-2. Series-900

TABLE 6-2. FOLDED UNIPOLE*

Type number	Frequency range, Mc	A,† in.	B,‡ in.
900–0	25–30	102	114
900–1	30–44	101	95
900–2	44–50	63	80
900–3	72–76	37	47
900–4	108–144	24	35
925–0	148–152	17	29
925–1	152–157	16	29
925–2	157–162	15	29
925–3	162–168	14	29
925–4	168–174	14	26

* Courtesy Andrew Corp.

† A is maximum length (lowest frequency); it is cut to the proper length for each installation.

‡ B is length of ground-plane rods.

antennas (five separate models) cover all communication bands in the 25- to 144-Mc range. Each model is supplied with a vertical radiating element long enough for the lowest frequency in its operating range. The vertical element is adjusted for the specific frequency required.

Series-925 antennas cover five bands in the 148- to 174-Mc range and may be used at any frequency in the band for which they are supplied without adjustment.

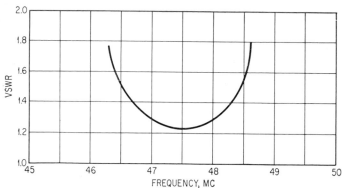

FIG. 6-27. Unipole VSWR for unipole (900-2) operating at 47.5 Mc. (*Andrew Corp.*)

The VSWR varies with frequency; Fig. 6-27 shows the variations in VSWR for a folded unipole cut for 47.5 Mc.

A single vertical reflector added to the unipole produces a cardioid radiation pattern, providing increased coverage over an angle of 180°; this antenna is shown in Fig. 6-28. It is useful for mobile services operating along city or state borders, shorelines, or back-to-back with other services. By concentrating its radiation the cardioid antenna gives a stronger signal in the desired operating area. Short-range communication to the rear is possible, as radiation in this direction is not entirely eliminated. This is shown in Fig. 6-29.

Figure 6-30 illustrates another modification of the unipole; here two driven elements are used which provide two large lobes, one front and one back. An antenna of this type provides for transmitting and receiving along a straight-line route such as for railroad or pipeline use; Fig. 6-31 illustrates this pattern.

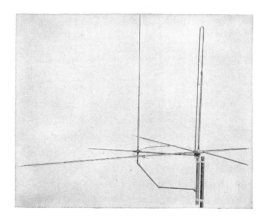

FIG. 6-28. Cardioid unipole. (*Andrew Corp.*)

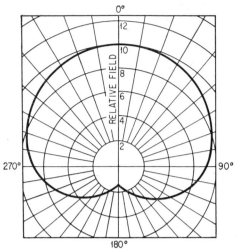

FIG. 6-29. Cardioid-unipole radiation pattern.

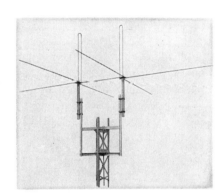

FIG. 6-30. Bidirectional unipole. (*Andrew Corp.*)

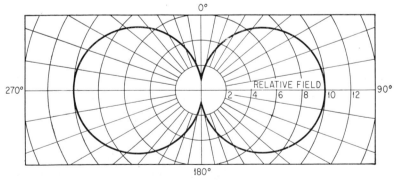

FIG. 6-31. Bidirectional pattern.

FIG. 6-32. Open-wire corner reflector. (*Andrew Corp.*)

Corner Reflectors. Vertical antennas with corner reflectors provide a single forward lobe with reasonably broadband characteristics, and Fig. 6-32 illustrates an open-wire corner reflector. Note that the dipole radiator is directly fed by the coaxial line. The VSWR for the 152- to 174-Mc model is shown in Fig. 6-33.

All of the radiation is concentrated in the forward direction, making the antenna useful for point-to-point and special-coverage problems. Limited signal to the side and rear frequently permits adequate range around the main station, combined with extended coverage in the desired direction.

Figure 6-34 illustrates a vertical stack of two corner reflectors; the horizontal patterns for the single and stacked open-wire corner reflectors (152 to 174 Mc) are shown in Fig. 6-35.

A solid-plane reflector is used for the 450- to 470-Mc band because of the shorter wavelength. Figure 6-36 shows a single dipole with this

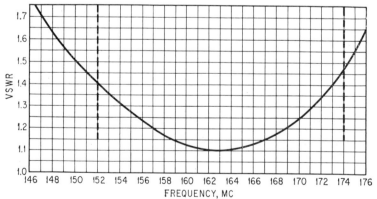

FIG. 6-33.   VSWR curve for corner reflector.   (*Andrew Corp.*)

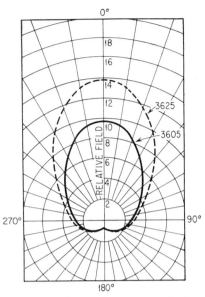

FIG. 6-35. Open-wire corner reflector for 152 to 174 Mc. (*Andrew Corp.*)

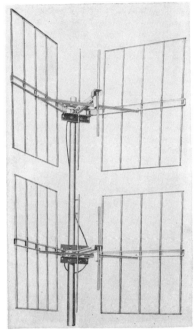

FIG. 6-34. Stacked corner reflector. (*Andrew Corp.*)

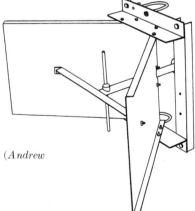

FIG. 6-36. Solid corner reflector. (*Andrew Corp.*)

171

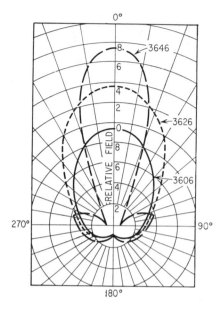

FIG. 6-37. Plane corner-reflector radiation patterns.

type of reflector. Radiation patterns for the single, stacked, and square-stack (two vertical and two horizontal) reflectors are shown in Fig. 6-37.

Collinear Arrays. A simple vertical half-wavelength dipole has a radiation pattern that is circular in the horizontal plane, but similar to a figure 8 in the vertical plane, with nulls along the axis of the dipole. By stacking a number of dipoles in a collinear array, and by feeding the dipoles in phase and with equal power to each dipole, the vertical radiation pattern is compressed. This increases the effective radiated power along the horizon.

The collinear array therefore can produce a power gain over the simple dipole. Collinear arrays have a high gain; in theory four dipoles have 6.5 db, six dipoles 8.5 db, and eight dipoles exceed 9.5 db. These are theoretical gain figures, but well-designed arrays approach these values.

Maximum gain is obtained when the center-to-center spacing between dipoles (Fig. 6-38) equals a wavelength at operating frequency.

Collinear antennas may have their elements driven (fed) or parasitically excited. Figure 6-39 illustrates two basic collinear arrays; *A* is a stack of folded dipoles; *B* is a vertical grouping of coaxial antennas. Feeding may be in series or parallel for either *A* or *B*.

High-gain Antennas. Antennas with nonuniform horizontal patterns are useful for special-coverage applications, but for almost any

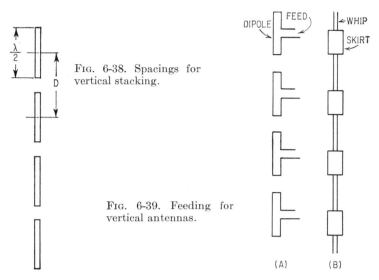

FIG. 6-38. Spacings for vertical stacking.

FIG. 6-39. Feeding for vertical antennas.

base station a stacked omnidirectional pattern will give increased coverage area. This is done by extending the vertical radiation pattern.

Figure 6-40 shows the vertical pattern for a stack of eight folded dipoles for the 148- to 174-Mc band. The proper vertical spacing and phasing of radiating elements produces a sharp pattern beamed at the horizon. High-angle or waste radiation is essentially eliminated. Horizontal radiation is omnidirectional. This model has 6.3 db gain over a dipole. The initial cost of achieving a given coverage in a mobile communication system is almost always lower when a high-gain antenna is used. Increasing the coverage with a high-gain antenna is less costly than making the same increase with a taller tower of a higher-power transmitter.

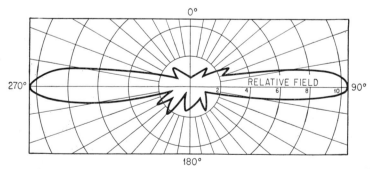

FIG. 6-40. Vertical radiation pattern for type-3000 and type-3001 stacked 148- to 174-Mc antennas. (Andrew Corp.)

FIG. 6-41. Side-mounting antenna for 25 to 50 Mc. (*Andrew Corp.*)

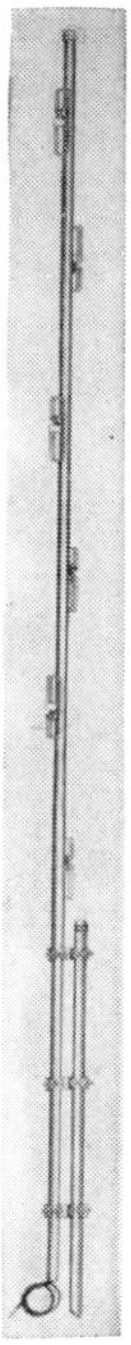

FIG. 6-42. Vertical-stack high-gain type-4000 antenna. (*Andrew Corp.*)

In mobile-radio systems the benefits of a high-gain base-station antenna are multiplied by the number of units in the system.

The side-mounting antenna in Fig. 6-41 has the advantage of having a firmly supported unit mounted directly to structural members of communication towers, allowing the top of the tower to be used for microwave or other antenna equipment; this is designed for 25 to 50 Mc.

The basic unit of this antenna is a center-fed, half-wavelength folded dipole. Two of these units, spaced 1 wavelength apart, make up the antenna. The rigid three-point mounting arrangement reduces the fluctuation of antenna impedance to a minimum under varying wind-loading conditions.

This antenna has an average gain of 2.5 db over a dipole, and a coverage pattern that is omnidirectional on ordinary communication towers. Larger towers may require additional bays to compensate for pattern distortion. Increased omnidirectional gain, or greater gain in a given direction, can also be obtained by using an additional number of half-wavelength units of the basic antenna. The harness design of the antenna permits these additional units to be incorporated with no appreciable effect on the low VSWR of the antenna.

Typical of a vertical stack for the 450- to 470-Mc band is the antenna shown in Fig. 6-42. Type 4000 has six folded dipole radiators for a 7.6-db gain; type 4002 has three elements for a 5.0-db gain. The radiation patterns and gain plots are shown in Fig. 6-43.

Another type of high-gain antenna for the 450- to 470-Mc band is shown in Fig. 6-44. This antenna has a gain of 10 db across the entire band and can be used at any frequency in the band without any tuning.

Special suppressor elements incorporate the desirable features of a single feed point, while providing high efficiency, eliminating wasted radiation, and producing superior mast isolation.

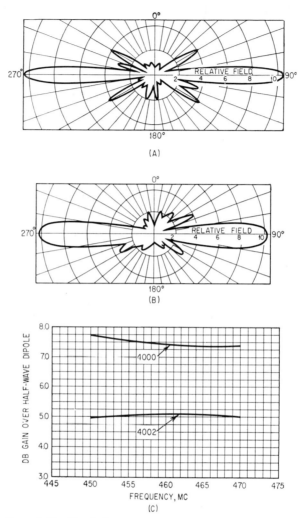

FIG. 6-43. Vertical antenna; (A) radiation pattern for six radiators; (B) for three radiators; (C) gains for both types. (*Andrew Corp.*)

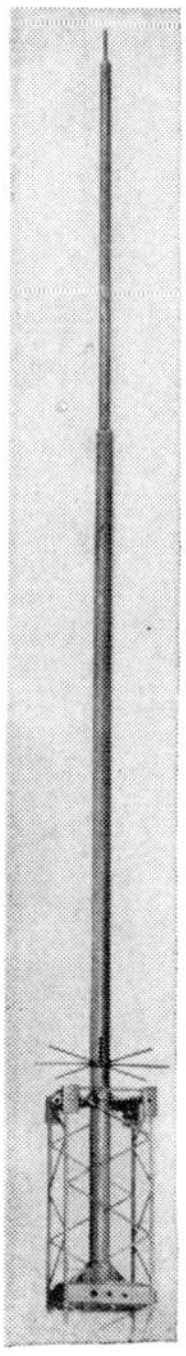

FIG. 6-44. Omnidirectional vertical antenna type 212. (*Andrew Corp.*)

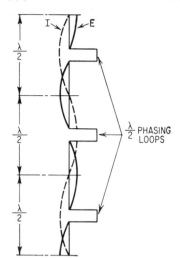

FIG. 6-45. Feeding method for type 212.

This lightweight antenna is enclosed in a Fiberglas radome which assures dependable systems performance under unfavorable weather conditions. The radiating elements are covered by the Fiberglas cylinder.

This antenna uses a new suppressor element.[1] This development permits the use of a long conductor, with the new elements properly applied at approximately half-wavelength intervals to "shield" the portions which normally cause cancellation, as in Fig. 6-45.

In one form, this element consists of a half-wavelength cylinder mounted over the conductor to be "shielded," and two additional quarter-wavelength cylinders over the first one connected to produce cooperative choking conditions. A cross-sectional view of such a device is shown in Fig. 6-46. A single end-fed wire is used for the radiator; the suppressor couples the vertical series of dipoles. The choking effect of the quarter-wavelength shorted cylinders prevents undesired radiation; the long cylinder acts as a one-to-one transformer.

[1] M. W. Scheldorf, Suppressor Improves Pattern, *Electronic Industries*, p. 78, January, 1958.

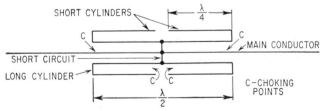

FIG. 6-46. Detail of RF antenna choke.

6-6. Coverage Area of Antennas

Antenna coverage in terms of distance or in terms of area is of specific importance; gain does not, of itself, indicate the coverage. The field patterns in this chapter are plots of relative field strength.

Stacked antennas can be used to provide increased gain by reducing the vertical angle of radiation. A large amount of energy of a simple coaxial antenna radiates at vertical angles which are not useful for mobile service. Power gain results from concentrating this energy in a useful direction. An antenna with power gain may be viewed as providing a signal strength of a simple antenna but with less power input provided to the power-gain antenna. Power gain should be rated against a standard half-wavelength dipole.

A method of obtaining gain is to stack the elements in a vertical direction which flattens, in the vertical plane, the normal pattern of a half-wavelength antenna, and the amount of gain increases with the number of elements.

Antennas are reciprocal, which means a power gain obtained when transmitting also has a power gain when receiving. Two or more antennas can be vertically stacked, and the horizontal pattern will remain about the same, while the added gain will be obtained by compressing, reducing the vertical pattern height.

As an example, in the 150-Mc band, eight 6-element antennas can be vertically stacked in a collinear array with a spacing between centers of 1 wavelength. If fed in phase, they will have a gain of 17 db over a dipole, which is the same as increasing the power by over 50 times.

The measure of relative field strength may be seen from Fig. 6-47 as an example; this is a two-element unipole with a bidirectional pattern as in A. This antenna has a 3.2-db gain, or in the direction of greatest gain (90 and 270° in A) the field is 3.2 db more than a half-wavelength dipole with the same polarization. Thus the arbitrary value 10 corresponds to 3.2 db at 90°, and a gain pattern as in B can be plotted by use of a gain-conversion graph. This is the horizontal pattern in terms of gain relative to a dipole. Zero decibels gain is the reference dipole, and only between 50 and 130° (or between 310 and 220°) does the gain of this antenna exceed zero. Negative values indicate where the antenna has less gain than zero decibels dipole.

But the gain pattern alone still does not give a complete picture of the area coverage. Based upon standard propagation data, frequency, power, and antenna height, a coverage pattern may be calculated. While this is again theoretical and the terrain and other conditions will modify this calculation, it does serve as a comparative basis for planning.

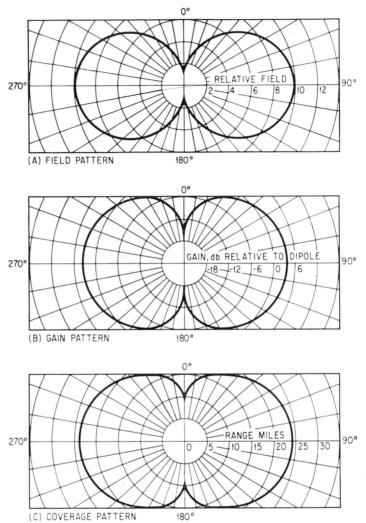

FIG. 6-47. Antenna patterns showing (A) field pattern, (B) gain pattern, (C) coverage pattern. (Andrew Corp.)

C is the coverage pattern, assuming 150-Mc operation with 50 watts, a two-element unipole at 150 ft, and a standard installation.

Based upon similar data, Fig. 6-48 offers several comparisons. A is a single unipole and cardioid at 50 Mc; B compares a dual unipole (bidirectional) with a corner reflector at 50 Mc; C shows a single unipole, corner reflector, and high-gain collinear array at 150 Mc; and D compares a single dipole, corner reflector, Yagi, and a collinear array at 450 Mc.

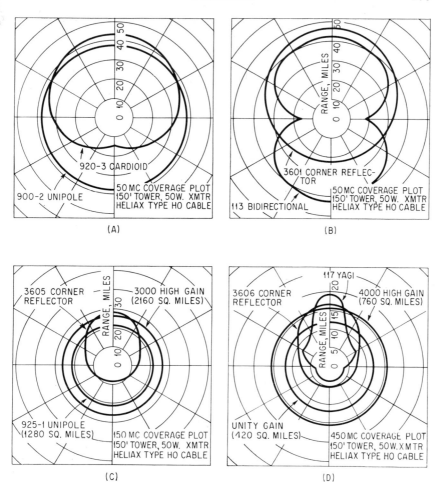

FIG. 6-48. Antenna patterns: (A) and (B) show 50 Mc; (C) is for 150 Mc; and (D) illustrates 450 Mc. Note antenna types as indicated. (*Andrew Corp.*)

CHAPTER 7

SELECTIVE CALLING

7-1. Calling Methods

In many cases of mobile communications a transmitter must select one station, or a group of stations, out of all the mobile stations on the same assigned frequency. The two basic types of selective-calling systems are those using different tones, or combinations of tones, which depend upon selection by frequency at the receiving end, and those which use tone pulses depending upon digital selection.[1]

Selective calling permits the selection of mobile units by the base transmitter either individually, in groups, or all at once in response to different codes created by the operation of a telephone dial or push buttons.

At the mobile station when the correct code is received for a particular vehicle, in a typical system, an alarm sounds a buzzer, and a lamp is lighted. The decoder may open a normally muted loudspeaker or turn on the headlights or sound a horn to warn the vehicle operator of a call if he is not in the vehicle when the call is received.

If the mobile units have a code sender and base stations have a decoder, vehicles can also call selectively. Base-station loudspeakers may then be muted until signaled by the proper code of a mobile unit. In this way drivers can select a specific base station or one of the control points of a base station without alerting the others.

Other electrical devices may be controlled from a mobile unit by selective calling, and mobile units can dial directly into land-based automatic-telephone systems without the aid of an operator.

By equipping both mobile units and base stations with code senders and decoder units, any radio station can dial any other station in the same system without alerting the others, just as if all stations were connected by a dial-telephone system.

The two basic techniques used in selective calling are tone signaling and digital pulses.

[1] Mininum Standards for Land-mobile Selective Signalling Equipment, *TR*-120, Electronic Industries Assoc., New York.

180

Tone Signaling.   Audio frequencies can be used for selective calling; these are known as tones.   A tone, or series of tones, modulates the transmitted carrier in a coded system.   Only a single receiver (or receivers for a group call) responds to the code, which allows reception of the following voice transmission.

A simple tone-code system is shown in Table 7-1; there are two sets of push buttons, one set for each of the digits in the code.   Where N is the number of tones, there are N^2, or 9, possible combinations of two tones. B is the first digit and A is the second digit.   Thus 31 is B_3A_1 and 12 is B_1A_2.

TABLE 7-1. SIMPLIFIED TONE-CODE SYSTEM

Tone A

		1	2	3
Tone B	1	11	12	13
	2	21	22	23
	3	31	32	33

First digit	Second digit
①	①
②	②
③	③
Tone B	Tone A

Digital Pulses.   A second type of selective calling uses a series of pulses representing digits in the code; each pulse represents the presence of tone modulation where a single tone is used.

An audio oscillator and telephone dial are used at the transmitter. When a number is dialed, a number of tone pulses is transmitted so that the number of pulses is the dialed number.

Digits may be directly represented by pulses, as where a 7 is seven pulses or a 5 is five pulses, but for a large number of code selections binary numbers, as in Table 7-2, are useful.   As an example, 555 can represent a decimal number of three 5 digits, but 15 pulses $(5 + 5 + 5)$ represent 32,768 in binary.   As shown, 0001 is 1, 0010 is 2, 0100 is 4, and 1000 is 8.   Thus the binary numbering system of 1's and 0's is a method for counting in powers of 2 rather than counting, as in the decimal system, in powers of 10.

TABLE 7-2. BINARY-NUMBER CODES

2^5	2^4	2^3	2^2	2^1	2^0		
32	16	8	4	2	1		
0	0	0	0	0	0	=	0
0	0	0	0	0	1	=	1
0	0	0	0	1	0	=	2
0	0	0	0	1	1	=	3
0	0	0	1	0	0	=	4
0	0	0	1	0	1	=	5
0	0	0	1	1	0	=	6
0	0	0	1	1	1	=	7
							$\vdots$
0	1	0	0	0	0	=	16
1	0	0	0	0	0	=	32

7-2. Tone-selective Calling Codes

Selective calling by frequency selection involves transmission and reception of tone-coded signals. An example of a simple coding system is shown in Table 7-3. There are two sets of tone generators in this system, each with a different frequency. For each tone there is a selective circuit in the receiver which responds to this frequency.

TABLE 7-3. A TONE-CODING SYSTEM

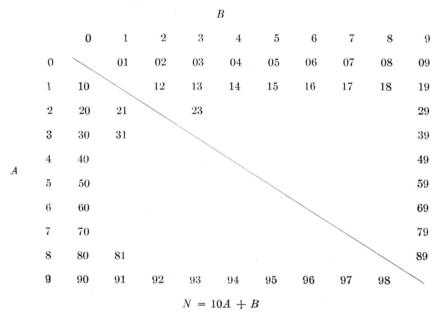

$$N = 10A + B$$

Assume, in a restricted example, that the code is a group of two tone signals in sequence. The first is A; the second is B. Thus for code 12 the signal is A_1B_2, for 23 it is A_2B_3, and for 69 it is A_6B_9. The only codes which are not in use are those where a digit is repeated, as 11, 22, 33, 44, and others. These are the codes which lie on the diagonal and are not indicated with code numbers. Repeated digits are not used to prevent false signaling or calling errors.

The decimal number for any code is $N = 10A + B$. Since this is a square chart ($A = B = 10$) there are 100 possibilities, less the double digits, a total of 90 different codes. There are 20 tone generators, but these can be arranged to form 380 separate codes.

A chart for this larger number of codes is shown in Table 7-4. Any code is made up of two tones and, where N is the code number, $N = 20A + B$.

This can be seen directly from the chart. But here A and B refer only to the sequence A, B, and there are only 20 different tones, A_0 through A_{19} and B_0 through B_{19}. Again the same digit cannot be used twice.

By switching arrangements two tones are used in proper sequence from the 20 generators. For code number 382 the signal is $A_{19}B_2$, which is the tone sequence 19, 2; for 282 it is $A_{14}B_2$, or the sequence 14, 2; and for 172 it is A_8B_{12}, or 8, 12.

A block diagram of a circuit for a code like the one in Table 7-4 is shown in Fig. 7-1. A series of individual tone generators, 1 through 19, are fed to both selectors A and B. The sequence is set by S, whose output goes to the transmitter. Codes are selected by A and B; with 19 tone generators any one of 380 different codes may be used.

But for ease in operation a system of code-calling identification

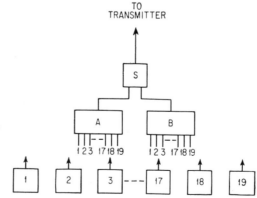

Fig. 7-1. Block diagram of a tone-coding system.

TABLE 7-4. A 20-BY-20 TONE-CODING SYSTEM

		0	1	2	3	4	5	6	7	8	B 9	10	11	12	13	14	15	16	17	18	19
	0		1	2	3	4	5	6	7	8	9	10	11	12	13	14	15	16	17	18	19
	1	20		22							29	30	31								39
	2	40	41								49	50	51								59
	3	60																			
	4																				
	5																				
	6																				
	7																				
	8													172							
A	9																				
	10	200																			
	11																				
	12																				
	13																				
	14			282																	
	15																				
	16																				
	17																				
	18	360																			379
	19	380	381	382																	

$$N = 20A + B$$

which is more direct is preferable.[1] With two sets of 10 tone generators each a calling system is mapped in Table 7-5. For a 3-digit code the first digit (as 1 in 132) sets up the sequence of the two banks of tone generators A and B. The digit 1 means B before A. The second digit, 3, refers to the third B tone, or B_{13}, and the third digit, 2, is the A_2 tone; the junction of B_{13} and A_2 is the required code 132.

[1] C. R. Roualt, Application of Voice-frequency Tone Signaling to Mobile Radio Systems, *Trans. IRE*, *PGVC*-2, p. 6, August, 1952.

TABLE 7-5. DOUBLE SET OF 10 TONE GENERATORS

First tone →

		A	A	A	A	A	A	A	A	A	A	B	B	B	B	B	B	B	B	B	B
		0	1	2	3	4	5	6	7	8	9	10	11	12	13	14	15	16	17	18	19
A	0	00	10	20	30	40	50	60	70	80	90	100	110	120	130	140	150	160	170	180	190
A	1	01									91	101									191
A	2	02									92	102			132						
A	3	03					53				93	103									
A	4	04									94	104									
A	5	05									95	105									
A	6	06									96	106									
A	7	07									97	107									
A	8	08									98	108									198
A	9	09									99	109	119							179	189	199
B	10	200	210							280	290	300	310							380	390
B	11	201									291	301									391
B	12																				
B	13															343					
B	14																				
B	15																				
B	16																				
B	17																				
B	18	208									298	308									
B	19	209								289	299	309									399

Second tone →

For codes from 00 to 99 the sequence is A, A; from 100 to 199 it is B, A; from 200 to 299 it is A, B; and from 300 to 399 it is B, B.   As examples: 53 is 053 and, since it begins with 0, the sequence is A, A; the first tone is A_5, the second tone is A_3, and their junction is 53. For 179 the sequence is B, A; the 7 indicates the seventh in B (17), and the 9 is the unit under A; their common point is 179.   For 289 the sequence is A, B; A_8 meets B_{19} (the ninth B) at 289.   For 343 the sequence is B, B or B_{14} and B_3 where they meet at 343.

Thus either a three-row push-button system or dial can be used to indicate the codes directly by decimal numbers.

7-3. Tone-selective Calling by Audio Signals

Tone signaling is a selective-calling system using the frequency to distinguish between the different signal codes.   The use of audio-frequency signals, within the voice-frequency range, permits the signals to pass over wire lines (telephone) as well as radio transmission. Because the tone signals are in the audio passband, the possibility of voice triggering must be considered in the equipment.

In many applications a fleet of vehicles can be divided into several groups; each group can be called by a different group code.   Figure 7-2 is a block diagram of a group selective system.   At the transmitter the calling-signal frequencies are produced by tone generators which are stable audio oscillators. B indicates a number of tone generators; in operation the desired code is selected from the appropriate tone generators by a telephone dial or by push buttons.   The operator then presses the *call* button on the microphone; this connects the transmitter to the tone generator for a short pulse, while the tone modulates the carrier.   After a short period (about 0.5 sec) the switch S connects the microphone for regular voice transmitter and disconnects the tone generator from the transmitter.

All mobile units on the same carrier frequency receive this transmission; all receivers have a frequency-sensitive vacuum-tube switch A,

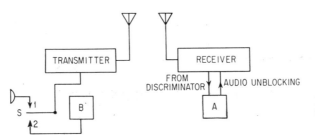

Fig. 7-2. Group selective-calling diagram.

as in the figure. Input to block A is from the detector output; when tone plus carrier is received, the switch in A unblocks, or unmutes, the audio stages. After the tone burst opens the receiver, the carrier signal holds the receiver in operating condition, and normal voice transmission is received. At the end of the transmission the switch A again blocks the receiver until the next proper tone plus carrier. All receivers in a group receive the same message, while all the other mobile receivers tuned to the same carrier frequency but with different tone codes are undisturbed.

7-4. Digital-pulse Codes

Using a dial system with digit values from 1 through 10 (zero is considered 10) a 4-digit code offers 10,000 possibilities, and a 5-digit code has 100,000. Since one number is reserved for clearing all code selectors before a call, there are 9 possible values for each digit, and for a 5-digit code this is 9^5, or 59,049.

Binary numbers (to the base 2) can also be used; this is shown in Table 7-6. For 6 pulse digits there are $2^6 - 1$ or 63 possibilities other than all zeros. A single tone is used for a pulse; a code is a series of pulses and spaces. Thus 63 is 111 111, 50 is 110 010, and 21 is 010 101.

For protection against errors, binary bodes can be mapped.[1] Figure 7-3 illustrates a simple cubic form showing messages 010 and 101. Moving along one edge of the cube a code changes by 1 digit only, as if a single error were introduced. Starting with 010 a single error will produce 110 or 000, or 011; starting with 101 a single error will produce 100 or 111, or 001. But no single error will change 101 to 010, and the two codes are error-protected from two single errors.

[1] R. C. Clark, Diagrammatic Methods of Code Construction, *Trans. AIEE,* vol. 58, p. 997, May, 1958.

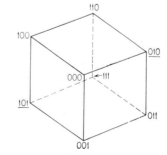

Fig. 7-3. Code mapping.

TABLE 7-6. AN EXPANDED BINARY-NUMBERING CODE

	2^5	2^4	2^3	2^2	2^1	2^0
	32	16	8	4	2	1
0	0	0	0	0	0	0
1	0	0	0	0	0	1
2	0	0	0	0	1	0
3	0	0	0	0	1	1
4	0	0	0	1	0	0
.						
.						
.						
10	0	0	1	0	1	0
11	0	0	1	0	1	1
.						
.						
.						
20	0	1	0	1	0	0
21	0	1	0	1	0	1
.						
.						
.						
30	0	1	1	1	1	0
31	0	1	1	1	1	1
32	1	0	0	0	0	0
.						
.						
.						
40	1	0	1	0	0	0
.						
.						
.						
50	1	1	0	0	1	0
.						
.						
.						
59	1	1	1	0	1	1
.						
.						
.						
62	1	1	1	1	1	0
63	1	1	1	1	1	1

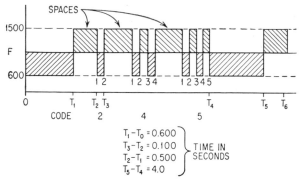

FIG. 7-4. A digital-pulse code.

7-5. Digital-pulse-code Selection

A digital-pulse code based upon the frequency change from one tone to another is shown in Fig. 7-4. A 5-digit code is used, using a standard telephone dial, where each digit lies between 2 and 10 (zero is considered as 10). Digit 1 is a clearing signal, and it is not used as part of the calling codes.

The number of digits may be between 1 and 5; any digit can have a value from 2 to 10, and there are 59,049 five-digit codes, or 9^5.

Two tones are used—600 and 1,500 cps—with one of these being transmitted at all times during the code.[1] Either the 600-cycle tone or the 1,500-cycle tone may be used to modulate the transmitter; the change from one tone to the other indicates the decimal digit of the code. Thus, as in Fig. 7-4, before each call there is a 600-cycle tone of 600 msec and a change from 600 cycles to 1,500 cycles at T_1. This is used to clear all selectors at the receivers; the interchange at T_1, for clearing, is the digit 1.

There is a space of 500 msec between digits, and each digit pulse is 0.100 msec. A code of 245 is shown in Fig. 7-4 to illustrate the pulse timing. In this example (where only 3 digits are shown) the clearing digit 1 resets all decoders.

There is a final interchange (at T_4) to 600 cycles, because the sum of the digits is odd. This final interchange rings the alarm signal (light or bell) at the decoder for a period of 4 sec ($T_5 - T_4$), after which there is a final change to 1,500 cycles. This change at T_5 removes the tone modulation and turns off the transmitter.

[1] W. Ornstern, A Selective Calling System to 106A Standards Employing Cold Cathode Thyratrons, *Trans. IRE, PGVC*-8, p. 17, May, 1957.

If the called station responds, the voice transmission begins; if there is not a response to the coded call, a light alarm (indicating a call but no answer) is lighted, and all decoders in the system are reset to zero.

A block diagram of the system is shown in Fig. 7-5. *A* shows the mobile unit and *B* is the fixed station. Coded transmission is from the base station to the mobile receiver. Only a single decoder will respond to the specific code, or perhaps a group of decoders, if this is a group code.

A block diagram of the decoder is shown in Fig. 7-6; interchanges are converted into pulses by the generator fed by the input. A decoder counter counts each digit-pulse series. When a number is recognized as digit 7, for seven pulses, or 5, for five pulses, the counter transfers the number to the digit register.

This register, as shown, has five stages, one for each digit. Assume the code is 23074. The first two pulses provide a count of 2, which is transferred to the digit-register first position and turns this stage on. Arrival of the next digit is a series of three pulses, which is transferred to the digit-register second stage. This continues until all stages of the register are turned on by their proper connection to the counter

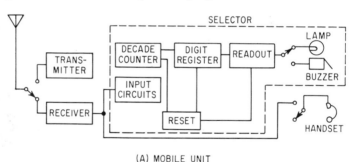

(A) MOBILE UNIT

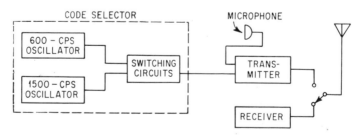

(B) FIXED STATION UNIT

FIG. 7-5. Digital-pulse system. *A* is the mobile unit and *B* is the fixed unit.

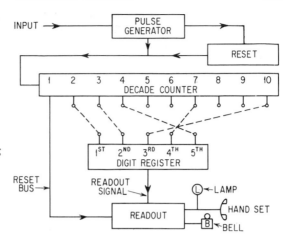

FIG. 7-6. Pulse decoding showing 23074.

stages. When the last digit is read into the register, a signal can pass to the read-out block, which turns on the alarm bell. If the handset is lifted, normal voice communication then begins. If, however, there is no answer, the bell is silenced, and the lamp goes on to show that the station was called but did not answer. In this way a driver can return to his vehicle and see that he received a call, on his code, during his absence.

The counter, as in Fig. 7-7, is a series of thyratrons, or gas-filled triodes. In the initial state V_1 is conducting while all the other tubes are cut off. All grids, except V_1, receive the pulses to be counted. But V_2 is the only primed stage; its grid potential is positive by the drop across R_1. All other tubes have zero grid voltage, and all stages, including V_2, have the same positive-anode voltage.

Positive pulses for a given digit will appear on all grids but will fire only V_2, because the pulse adds to the direct current across R_1. When V_1 fires, the next tube is primed; thus a 2 passes through 2 stages, a 5 passes through 5 stages, and the string of tubes counts the digit pulses; this is the count transferred to the digit register.

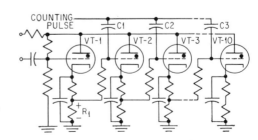

FIG. 7-7. Counter circuit.

Other Counter Types.   Other possible electronic counters[1] include the multivibrator, which is a two-stage resistance-coupled amplifier with the output of the second stage fed back to the input of the first stage.

Transistor flip-flop circuits are becoming increasingly important in counter applications.   Typical junction transistor circuits function in much the same manner as the vacuum-tube flip-flop.   One transistor is always conducting, and one is always nonconducting.   *On* is 1 and *off* is 0.

A series of flip-flops constitute a binary, or count-by-two, counter, as in Fig. 7-8.   Four stages are shown; each counts by two, so the count goes 2, 4, 8, and 16.   Zero-one is the first state of a given stage, and one-zero is the other state of any given flip-flop stage.

One stage of a flip-flop changes state every second pulse and drives the other half.   For every second pulse from any succeeding stage the next is driven.   A binary counter with N stages counts 2^N pulses; thus two complete four-stage counters (or an eight-stage counter where $N = 8$) will provide a single output for every 256 pulses, for the series is 2, 4, 8, 16, 32, 64, 128, and 256.   This is, again, the binary numbering system.   By proper feedback a decade counter can be made, which counts by 10.

Binary-code Selectors.   Binary codes are a series of pulses and spaces where 1 is a pulse and 0 is a pulse absence, or a space.   Codes, as for example 101 001, 010 111, or any series, are transmitted in sequence. At the receiver the pulse pattern is recorded and compared with the stored information; a logic circuit recognizes only the proper code.

Active devices for a decoder can be magnetic cores, transistors, or vacuum tubes.   Any device with two stable states may be used.

One method of synthesizing a circuit for detecting a sequential code is illustrated in Fig. 7-9.   This block diagram of the circuit may be broken down further into its function.   The information register can

[1] J. R. Pollard, Selective Calling for Radio Telephone Systems, *Electronic Engineering* (British), p. 490, December, 1953.

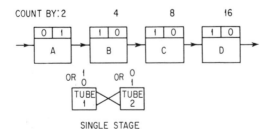

FIG. 7-8. Flip-flop counters.

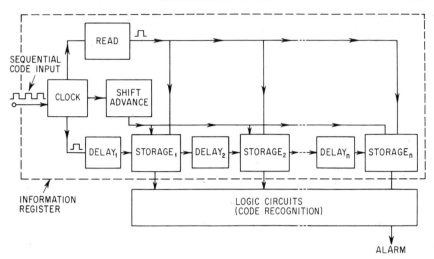

Fig. 7-9. Sequential-code recognition.

be divided into the five functions: clock, shift advance, read, delay, and storage. There is one clock, one shift advance, and one read, but there are as many delays and storages as there are bits of information (1's or 0's) in the code. The received incoming code will first trigger the clock, which produces a series of pulses which control the timing of the circuit. Each shift-advance pulse will shift the stored information from a storage block to the next delay block. Delay permits the shift advance to operate before new information is stored.

The operation may be seen by the chart in Table 7-7. Assume that a 01 011 (five-bit) code is to be received; this is the sequential-code

TABLE 7-7. PULSE-CODE SHIFTING

Digit storage

Shifts	S_1	S_2	S_3	S_4	S_5
	0	0	0	0	0
1	1	0	0	0	0
2	1	1	0	0	0
3	0	1	1	0	0
4	1	0	1	1	0
5	0	1	0	1	1

Shift of code 01011

input.   Each of the five storage stages, which can be either 1 or 0, is in the 0 state.

A timing series of pulses is started when the code enters the clock. First, a bit is read into the delay; at the same time a shift-advance pulse moves (shifts) the preceding bit from storage to delay.

Using the 01 011 code the contents of five bits of storage is shown in the table.   The first bit is a 1, and when added to the all-zero (empty) storage this produces 10 000.   As the successive bits enter, the code 01 011 appears in the storage.

At the end of the code, five bits in this case, the clock pulses the read, which feeds the code, in parallel, into the logic, or code-recognition, circuit.   If (and only if) this is the proper code for this decoder, an alarm signal is turned on; all other codes are rejected.

Modifications include provision for group calls, all calls, and individual codes.

Electromechanical Selectors.   A telephone type of dial can be used to code pulses with a 2,800-cps tone as breaks in the steady tone.

A typical code sender consists of an audio oscillator between 200 and 3,000 cycles.   This output is interrupted by telephone-dial pulses through a relay.   The tone pulses are fed to the audio input of the transmitter; the tone generator is turned on when dialing starts. The dial pulses break the tone, and the coding operates as a break system instead of a make system.   The decoder unit shown in Fig. 7-10 has a tuned audio amplifier, a signal rectifier, and a d-c amplifier for keying the decoder.   The call indicator is on the right.   The circuit operates under conditions where incoming pulses are of lower intensity than background noise.   A typical frequency is 2,800 cps.

This decoder is an electromechanical switch activated by direct current, stepping with each pulse.   It will respond to any of over 100,000 code combinations.   The schematic of the tone-pulse decoder is shown in Fig. 7-11.   Model 49HS has about 300,000 combinations; the newer model 59HS has a capacity of almost 100 times the previous unit.   Both are made by Secode.

Fig. 7-10. Dial-pulse decoder (center) and call-indicator head (right).   (*Secode-Electrical Communications.*)

A mechanical code wheel is used. When the coil of the selector is energized by a d-c pulse, both the pulsing armature and the slow-to-release armature are pulled in.

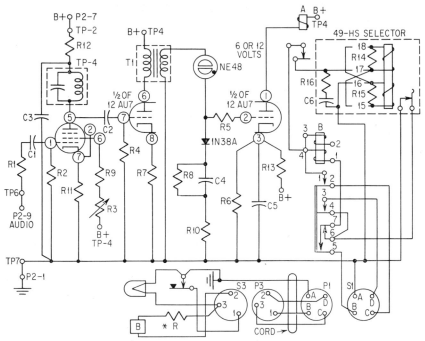

FIG. 7-11. Schematic diagram of tone-pulse decoder RPS-634 shown in Fig. 7-10. (*Secode-Electrical Communications.*)

The action of the pulsing armature causes the code wheel to step in a counterclockwise direction with each pulse, a ratchet assembly holding the code wheel ready to receive the next impulse. The pulsing armature will not cause the code wheel to step unless the slow-to-release armature is also pulled in.

The code wheel continues to step with each impulse until a code pin is reached. If the number of pulses in the first train of impulses is in excess of the number required to step the code wheel to the code pin, the stepping action stops. Subsequent pulses will cause no further action of the code wheel, which remains stopped at the setting of the first code pin. After the entire code combination has been received, the code wheel is released and returns to stand-by position ready to intercept another code.

If, however, the first train of pulses has fewer pulses than that necessary to step the code wheel to the position of the first code pin, the code wheel will return to stand-by at the end of the code combination.

When the number of pulses in the first train of pulses is the same as the setting of the first code pin, the code wheel will continue to step with incoming impulses until it reaches or falls short of the second code pin. At the end of each train of pulses, the slow-to-release armature drops out and is pulled in again with the next impulse, permitting the code wheel to step if earlier trains of pulses were of the correct number. This action is repeated with each train of pulses, until the code wheel has stepped a sufficient number of times for the contacts to make.

After the contacts have closed, they hold until one pulse (or more) is received, which releases the mechanism and allows the code wheel to resume its stand-by position, ready to intercept a new code combination. In most applications the contacts will be allowed to close only for a short period, and external latching or timing circuits will be used when continuous or prolonged operation of the controlled device is required.

The decoder responds to d-c pulses more than 31 msec in duration, spaced 19 msec or more and occurring at rates from 4 to 20 pulses per sec. These pulses are created by a standard telephone dial. The decoder mechanism requires 5 watts of electrical power during pulsing.

The decoder may be set, for example, to 4, 3, 2, and it will then respond to four pulses, a space, three pulses, a space, and then two pulses. Combinations of pulses such as this may be generated by dialing the numbers 4-3-2 on an ordinary telephone dial just by dialing as when placing a telephone call. Upon reception of this combination by a decoder set to accept this particular code, it closes a pair of contacts. The contacts are released by dialing the single digit 1, which results in a single release pulse. The decoder then restores itself to stand-by ready to monitor and accept or reject following combinations of pulses. If the combination 4-3-4 is dialed, for example, when the decoder has been set for 4-3-2, the contact will not close, and the decoder restores itself to stand-by.

Dial Codes. In this system, which may be considered typical of this type of decoder, the digit 1 is used for a clearing signal, and the total sum of the digits in a 4-digit code cannot exceed 42.

A code table is shown in Table 7-8. The code to which an individual selector will respond is determined by the settings of the code pins in the holes in the code wheel. They can be set so that the selector will close its contact upon receipt of a series of pulses consisting of one or more digits whose sum total of pulses does not exceed 42. For example, the code 9-9-9-9-9-9 cannot be used, since

$$9+9+9+9+9+9 = 54$$

However, 9-9-9-9-4-1 can be used, since the digits add up to 41.

When two sets of contacts are provided on a selector, the second

TABLE 7-8. DIGIT CODES

Examples	2-digit code	3-digit code	4-digit code
First code.............	3-2	3-5-2	4-3-3-3
Second code...........	3-4	3-5-4	4-3-3-5
Third code............	3-6	3-5-6	4-3-3-7
Fourth code...........	3-8	3-5-8	4-3-3-9

code must be an extension of the first code. For example, if the selector is set to respond to 4-3-3-3 to close the first contact, the code for closing the second contact must be 4-3-3-5, or the same number plus 2. The last digit is the sum of the previous last digit and 2. Thus, the two-code selector may be used to start a motor by sending the code 4-3-3-3 and to stop the motor by sending the code 4-3-3-5.

A four-code selector makes use of an arm containing four stationary contacts and one adjustable contact pin, making it possible to control four functions. Four codes are assigned, the first of which can be any convenient combination of digits. The last digit, for example, may be 2. The other three codes must be the same as the first code except for the last digit. The last digit of the second code must be the same as the last digit of the first code plus 2. The last digit of the third code must be the same as the last digit of the second code plus 2, and the last digit of the fourth code must be the same as the last digit of the third code plus 2.

Two, three-, and four-code selectors are provided with two, three, or four stationary contacts and one adjustable contact pin. The adjustable contact pin is common to all the stationary contacts. Contact between the adjustable contact pin and the stationary contact for the first code is not made, even momentarily, when the second code is dialed, nor by the contacts for codes 1 and 2 when the third code is dialed, and so on. The adjustable contact pin does not wipe across the stationary contacts as it passes them. Instead it drops into place after receipt of the correct code.

7-6. Telephones on Wheels

Several automatic systems have been proposed for dialing from vehicle radios to land telephones through special termination equipment installed to connect with the land-telephone system. One such system which has been demonstrated is the DuMont Dial-Direct.

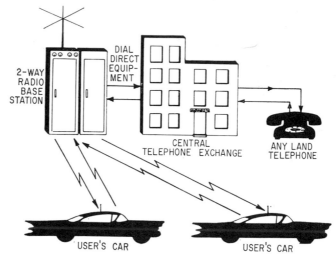

FIG. 7-12. Block of the Dial-Direct telephone system. (*DuMont.*)

This is shown in Fig. 7-12 and provides three basic functions: dialing from a vehicle directly to any land telephone; dialing from any land telephone directly to any vehicle; and direct dialing from vehicle to vehicle.   Long-distance calls to or from the mobile units are made through normal long-distance facilities.

As an example, the system operation would be used for dialing car-to-land; a mobile user picks up the handset of his car and, if the system is not in use, hears the normal rush of the FM receiver.   By dialing a key number, normally 9, the base-station transmitter is automatically activated, the local telephone system is switched in, and the user hears the normal dial tone.   He then dials the desired number directly.

In dialing land-to-car the land-telephone subscriber looks up the mobile user's number in the telephone directory.   It might be 166-53. He dials 166 and receives a special radio dial tone if the system is not in use.   Upon dialing 53, a call lamp in the car is lighted and an audio signal sounded.   Conversation begins when the handset in the vehicle is picked up.

For dialing car-to-car the mobile user picks up the handset in his car, and if the system is not in use, he hears the normal rush of the FM receiver.   By dialing a key number, which might be 9-9, the base-station transmitter is automatically activated, and a busy signal appears on the lines to and from the local telephone system.   The user then dials the number of the desired mobile unit, which might be 54, lighting a call lamp in the car and sounding an audio signal.   Conversation begins when the handset in the called vehicle is picked up.

The basic base-station dialing equipment is entirely contained in a 6-ft rack cabinet. The radio base station varies in size according to the area to be covered.

In the vehicle the additional equipment is usually mounted in the trunk compartment along with the two-way radio.

Flexibility is important, and if the driver is not in his vehicle when the call is received, a call light is lighted and an alarm bell rings. It is possible to arrange the equipment so that the call light stays on, if the driver does not answer, and this indicates the presence of a call when he returns to the vehicle.

7-7. Other Selective-calling Functions

Selective calling can also be used for controlling electronic or mechanical systems at a distance as well as for calling certain receivers for communications. A base station used for two-way communications is connected to the remote-control unit through a single-pair line.[1]

With the addition of a telephone dial and a d-c power supply at the remote-control point plus two rectifiers, D_1 and D_2, two relays (K_3 and K_4), a decoder, and a d-c power supply at the base station, remote control of up to four different functions can be provided. A typical circuit is shown in Fig. 7-13. D_1 is in series with the line relay K_2 at the base station, and the relay will respond only when relay K_1, at the remote-control point, is energized by the press-to-talk switch.

When the base station is in receive, in stand-by, or turned off, relay K_1 in its deenergized position will allow use of the dial to control functions at the base station. The dial is not in the circuit when this relay is energized.

[1] Leo G. Sands, The Telephone Dial in Control Applications, *Wire and Radio Communications*, vol. 5, p. 25, May, 1959.

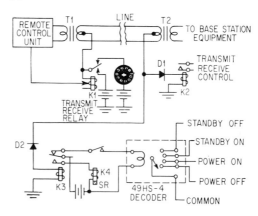

FIG. 7-13. Control of base-station functions by mobile selective calling. (*Secode-Electrical Communications.*)

When the dial breaks the circuit with the dialed code, relay K_3 causes the decoder to step. The contacts are held closed by K_4 during pulsing, completing the circuit to the selector. This relay drops out when the dialing sequence is completed, after allowing a single clearing pulse.

Two of the four contacts of the decoder, each closed by an individual code, are used to apply primary (but not keying) power to the base-station equipment and to disconnect power totally. The third contact is used for energizing relays which switch in stand-by base-station equipment, while the fourth contact releases the transfer relays to put the regularly used equipment back into service.

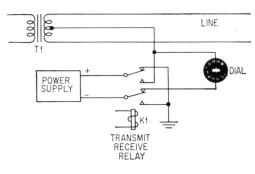

Fig. 7-14. Polarity-reversing relay.

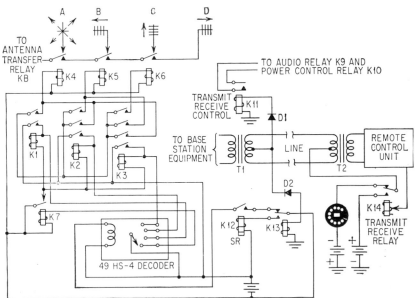

Fig. 7-15. Base-station antenna selection. (*Secode-Electrical Communications.*)

By use of the same techniques it is possible to control tower lights, emergency power supplies, and electrically actuated door locks to prevent entry to the base-station building until the operator at the remote-control unit dials the proper code number.

The circuit in Fig. 7-13 shows separate power supplies for press-to-talk and dialing functions. A common power supply can be used at the remote-control point by a relay, as in Fig. 7-14, for reversing polarity. As the press-to-talk switch is operated, the polarity is automatically reversed, and the dial is disconnected from the circuit.

In addition to the remote control of base-station power, selective calling codes may be used for remote selection of base-station antennas as illustrated in Fig. 7-15. By dialing the proper numbers, the base-station operator may select a specific antenna for optimum communication with a given station.[1]

As shown, in normal operation, the station uses an omnidirectional (A) antenna. By dialing 5-4, for example, a Yagi array (B) pointing north is switched in; dialing 5-6 switches in another Yagi array (C) aimed east; and dialing 5-8 causes still another Yagi antenna (D) to be connected to provide maximum signal strength to and from the south. By dialing 5-2, the omnidirectional antenna is placed back into service.

[1] Selective Calling Grows, *Electronics*, vol. 32, no. 22, p. 52, May 29, 1959.

CHAPTER 8

POWER SUPPLIES

8-1. Introduction

Power for the radio receiver and transmitter may be obtained from the a-c lines, as with a base station, or from the vehicle battery or generator, as with the mobile equipment. The most common d-c source is a vehicle battery, 6 or 12 volts, in automobiles, trucks, and buses.

Inverters are used for conversion of direct current into alternating current, and these can be vibrators, motor-generator sets, or electronic oscillators. Typical vibrators produce up to 150 watts or more of a-c power, depending upon the voltage source and vibrator design. Vibrators in this class are used to operate 110-volt a-c equipment from direct current.

A mobile motor-generator is a d-c motor driving a higher-voltage d-c generator. Power output is a function of the size of the motor and generator.

For small amounts of power, electronic oscillators and amplifiers are used. Tubes or transistors can supply the conversion from low-voltage direct current to high-voltage direct current. Mobile radios require high-voltage plate voltage, and because only a low-voltage direct current is available, a converter is used. Among the newer systems is the power-transistor converter, which can supply voltages and power in the same range as the electromechanical vibrator, at higher present cost but without moving parts. This unit is a self-excited oscillator feeding a step-up transformer with diode rectifiers providing the d-c high voltage.

A typical commercial unit is shown in Fig. 8-1. This model has a regulated output which corrects for variations of input current and load current; efficiency is 70 per cent.

8-2. The Battery

For vehicle radios the battery is usually the prime d-c source. It can be used directly for the filament power and, by conversion, as the power source for the d-c plate supply. Both 6- and 12-volt batteries are in use; newer vehicles have 12-volt batteries.

Because the radio transmitter-receiver is an extra drain on the battery, which has other functions in the vehicle, heavy-duty batteries and larger d-c generators for charging the battery are often used.

Transistorized radio equipment can use small, lightweight batteries because of the low power drain of the receiver-transmitter. The power needed for a typical 17-transistor receiver is about that for a single vacuum tube in the ordinary receiver.

Fig. 8-1. GE transistorized power supply. (*General Electric.*)

8-3. D-C Generators

A d-c generator can be driven by the vehicle motor and used, in a vehicle, as a source of power. While low-powered radio transmitters can operate with an ordinary battery-generator combination, as found in any automobile or truck, high-power transmitters require a heavier generator.

The dynamotor is a special type of motor-generator combination. A dynamotor differs from a motor-generator in that it is a single unit having a double armature winding. One winding serves for the driving motor, while the output voltage is taken from the other. Dynamotors usually are operated from 6-, 12-, or 32-volt storage batteries and deliver from 300 to 1,000 volts or more at various current ratings.

Genemotor is a term which is used for a dynamotor which is designed especially for automobile receivers and transmitters. It has good regulation and efficiency, with economy of operation. Standard models of genemotors have ratings ranging from 135 volts at 30 ma to 300 volts at 200 ma or 600 volts at 300 ma. The normal efficiency is about 50 per cent, increasing to better than 60 per cent in the higher-power units.

Proper operation of dynamotors and genemotors requires heavy direct leads, mechanical isolation to reduce vibration, and complete filtering for RF. The shafts and bearings should be thoroughly "run in" before regular operation. The tension of the bearings should be checked occasionally to make certain no looseness has developed.

The support for the genemotor should be in the form of rubber mounting blocks, or their equivalent, to prevent the transmission of vibration. The frame of the genemotor should be grounded through a heavy flexible connector. Brushes on the high-voltage end of the shaft should be bypassed with 0.002-μf mica capacitors to a common point on the genemotor frame, preferably to a point inside the end cover close to the brush holders. Short leads are essential, and it may be necessary, in some cases, to shield the entire unit, or even to remove the unit to a distance of 3 or 4 ft from the receiver and antenna lead.

When the genemotor is used for receiving, an additional RF filter should be used.

8-4. Vibrator Power Supplies

The vibrator type of power supply consists of a special step-up transformer combined with a vibrating interrupter (vibrator). This unit is connected to a storage battery, and plate power is obtained by passing current from the battery through the primary of the transformer. The circuit is made and broken rapidly by the vibrator contacts, interrupting the current to produce a magnetic field which induces a voltage in the secondary. The resulting d-c square-wave pulses in the primary of the transformer cause an alternating voltage to be developed in the secondary. This high-voltage alternating current is rectified, either by a vacuum-tube rectifier or by an additional synchronized pair of vibrator contacts.

The most popular vibrator circuit shown in Fig. 8-2 is the simple full-wave vibrator. It is electrically driven to perform the function of a single-pole double-throw switch. Current from the battery flows through the primary first in one half and then in the other. The center tap of the two halves of the transformer primary is connected to the battery. An alternating current appears on the secondary at the frequency of the vibrator. This alternating current on the secondary may be applied to a full-wave rectifier tube as shown, after which it is filtered, and used to supply high-voltage direct current to the receiver-transmitter.

A "buffer" capacitor is used across the secondary winding because

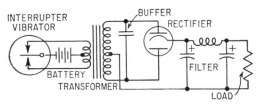

Fig. 8-2. Vibrator power supply.

of the highly inductive circuit. The buffer capacitor is of a value which, together with the inductance of the transformer, tunes the circuit. The capacitor absorbs the inductive kick when the circuit is broken and releases the stored energy in the reverse direction, while the vibrator is moving from one side to the other. Contact action thus is free of heavy arcing, and long vibrator life is possible, since the points of the contacts are protected.

Buffer capacitors are frequently operated across the high-voltage secondary winding, and the vibrator circuit gives transient peaks. These add to the steady d-c voltage. Near the end of vibrator life the transients can become excessive. Proper operation of the buffer capacitor should always be checked when a new vibrator is installed, since it is possible to obtain almost correct voltages and actual operation of a receiver with a poor buffer condition. This will cause the vibrator to fail long before it normally would. In applications requiring longer vibrator life or requiring heavier loads than can normally be provided by the single interrupter, paralleled interrupters are frequently used. Such vibrators contain an additional pair of contacts wired internally in parallel with the other pair. Externally the circuit is the same as the simple interrupter, except that heavier transformers and components are usually used.

In some cases, where heavy-load-handling ability and long service life are desirable, a dual primary may be used with a dual vibrator. There are two independent primary circuits operating from two independent sets of contacts. The only common connection exists at the vibrator and the transformer center tap.

Figure 8-3 shows a dual interrupter with a dual primary which divides the primary current. This gives more resistance in each half to control arcing and also forces independent action of the contacts in sharing the load, which increases vibrator life. There are disadvantages to this arrangement, which include added cost and complication of the transformer, and the need for bringing out separate leads for all the vibrator contacts.

A single vibrator can be used for pulsing and rectifying. This takes

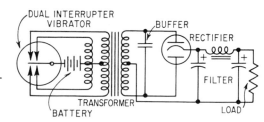

Fig. 8-3. Dual-interrupter vibrator.

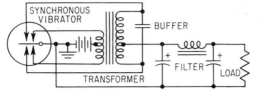

FIG. 8-4. Synchronous-vibrator circuit.

the place of the rectifier tube, its socket, and the filament power required.

This is the synchronous vibrator shown in Fig. 8-4. The ends of the secondary winding alternately change polarity, and a rectifier tube has two plates, each of which conducts in one direction only, so that the output of the tube is a series of unidirectional pulses. These pulses are caused by the vibrator, and a second pair of contacts operated in synchronism with the primary contacts could be used to connect the end of the secondary winding that has the proper polarity. The result would then be that a series of d-c pulses would be delivered to the filter exactly as with the dual-diode tube rectifier.

Figure 8-4 shows a typical synchronous-rectifying circuit, or a self-rectifying vibrator. The circuit is just like the simple interrupter. In this synchronous-rectifying vibrator, one side of the secondary high-voltage circuit must be common with one side of the battery, and the polarity of the high voltage will depend upon the polarity of the battery.

There are two ways of connecting a vibrator drive coil, as shown in Fig. 8-5. There are basic advantages in both types of drive. These methods are the shunt drive and the series drive.

In the shunt-driving method, as in *A*, the coil is connected across, or in shunt with, one pair in the primary contacts. All the contacts are open when the vibrator is at rest. Voltage is applied to the coil,

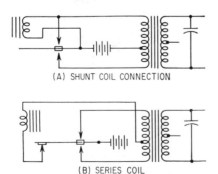

(A) SHUNT COIL CONNECTION

(B) SERIES COIL

FIG. 8-5. Shunt and series coils.

causing a current which attracts the reed, which then short-circuits the coil through the contacts that shunt it. The reed is then released to swing back and make connections with the opposite contact. During this interval, the coil energy is again built up to cause a continuous repetition of the driving process.

In the shunt-driving method, the vibrator will operate regardless of which side of the circuit the coil is connected to. The exact resistance of a shunt-driving coil is not significant in determining the condition of a vibrator. Coils for a single operating voltage may differ widely in resistance value.

Shunt-driven vibrators are suitable for operation in circuits designed for a single voltage only, which is a disadvantage in certain types of commercial equipment.

Series driving is shown in *B* of Fig. 8-5. To permit proper operation of a vibrator from different voltage sources, it is necessary to include a separate driving-coil circuit. A separate lead for this coil is brought out of the vibrator for connection directly to battery or through a resistor to the battery, if required.

Series drive requires an additional pair of contacts, one of which is added to the center reed and carried by means of a very lightweight spring contact. The other contact is usually in the form of a screw, set in the vibrator frame. The connection from the frame is then made to the center of the vibrator coil, with the outside of the coil being brought out of the vibrator for separate connection.

The driving contact is closed when the center reed is at rest. Application of voltage causes a current in the coil which attracts the reed. This opens the driving contact and deenergizes the coil, which allows the reed to swing back. The driving contact is again closed, so that energy is reestablished in the coil and the cycle is repeated.

A driving coil of this type will have a much lower resistance than a similar shunt-connected coil for a given vibrator voltage. But the exact resistance of such a coil will vary greatly in vibrator designs. If the coil resistance on a replacement is much higher than on the original in a series-resistor circuit, the driving voltage will be higher than normal, so that vibration will be extreme and life will be short. Also, a mismatch in the other direction would result in a feeble vibration with abnormal arcing, which would also result in short life and low voltage delivered to the circuit.

8-5. Transistor D-C–to–D-C Converters

Transistor power supplies, or d-c–to–d-c converters, are a new answer to the d-c power needs for mobile radio. Figure 8-6 illustrates a

FIG. 8-6. A d-c–to–d-c converter showing heat-sink case. (*General Electric.*)

converter and its heat-sink case mounted on a radio. Transistor d-c–to–d-c converters are used because they are more efficient and reliable than other types of d-c power sources.

Figure 8-7 shows a schematic of a transistor power supply designed to be added to, and used with, GE mobile radios. The unit is illustrated in Fig. 8-8. As shown in the schematic diagram, two triode power transistors operating as a flip-flop oscillator are used. This form of oscillator is a square-wave generator; the frequency is approximately 100 to 3,500 cps, which reduces the size and weight of transformers and filters. The vibrator supply requires an iron-core transformer with materials and construction similar to 60-cycle equipment, but the transformer, operating at 3,500 cps, becomes a small assembly weighing only a few ounces. Filtering and shielding can be reduced, because current switching in the transistors is electronic. Square waves are a

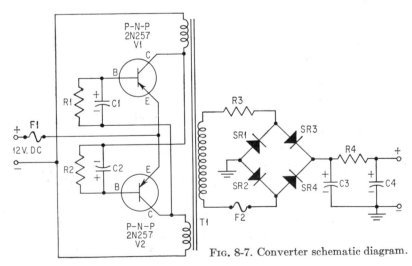

FIG. 8-7. Converter schematic diagram.

source of harmonics into the RF range, but the technique of suppressing these undesired components is not difficult.

Rectification of the stepped-up voltage appearing at the secondary of the transformer takes place in a bridge circuit using four silicon diodes. Ripple filtering is accomplished in a conventional RC network following the rectifiers. Power output of the transistor supply shown is approximately 195 volts at 100 ma, which is sufficient to power a 15-tube FM receiver. Over-all efficiency of the supply is 70 per cent, which is approximately the efficiency of a vibrator

FIG. 8-8. Construction of the d-c-to-d-c converter. (*General Electric.*)

supply employing a nonsynchronous vibrator and selenium rectifier.

All components except the transistors are mounted on a small printed circuit board. The transistors are mounted directly on the outside surface of the case, which acts as a heat sink. A protective bracket covers the transistors but still permits free-air circulation around the heat sink to maintain the transistors within the recommended operating temperature.

The current flow in this transistor supply limits the present use of the converter to the low-power stages of the radio.

Figure 8-9 shows another converter. The circuit is two PNP power

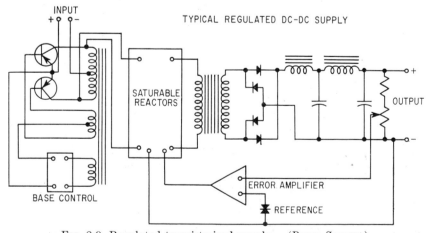

FIG. 8-9. Regulated transistorized supply. (*Power Sources.*)

transistors in a push-pull switching circuit which is connected to the d-c power source by a control circuit. The two transistors alternately connect the d-c battery across each half of the primary of a toroidal transformer. The transistor dissipation is low and the conversion efficiency high. In addition to the primary and secondary the toroid also has windings for positive feedback from each transistor collector to its emitter.

When one transistor conducts, the supply voltage is placed across half the primary, and the opposite collector is driven negative to twice the supply voltage. At this point the base feedback voltage is reduced, and the collector current and voltage across the primary are also reduced, which makes the base drive less. This action regeneratively shuts off the conducting transistor and starts the conduction cycle in the opposing transistor. The resulting waveform is a series of square waves which appear across the primary.

The frequency of oscillation is a function of the characteristics of the transformer core, the number of primary turns, and the supply voltage. A base-control circuit is used to prevent excessive transistor dissipation when the oscillator is effectively operating at no load. The control circuit used also improves quick starting and prevents transistor failure in the event of accidental reversal of the supply voltage.

The base-control circuit takes advantage of the reversal in polarity between PNP and NPN transistors, which permits the bases of the PNP oscillator transistors to be directly connected to the collector of an NPN control-transistor circuit and then to the positive end of the d-c supply.

The control transistor has a negative bias voltage obtained from an additional winding on the exciter transformer. The collector current of the control transistors and hence the maximum base current of the oscillator pair are determined by this bias voltage.

The control transistor has a high effective collector resistance; hence the oscillator transistors act as though they were operating with a constant-current bias. Thus, if for any reason the output should become shorted, there will be no bias voltage, and the base current will drop to a very low value. This protects the converter from accidental shorted loads, as other d-c power sources are not protected.

Base-circuit regulation may be used; a sample of the rectified and filtered output voltage is compared with the accurate, stable reference voltage of a Zener diode. The difference voltage is then amplified by one or two transistors and applied to the base of a regulator transistor in series with the base return circuit of the switching transistors. The control-transistor impedance varies in proportion to the error voltage, which changes the output of the switching transistors.

A saturable-reactor regulator may be used between the free-running-transistor oscillator and the load. Saturable reactors are switches opening or closing as controlled by an error voltage obtained by comparing the rectified and filtered d-c output voltage with a Zener diode.

A Univistor[1] is a transistorized direct plug-in replacement for the less efficient electromechanical vibrators.

Plugging the Univistor into the vibrator socket converts an electromechanical power supply into an all-electronic power supply with all the advantages of a transistorized unit including greater reliability, higher operating efficiency, elimination of moving parts and maintenance costs, and longer operating life, which is estimated at 10,000 hr compared with an average vibrator life of 400 to 500 hr.

The Univistor is an astable multivibrator used in conjunction with an external-vibrator transformer to deliver a-c power output from d-c input. Since the external-vibrator transformer is a part of the basic power-supply circuit, the Univistor can be interchanged with a vibrator without any alteration in the power-supply circuit.

Two germanium power transistors are used as the basic switching elements. The existing vibrator transformer is used. Replacement Univistors can be obtained with bases corresponding to any commercially available vibrator socket.

The Univistor output, as with other d-c–to–d-c converters, is cleaner than that of the vibrator. The filtering provided by the rectified and filtered portions of the basic power supply produces a smoother d-c output from a Univistor than from a vibrator.

Operation of a vibrator power supply using a Univistor eliminates damage to the buffer capacitor and saves some of the costs of repair.

8-6. Base-station Rectifiers

Full-wave rectifiers are used to convert the a-c power from a transformer fed by the line into direct current for the receiver-transmitter. For the filaments, alternating current can be used directly.

A typical power supply is shown in Fig. 8-10. This is designed to provide heater, plate, and screen voltages to the units of a communication base or repeater-station system.

It consists of three sections, one operating continuously for the receiver and control portions of the base station while the remaining two are controlled by the *power-transfer* relay, operated as required to place the transmitter on the air. The relay is operated by an external handset or microphone switch controlled by the operator.

The input voltage normally required is 117 volts alternating current,

[1] Universal Transistor Products.

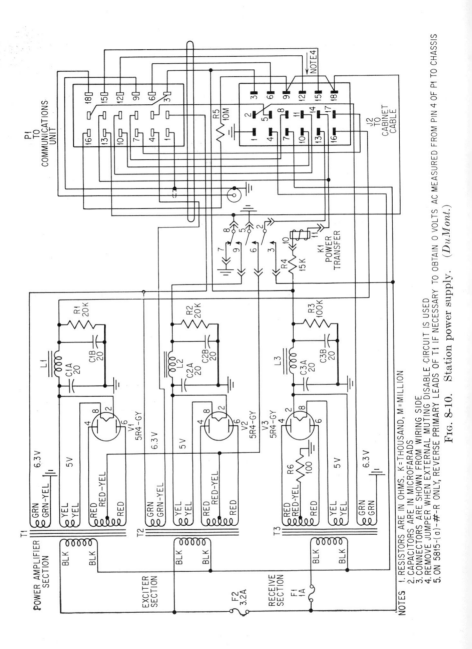

FIG. 8-10. Station power supply. (*DuMont.*)

212

60 cps, at a power level which varies with the power output of the transmitter.

External connections to the supply are made through P_1, J_1, and J_2. P_1 is a multicontact plug connected to the power supply through a cable of sufficient length to permit insertion of the plug into the mating receptacle of the communications unit comprising the receiver and transmitter portion of the base station.

J_1 is the audio input receptacle connecting directly to P_1 and so to the transmitter. J_2 connects to the cabinet cable for the a-c input, filament- and plate-power output, and control-voltage connections required for the complete base-station operation.

The output voltages and power developed by this particular unit are both alternating current for the filaments and direct current for the plate supply.

(A) 12.6 volts alternating current center-tapped, at 5 amp maximum, and (B) 6.3 volts alternating current at 5 amp maximum are for the filaments. Output A is obtained by the series connection of the 6.3-volt winding of the power transformers T_1 and T_2. Output B is obtained from the 6.3-volt winding of the power transformer T_3.

Plates and screens have three d-c voltages. These are:

(A) +160 volts at 125 ma maximum (receive section)

(B) +325 volts at 300 ma maximum (exciter section)

(C) +325 volts at 300 ma maximum (power-amplifier section)

Output A is supplied continuously to P_1 and J_2 for the receiver and audio sections of the base station. Outputs B and C are controlled through the contacts of the power-transfer relay. This relay is keyed by the microphone or handset switch of the operator to place the transmitter on the air by applying the two output voltages to P_1. The output voltage of the power-amplifier section is routed through J_2 to a plate-current meter located in the associated cabinet housing the base-station units. The wiring of the power supply completes the circuit to the communications unit and the power-amplifier stage.

CHAPTER 9

INSTALLATION

9-1. Planning the Installation

Long-life and trouble-free mobile-radio operation depends a great deal upon the original installation. Specific data are best obtained from the manufacturers' published instructions and diagrams, which are also the best source of information for servicing. The general procedures for installation are given in this chapter; they apply to most mobile receiver-transmitters. Proper operation can only result from a careful and well-planned installation.

Noise reduction in some vehicles can, in many cases, become quite a problem. Noise may be eliminated, if the receiver is correctly tuned to the frequency to be received, by installing a suppressor in the distributor-center lead and a capacitor between the generator-armature terminal and ground. If this does not prove to be effective, bypass capacitors can be tried at various points in the electrical system. Bonding straps installed between motor block and frame, between exhaust pipe and frame, and between other points may be helpful. There is no sure cure for noise in all vehicles. Many of the noise sources and possible steps to eliminate noise are discussed in the following sections of this chapter.

Units for installation are shown in Figs. 9-1a and 9-1b. Figure 9-1a illustrates the four parts of a trunk mounting, showing the separate speaker, the microphone, and the control head, all used alongside the driver, and the unit for mounting in the trunk. Figure 9-1b shows the control head, with the speaker, as an integral part of the unit for front mounting. Both types of mountings are shown in Fig. 9-2.

There are, of course, many possible arrangements for base stations, depending upon the type and size of the equipment; a unit designed to match a desk is shown in Fig. 9-3.

9-2. Trunk Installation

For automobile-trunk installations there are several possible locations in the trunk for the receiver-transmitter case, as shown in Fig. 9-4. A shows the mounting just above the gas tank. This is convenient

FIG. 9-1a. Unit for trunk mounting showing speaker, control head, and microphone, which are near driver. (*General Electric.*)

FIG. 9-1b. Unit for front mounting with integral control head. (*General Electric.*)

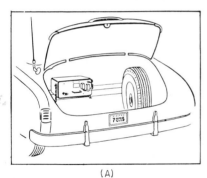

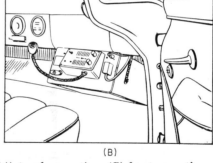

(A)

(B)

FIG. 9-2. The two types of mounting: (A) trunk mounting; (B) front mounting.

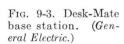

FIG. 9-3. Desk-Mate base station. (*General Electric.*)

215

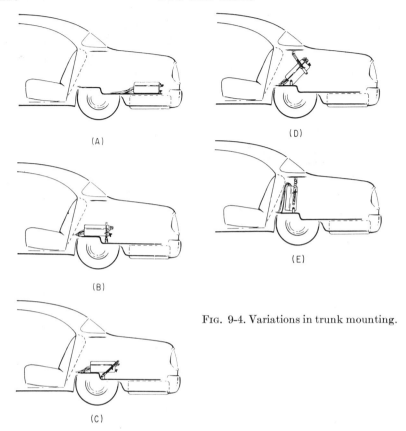

FIG. 9-4. Variations in trunk mounting.

for the adjustment of controls or for servicing, but it also means that there is less room in the trunk for other things.   The unit may also be arranged on the trunk step, as in B or C, with the bracket on the trunk floor.   Both of these provide more room in the trunk.   But the most compact installation is with the vertical mounting as in E.   For adjustment the unit may be tilted forward as illustrated in D.

A general view of the over-all layout for trunk mounting is shown in Figs. 9-5A and 9-5B.   When drilling for the mounting holes, care must be exercised to prevent damage to the gas tank or gas line.   A good electrical and mechanical contact should always be made between the case and the vehicle where the case is directly mounted on a metallic portion of the vehicle.   However, if the case is mounted on a non-metallic surface or where a good electrical connection is impossible, it is preferable to avoid grounding the case and to allow the primary power-return lead to supply the ground.   It is better to have no ground connection through the equipment case than an intermittent connection which can cause trouble.

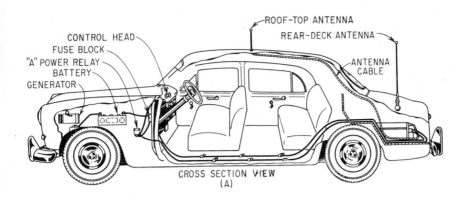

CROSS SECTION VIEW
(A)

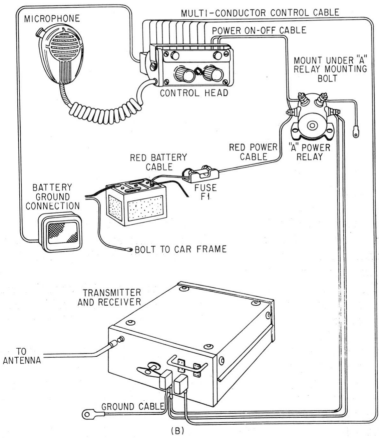

(B)

FIG. 9-5. Layout of parts and cables. (*Motorola.*)

Both the control and power cables may be brought through the forward trunk wall, under the rear seat, and under the floor mats next to the drive shaft. If the cables are run under the chassis, they should pass through protective covering. Use cable clamps where necessary to eliminate sag or undue tension on the cables. If the cables are run under the floor mats, it is important to make sure that foot traffic or the moving of the seats will not injure the cables. Protect the cables where they pass the edges of the seats by a length of conduit tubing slipped over them at these points of wear, or bend the seat-support bar to prevent kinking the cables.

Near the radio equipment clamp the cables so that they will not interfere with tools or baggage. Also arrange the clamps so that the power and control cable tends to push the plug into the receptacle rather than pull it out, to prevent possible disconnections.

Cable routing is important; in addition to the drive-shaft position and under-chassis runs it is also possible to have the cables along the side of the car.

Many cars now use aluminum strips to hold down the mats and rugs to protect the edges of the mats. These strips usually are held in place by means of short screws. Usually, the channel in the floor pan near the sides is about the proper depth for these cables. Rugs in modern cars are placed on top of a heavy jute padding. If necessary, tear or cut a strip along the side, which will allow the rug to fall back into place.

Some cars have a small channel along the side of the floor, and there is in this channel some wiring. There is enough room in this channel for the radio cables. In four-door cars, there usually is enough space under the base of the center post for the cables. Run the cables along the side, and up behind the fiber kick pad, on the side of the driver's compartment. But some of the new cars are quite long, and the standard length of cable may not reach unless the proper place for mounting is carefully chosen.

The power cable can go through the fire wall high enough from the floor so that water will not enter the vehicle around the cable. Rubber tape or a rubber grommet should be used where the cable goes through the fire wall.

The cables on the engine side of the fire wall should be positioned so that they will not come in contact with the engine to prevent damage from the heat. Some cables or parts of cables may have to be moved or repositioned to reduce ignition noise. If possible the ground cable should connect to the grounded side of the battery.

The fuse mounting and relay assembly, as in B of Fig. 9-5, are normally mounted on the front, or engine, side of the fire wall on a fender panel or on some other convenient mounting surface beneath the hood. It should be mounted at a point which will be close to the power source and which will allow as direct running of the power cable to the transmitter-receiver as possible. The fuse mounting and relay assembly should be kept from hot spots such as the engine block or manifold.

Details of the primary power wiring are illustrated in Fig. 9-6. The power-relay assembly, distributor-noise suppressor, fuse block, and generator capacitor are shown.

The control head, microphone, and speaker are all near the driver in the front of the vehicle.

The *control head*, or unit, has the on-off controls, the volume control, and the squelch control. The control unit should be mounted in a location where the controls will be within convenient reach of the operator. Usually this will be beneath the middle of the dashboard. Since the microphone cord connects to the control unit, the unit should be placed so that the microphone cord does not interfere with the operation of the vehicle. A typical arrangement is mounted under the instrument panel as in Fig. 9-7. In some of the newer cars

"A" POWER RELAY
MOUNTING BRACKET
"UP" & TERMINALS
"DOWN"

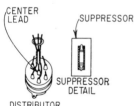

CENTER
LEAD   SUPPRESSOR

SUPPRESSOR
DETAIL

DISTRIBUTOR

Fig. 9-6. Primary power components.

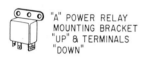

FUSE BLOCK

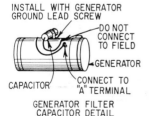

INSTALL WITH GENERATOR
GROUND LEAD SCREW

DO NOT
CONNECT
TO FIELD

GENERATOR

CAPACITOR   CONNECT TO
                 "A" TERMINAL

GENERATOR FILTER
CAPACITOR DETAIL

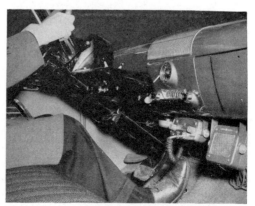

Fig. 9-7. Microphone, control head, and speaker, as in Fig. 9-1a, shown above in their proper positions. (*General Electric.*)

the bottom edge of the panel is not easy to use as a place to mount the control head. The other panel instruments and controls also allow little room for the head mounting. The opening provided for the ordinary car radio can be used if the car has no broadcast-band radio. By using a dummy plate for the radio opening on the instrument panel the control head may be mounted behind the plate with an opening cut in it, or it may be mounted on the front of the dummy plate.

The *loudspeaker* should be mounted in a position where it will direct the sound to the operator, but not where it will interfere with his vision. This will usually be just above or below the center of the windshield or on the fire wall. Some installations have also been made with the speaker mounted on the deck in front of the rear window.

In some cars the speaker can be mounted under the instrument panel, or where there is again a shortage of clear space, the opening provided for the use of a speaker on the panel may be used. The mobile-radio speaker and case may be mounted behind this grille, or the speaker may be removed from the case and bolted directly to the grille.

The speaker may be mounted underneath the dash on the fire wall,

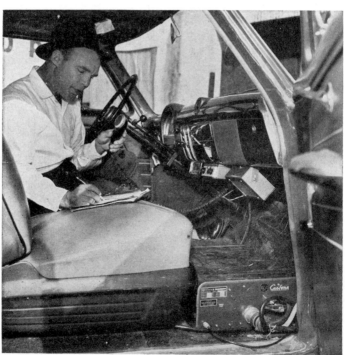

Fig. 9-8. Front-seat use of radio. (*RCA.*)

but if the vehicle is to be used in a noisy area, the speaker might better be mounted on the steering column, or on the dash. Recently one manufacturer has announced a speaker with built-in transistor audio amplifier with a power output of 5 watts at 6 volts and 15 watts when used with a 12-volt source. This is very helpful when a vehicle is used in a noisy location or if the operator is some distance from the vehicle and is called.

9-3. Front Mounting

Units designed for front mounting have built-in controls and a speaker as shown in use in Fig. 9-8. It is usually mounted, as illustrated, on the center drive-shaft well. Mounting brackets or braces are often used. The microphone is usually mounted on the unit, but in some cases it may be mounted closer to the driver or the operator. Figure 9-9 is a close-up.

Figure 9-10 shows the use of the front-mounting bracket which permits the unit to be lowered for removal. A front-mounted unit requires only a single cable through the car behind the driver's seat; this cable is to the antenna.

FIG. 9-9. Close-up of the front-mounted unit. (*General Electric.*)

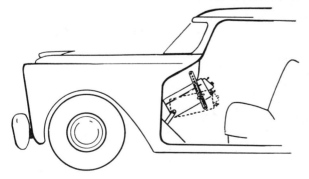

FIG. 9-10. Bracket for use in front mounting.

Power cables, as in Fig. 9-11, connect through the fire wall as shown. The electrical connections to be made in the forward installation are the same as in the trunk-mounted case. The antenna transmission line will be led forward under the roof to the front corner post and down to the unit.

To lead the control and power cables to the transmitter-receiver, it will usually be convenient to secure the lines along the fire wall until it is necessary to lead them down to the unit. Avoid routing of the cables where they may be stepped upon. Leave enough slack so that there are no sharp bends at the plugs to the chassis, so that removal of the unit is not difficult.

9-4. Truck Installation

Truck radios usually require more time for installation, and the job can be more difficult than for an automobile.

The transmitter-receiver unit may be mounted behind the seat or underneath the seat, as well as on top of the cab, in the rear of the truck using a weatherproof housing. The cables are routed partly or completely on the exterior, using flexible conduit and terminating on the engine side of the fire wall. Any excess opening is filled to prevent water from entering. The conduit may be fastened along the route

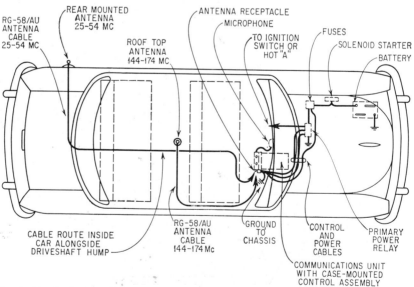

FIG. 9-11. Typical cable layout for an automobile installation. (*General Electric.*)

with conduit straps or heavy wire. Illustrations of possible truck mountings are shown in Chap. 1; a truck installation showing the antenna and external speaker is shown in Fig. 9-12.

9-5. Industrial-vehicle Installations

Several different types of mountings can be used on trucks and materials-handling vehicles as used by industry. Figure 9-13 shows a fork truck with the driver-operator. Vehicles like this are used to transport materials in or near a manufacturing plant or warehouse. It is possible, on some installations, to have the antenna mounted

FIG. 9-12. Truck-mounted unit. (*General Electric.*)

FIG. 9-13. Unit mounted in an industrial vehicle. (*DuMont.*)

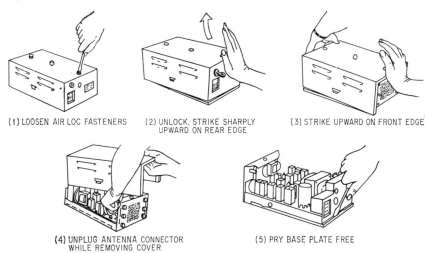

(1) LOOSEN AIR LOC FASTENERS   (2) UNLOCK. STRIKE SHARPLY   (3) STRIKE UPWARD ON FRONT EDGE
                                     UPWARD ON REAR EDGE

(4) UNPLUG ANTENNA CONNECTOR   (5) PRY BASE PLATE FREE
    WHILE REMOVING COVER

FIG. 9-14. Low-power industrial unit for AM.   (*Karr Engineering*.)

directly on the unit case.   Figure 9-14 shows the simplicity of the
cover removal of a low-power industrial AM radio.

9-6. Vehicle Noise

An FM receiver with high sensitivity can be greatly degraded by
the amount of ignition, generator, and other noises present in most
modern automobiles and trucks.   If an automobile generator is permitting, for example, 10 μv of noise to be picked up by the receiving antenna
and the desired signal input is only 1 μv, the receiver will be captured
by the 10 μv of noise instead of the signal, and it is likely that the signal
will be completely unreadable.

It is generally stated that a signal must be at least 6 db above another
signal to take control of an FM receiver.   In the case of a receiver
receiving a high noise level, the desired signal input must be many
times stronger in order to provide a signal-to-noise ratio sufficient to
provide good intelligibility in the audio output.

It will be found that different makes of cars and even cars of the
same make have different sources and levels of noise.   No set rules can
be stated for the elimination of such noise, but the following suggestions
are given:

Radio receivers in automobiles and trucks suffer from the noise
sources which are a part of the vehicle itself.   Some of these are
associated with the ignition system, but there are also other sources of
noise.

Any pulse (square wave) has a high harmonic content, and the more square, or sharp, the pulse, the greater are these harmonics. This may be shown by the high-frequency response required of an amplifier which must pass an undistorted square wave. With a 1-kc square wave, as an example, the amplifier must have a response to 20 or 30 kc to amplify and pass the undistorted square wave.

The ignition system is the major noise source, and the potential trouble spots are the spark plug, the distributor gap and breaker points, the ignition coil, and possibly the connecting wires. There are also other sources of noise which include the generator, the voltage regulator, electrical instruments, and accumulations of static electricity caused by poor bonding between the automobile parts.

Noise sources can be located, in many cases, by their characteristic sound. A popping or crackling sound is usually an ignition noise changing as the speed of the engine changes. A whinelike noise is created by the generator; turning off the ignition, while the car is moving, will stop the ignition noise and allow the generator noise to be heard. Voltage-regulator noise is characteristically of a random sort. Some sorts of static are also identifiable; wheel static will disappear when the brakes are put on, and tire static will be eliminated when the car is driven off the road onto the shoulder.

Early radio transmitters were spark-gap devices, and any arc or spark gap is a miniature transmitter generating RF.

A diagram of an automotive ignition system is shown in Fig. 9-15. Battery B is, of course, the source of the d-c power. When the breaker points (P) close, current flows through the primary (L_1) of the spark coil. After this current has reached a steady-state value, the points P open and break the circuit. L_1 and capacitor C form a resonant circuit at about 12 kc. L_1 to L_2 is a voltage step-up, and when the distributor connects to a spark plug, there is a sharp spark across the points of the plug, and this gap fires. The spark-plug points are in the cylinder, and because of this they are shielded. But the high-voltage lead to the spark plug is *not* shielded; hence it carries the RF components which cause noise interference. Thus the *spark plug* and its leads form the first ignition-noise source. The solution is to use a wider-than-normal

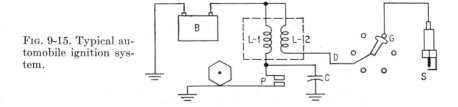

FIG. 9-15. Typical automobile ignition system.

gap adjustment to reduce the peak current and to use resistor plugs that reduce the levels of the RF interference in the high-voltage leads. Resistor spark plugs may also require a recheck of the engine timing.

Breaker points P, as in Fig. 9-15, may contribute to the noise.   An arcing across the points with a consequent generation of noise may be caused by two things: the point setting or the capacitor *C*.   Often both point adjustment and capacitor replacement are used.

When the points are too close, the engine may cut out at high speeds. With the points too close high speed makes for continuous flow of charging current in the coil, and the high voltage is lost.   But if the points are set too wide, the engine runs rough on idle, and it also will not accelerate smoothly because of a low value of current in the coil primary.   The points do not stay closed enough to permit the maximum current flow in the primary of the coil.   The engine performance will probably be poor in either case, and the points should be readjusted.

A third potential noise source is the high-voltage *spark coil*, which generates only low-frequency noise but which can radiate other noise from different sources.   It is sometimes necessary to shield the coil, and an RF bypass in the battery lead to the coil primary is also helpful.

Lead *D*, from the spark-coil secondary to the distribution cap, is a fourth problem.   Ordinary leads have stainless-steel conductors and brass ferrules; any carbon deposit on the ferrules is a probable indication of arcing and noise.   A copper conductor cable with soldered-lead terminations will prevent some of this arcing and radiated noise. Suppressors may be used to reduce the noise level but *never* on the special composition leads which are specifically designed for reducing noise, and they should be left intact and not cut.

A fifth noise source is the *distributor* itself, and this is another spark gap which can produce arcing.   In operation the switch arm rotates, and wear or improper setting not only causes noise but decreases the engine performance as well.   Leads from the distributor to the spark plugs can also radiate noise and should be treated as is the lead to the distributor.   The distributor cap may, itself, require replacement because of the presence of small metal particles.

Any source of static or sparking can cause noise.   Bonding of metal parts of the car together, such as providing positive low-resistance flexible connections between the car hood, fenders, and frame, becomes necessary because of the use of rubber insulation to reduce squeaks in modern cars.   This bonding tends to shield the ignition noise from the antenna.   The lead from the battery connection of the ignition coil through the ignition switch quite often carries a high level of noise. A coaxial capacitor of approximately 0.1 μf located at the ignition coil and connected with short leads will prevent this noise from being conducted through the ignition switch to other wiring. Oftentimes the ignition noise is carried by the wiring to the dome light or tail-light and is coupled to the antenna base.

Generator noise is often troublesome in the low band, and because of its high average level, it can reduce receiver performance. This can generally be identified by a "whine" when the receiver squelch is open and the engine raced. A coaxial capacitor of 0.1 to 0.5 μf, installed at the generator, will reduce this interference. It is important to note the automobile manufacturer's warning about putting capacitors on the armature winding. In some extreme cases, it will be necessary to install a series choke in addition to the coaxial capacitor. In both cases, the rating of the capacitor or choke will have to be able to stand the maximum generator voltage and current without appreciable voltage drop.

The contacts in the *voltage regulator* interrupt the generator-field current and can create a high level of noise which appears to be ignition noise. The noise from the sparking of contacts in the regulator is often not severe but becomes severe because of resonance in the field of the generator. Coaxial capacitors in the lead between the battery terminal of the regulator and the battery, and the lead between the armature terminal of the generator and the generator terminal of the regulator will prove helpful. A third capacitor unit connected between the field terminal and ground is also helpful.[1] This unit should consist of a 0.002-μf capacitor with a carbon resistor of approximately 4 ohms in series. In some cases shield braid pulled over the leads between the generator and grounded at both ends of the braid will reduce noise.

Tire static is caused by the static charge that accumulates on tires through flexing on the road. It is more noticeable on dry, smooth roads, and sounds somewhat like interference from a leaky power line. Most automobile dealers sell antistatic powder for injecting into the tire tubes. Front-wheel static shows up as a steady popping in the receiver at speeds over approximately 15 mph, on smooth streets. It is caused by grease in the front-wheel bearings that insulates the wheels from the car, so that the static picked up by the wheels is discharged to the car frame, jumping through the grease. The remedy is a static collector which fits inside the dust cap and bears on the end of the front axle, effectively grounding the wheel at all times.

Static built up in brake shoes can be removed by grounding to the backup plate.

Several *other possible sources* of static are body pickup and noise

[1] Do *not* bypass the generator-field terminal without a series resistor.

from exhaust pipes and their brackets.   Exhaust pipes can cause noise, and grounding straps or penetrating oil with large amounts of graphite can be used as a remedy.   Grounding straps are effective at first, but they do not, usually, have a long life.   Graphited oil appears to give better service, since the conductive graphite remains after the oil is evaporated.   Where bonds are used, they must be of low impedance for RF.

RF bypasses require a very low impedance to ground.   Some capacitors have a high value of series inductance which is integral to the capacitor itself.   Hence for noise suppression mica, coaxial, or high-quality paper capacitors are required.   For greatest effectiveness the RF bypass must be located as near to the actual noise source as possible.

9-7. Antennas

Mobile and base-station antennas are discussed in Chap. 6.   For some high-band and UHF units the vehicle antenna is mounted in the center on top of the vehicle roof.   The antenna-mounting hole can be made by using a lip saw.   The transmission line is fished from the trunk with a tape.   In some cases it is easier to remove the trim from one of the rear windows and fish the transmission line first to the window and then to the antenna-mounting location.

For a roof-top antenna, as in Fig. 9-16, first select a position as near to the center of the metal roof of the vehicle as possible, making sure that this location is clear of any structural ribs.   Next a hole is drilled as required by the instruction sheet supplied with the antenna assem-

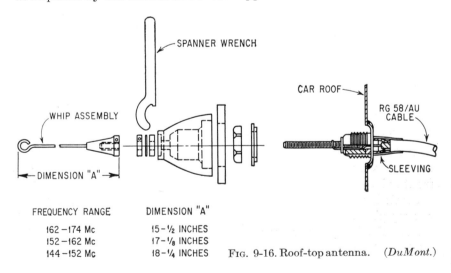

FREQUENCY RANGE	DIMENSION "A"
162 –174 Mc	15-½ INCHES
152 –162 Mc	17-⅛ INCHES
144 –152 Mc	18-¼ INCHES

Fig. 9-16. Roof-top antenna.   (*DuMont*.)

bly. Be careful not to allow the drill to puncture the upholstery under the roof during the drilling. A rotary hack-saw type of tool driven by a $\frac{1}{2}$-in. drill is useful for this operation.

Remove all burrs above and below the hole in the roof, and remove as much of the sound-deadening material as possible from the underside of the roof for a distance about $\frac{1}{2}$ in. around the hole.

Next, insert one end of an electrician's snake in the hole in the roof, and snake it between the roof and the upholstery in the desired direction. In most passenger cars, it is recommended that the snake be led over to the left side of the car to the top of the window or door frames. To lead the snake back to the trunk or forward to the dash more easily, the frames should be removed.

Usually it will be necessary to pull down the cross ribs to provide clearance for the snake. Use an awl or other small pointed tool to lever the ribs. The small hole in the upholstery can be hidden after removal of the tool, by using a whisk broom. The end of the snake protruding from the roof hole should be attached to the antenna transmission line. Tape about 6 in. of the line to the last 6 in. of the snake.

Check that the transmission line will not bind on any window-frame mounting screws; remove these screws if necessary.

Pull the transmission line through the roof to the proper location. Pull until the base of the antenna arrives at the roof hole. Mount and assemble the antenna as directed in the manufacturer's instructions.

After removing the snake, cut the transmission line, leaving sufficient slack to avoid strain when finally connected.

A good ground connection is essential at the mounting location. For an antenna used with a unit operating in the low band the antenna is usually mounted at the upper-left corner of the trunk lid, between it and the left corner of the rear window. This is usually a strong part of the vehicle body and as high as possible to mount an antenna of this length.

An antenna hook, included with the mounting hardware, is used, so that the whip antenna may be hooked down in locations where the antenna would interfere with or damage objects overhead, such as the lights in a garage. This is designed for installation just under the gutter at the edge of the roof on a vehicle, though it may be bent or flattened for installation at other locations. To locate the mounting position for the hook, grasp the antenna near the middle, bend the antenna down near the gutter, and place the hook over the antenna (at least a foot from the tip) at the point where it will hold the antenna in the desired position. In most installations, the antenna spring will be flexed with the antenna hooked down.

9-8. Power Sources

Battery voltage should read at least 5.8 for a 6-volt system and 11.6 for a 12-volt system.

Battery-charging-equipment requirements vary with the unit drain, cycle of transmitter use, speed of the vehicle, etc. For 30-watt units or less, the vehicle's standard battery-charging equipment is usually sufficient. Units requiring 60 amp or more when transmitting sometimes require larger battery-charging equipment, such as heavy-duty generators or alternators.

Alternator systems are preferred, since they can charge at a 25-amp rate when the engine is idling, and they have a long and comparatively trouble-free life.

The power cable, fire mounting, and the power relay have all been discussed in detail in Sec. 9-2.

9-9. After the Installation

The installation of the radio in a vehicle or at the base station is not actually complete until the transmitter-receiver is operating properly in its system.

Once the equipment is installed, the crystals should be rechecked to make certain their frequencies are correct. The power is turned on, and, after a short warm-up period, both squelch and volume are turned up full. Volume is adjusted to the desired level, and then the squelch is varied to a point just beyond the point at which the noise is silenced.

Once the operator has become familiar with this procedure, the only check necessary after a brief warm-up period is to advance the squelch control slightly until set noise is heard, then return it to the "threshold" position as described below.

The squelch control cannot be adjusted if a signal is being received. The presence of a usable signal will quiet the background noise regardless of the squelch-control position.

After the radio equipment has been placed in operation and checked out, the installation should be analyzed for noise pickup. This check should be made with a very weak signal entering the receiver. In the absences of any signal the second limiter is saturated and limiting on thermal noise originating in the receiver. With the receiver unsquelched, it would be impossible to recognize any ignition noise through the normal receiver noise. A very weak signal should be fed into the receiver so that the normal receiver noise is reduced to a very low value but not quite eliminated. If any ignition noise is present, it will then be noticed as a "popping" effect against the receiver noise in the background. If noise is present and is originating in the ignition or generating system, it should stop immediately when the ignition switch is turned off. Other noise sources may be identified and suppressed.

To transmit, depress the push-to-talk button on the microphone, and speak in a normal tone of voice, while holding the microphone about an inch away from the lips. It is not necessary or desirable to shout. Shouting may actually make the received signal less intelligible. Good operating technique is marked by speaking distinctly and by keeping each transmission brief. If there are several instructions to be given, it is usually better to state them one at a time and have each acknowledged. Avoid long one-sided discussions; before calling other units, be sure the air is clear.

If another unit can be heard, even though the call is not for you, do not attempt to call, as the communication already in progress may be garbled and distorted.

As soon as a call has been made, release the push-to-talk button immediately. If it is held down, it keeps the transmitter on the air; and it is impossible to hear the reply.

To turn the equipment off, throw the power switch to the off, down, position. In some installations, the vehicle ignition switch is wired to include this function so that it is impossible to energize the radio equipment if the ignition switch is in the off position, thus preventing unauthorized radio operation.

Selective-calling-equipment check-out depends upon the type of calling system. In each case an operating check should be made.

CHAPTER 10

TEST EQUIPMENT

10-1. Introduction

Television and radio repairmen already have and use some test
equipment which may be used for mobile-radio servicing. This
includes a volt-ohm meter, vacuum-tube voltmeter, tube tester,
oscilloscope, signal generator, signal tracer, and battery eliminator.
But some of this equipment, such as the RF signal generator, is
probably not accurate enough for use in mobile-radio servicing, and
additional equipment will be required.

This chapter discusses the new test equipment needed by the tele-
vision-radio shop; the servicing techniques are discussed in the following chapter.

A list of test instruments is given in Fig. 10-1; those which are
underlined are probably found in any complete television or radio shop.
Since their use and operation are already familiar, they will be discussed only briefly. The additional test equipment will be described
more fully.

Instrument	Function	Indicates
Frequency standard	Signal source	Exact frequency
Heterodyne meter	Measures frequency	Coincidence of two signals
Interpolation meter	Measures frequency	Compares signal to standard
Signal generator	Signal source	Signal for alignment
Absorption meter	Measures frequency	Approximate frequency
Grid-dip meter	Measures frequency	Approximate frequency
Modulation meter	Measures deviation	Deviation of carrier
VTVM and multimeter	Measures R, E, and I	Measured value
Tube checker	Tests tubes	Tube characteristics
Oscilloscope	Displays trace	Alignment and modulation
Signal tracer	Traces signal	Path of applied signal
Bridge	Measures R, L, C, and Q	Measured value
Dummy load	Replaces antenna	Prevents radiation
Wattmeter (RF)	Measures power	Power
Power source	Replaces battery	

FIG. 10-1. Test instruments and their functions.

232

10-2. The Test Bench

The mobile-radio test bench is more than a collection of electronic test equipment for servicing radio.   A receiver, in good working condition, is an excellent means of checking the operation of transmitters mounted in vehicles.   Several receivers each with two or more channels may be required for different frequencies.

A test bench fitted for a mobile unit is a big timesaver.   This includes a speaker, control head, microphone, antenna, a 6- and 12-volt d-c power source, and the necessary adapters for the different types and models of radios which are serviced.

10-3. General Test Equipment

This is equipment familiar to most servicemen and is usually part of the radio-television repair-shop bench.

A multimeter (a-c and d-c) is the basic test instrument for checking operating voltages and measuring component values.   The range should go up to 1,000 volts and the meter should be 20,000 ohms per volt or higher for accurate readings.

For greater accuracy, less circuit loading, and greater sensitivity a VTVM is required.   Transistorized portable models are useful for field work.

For trouble shooting, alignment, and testing on the bench a d-c range from 100 mv up to 1,000 volts is required and an a-c range from 100 μv up to 300 volts will be useful.   A center-reading scale is required for discriminator alignment.

In addition to these uses a VTVM can be used to measure RF power and to locate interference with the circuits shown in Fig. 10-2.   The

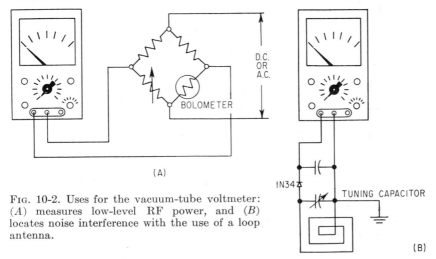

Fig. 10-2. Uses for the vacuum-tube voltmeter: (A) measures low-level RF power, and (B) locates noise interference with the use of a loop antenna.

bolometer bridge can be used to measure RF power, and the loop antenna can help to locate interference.

A general-purpose tube tester will serve as check for receiving-type tubes. Grid-emission testing is an important servicing aid which should be included. As in many applications the final and best test of an individual tube is its proper operation in the circuit.

The oscilloscope can be used in several ways: it serves as an alignment indicator, a modulation indicator for AM, and a peak-reading voltmeter.

10-4. RF Signal Generators

RF signal generators are stable and accurate signal sources for checking and aligning RF and IF amplifiers and oscillators in either transmitters or receivers. There are many types, but they can be divided into AM and FM classifications. An AM signal generator provides either an unmodulated signal or, as in most models, also an AM signal. The FM signal generator, or sweep generator, is, in effect, a small FM transmitter and provides a band of frequencies with deviation about a center frequency.

AM Signal Generators. A signal generator is used for circuit alignment; normal accuracy is about ± 0.5 per cent for reliable instruments. This is *not* accurate enough for FCC frequency measurements, but it does provide a signal source for alignment.

One generator may cover all the required frequency bands, or several may be required. The general functions of a typical AM signal generator may be seen from Fig. 10-3.

The radio-frequency oscillator generates the RF signal, which is fed through a buffer and power amplifier to the output jack of the signal

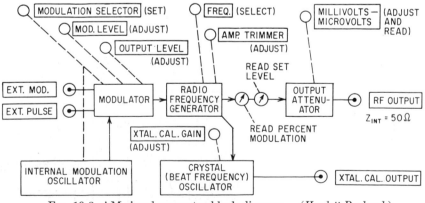

FIG. 10-3. AM signal-generator block diagram. (*Hewlett Packard.*)

generator. The oscillator provides a continuously variable sine-wave signal of high stability. The buffer stage is used to isolate the oscillator from the power amplifier. This minimizes interaction between the two circuits. Both the oscillator and buffer are in the block marked radio-frequency generator.

A radio-frequency power amplifier receives both the RF and modulation signals. It amplifies the RF energy for application to the output attenuator. The RF amplifier also receives variable bias from the modulator, which provides for adjustment of the power level fed to the output attenuator. Controls include frequency selection, frequency adjustment, and output level.

The output-power meter samples the energy fed to the output attenuator and indicates the power and voltage level on a front-panel meter. The output attenuator obtains energy from the power amplifier and applies the selected degree of attenuation.

A beat-frequency oscillator (crystal-controlled) generates harmonics of a crystal signal and mixes these harmonics with energy from the RF amplifier. The beat-frequency signal is amplified and fed to the front-panel earphone jack. A low frequency, of perhaps 5 Mc, is used for the crystal oscillator, and there will be beat notes every 5 Mc throughout the output band.

An internal-modulation oscillator generates either a 400- or 1,000-cps sine wave for the modulation. Provision is also made for external modulation.

The modulator receives all signals for modulation of the RF power amplifier and also controls the output level of the modulating signal. Figure 10-4 is the General Radio signal generator.

FM Signal Generators. FM signal generators, or sweep generators, provide a standard RF signal frequency-modulated about a carrier center frequency. An internal modulator is used to sweep the output

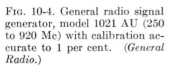

Fig. 10-4. General radio signal generator, model 1021 AU (250 to 920 Mc) with calibration accurate to 1 per cent. (*General Radio.*)

over deviations several times the bandwidth of the radio system. The center frequency is the transmitter carrier frequency of the radio system, in any of the mobile bands. Deviation up to 50 kc or higher is available. Modulation frequencies are normally 400 or 1,000 cycles.

The instrument also can function as an ordinary signal generator with or without AM modulation. An oscillator used as the signal source is a VFO covering the desired bands. An audio oscillator is the modulating signal source; modulation is by a reactance tube, a ferrite modulator, or other electronic means. Modulation control is continuously variable, or it may be variable by steps.

A typical generator is shown in Fig. 10-5; V_1 is a self-excited oscillator covering the desired frequency range for the center frequency of the equipment to be tested.

There are several methods of obtaining a swept band of frequencies. Here an a-c signal, on the grid of V_4, varies the plate current through an inductor. Variations in the magnetic field are linked to the oscillator plate inductance; this varies the oscillator frequency on either side of center. Bandwidth control changes the amplitude of the a-c signal and hence the band which is swept. Center frequency varies the average plate current of V_4 and the center frequency of the oscillator.

An AGC circuit provides a constant signal amplitude from the RF oscillator and (AGC control) a variable bias to adjust the output level.

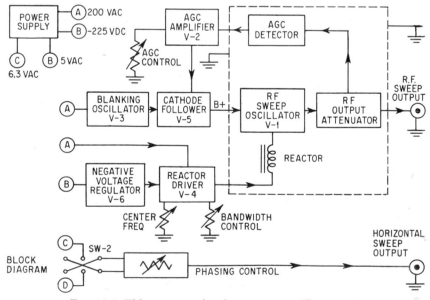

FIG. 10-5. FM, or sweep-signal, generator. (*Transitron.*)

FIG. 10-6. Combined FM signal generator and oscilloscope for the range from 15 to 400 Mc with 0.01 per cent accuracy. (*Transitron*.)

Blanking provides a zero reference line on the oscilloscope during visual alignment. The horizontal-sweep output is the sweep for the oscilloscope time base; phasing is required to start the sweep waveform at the proper point.

Figure 10-6 is a combination FM signal generator and oscilloscope.

10-5. Frequency Measurement

The frequency of a resonant circuit may be determined by using a signal generator and an indicator such as an oscilloscope or an output meter. But frequency is usually determined by devices built for this purpose; there are wavemeters, grid-dip meters for approximate measurements, heterodyne-frequency meters for more accurate determination, and secondary-frequency standards for calibration.

Wavemeters. A wavemeter is a calibrated resonant circuit as in Figs. 10-7*A*, 10-7*B*, and 10-8. The reaction wavemeter has no resonance indicator of its own and also takes very little power from the circuit under test, as in Fig. 10-7*A*.

An absorption wavemeter is a calibrated tuned circuit as in Fig. 10-7*B*. When the coil of the wavemeter is brought near a tuned circuit in operating equipment, the RF energy is coupled to the wave-

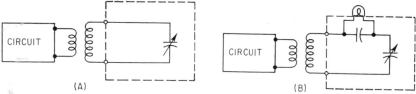

(A)   (B)

FIG. 10-7. Wavemeters: (*A*) with resonance indicator; (*B*) with calibrated dial.

FIG. 10-8. Type–724-B precision wavemeter for the range from 16 to 50 Mc. (*General Radio.*)

meter coil.   A detector, fed from the resonant circuit, rectifies the RF, which is indicated by a meter or a lamp.   Extended ranges are possible by using plug-in coils.   As the wavemeter is tuned through resonance by a variable capacitor, a variable inductance, or both (in the case of a butterfly circuit), the RF circulating current increases in the wavemeter; this is shown in Fig. 10-9.

Wavemeters are useful for preliminary transmitter alignment and for determining the operating range of an oscillator.   Because of the simple nature of these instruments, their accuracy is limited to about 2 per cent for ordinary wavemeters and to about 0.25 per cent for more advanced types.

Grid-dip Meters.   A calibrated oscillator with provisions for a grid-current reading and coupling to an external tuned circuit can be used as a grid-dip meter.   Grid-current flow is a function of the signal strength from an oscillator.   Measurement of this current flow through the grid resistor is one well-known method of checking on the operating conditions (but not the frequency) of an oscillator.   Current flow from cathode to grid depends upon the signal amplitude on the grid; this is the basis for the grid-dip meter.

A tuned circuit is to be checked for frequency; the grid-dip meter is coupled to the tuned circuit by bringing the coil of the grid-dip oscillator near the coil of the circuit to be measured.   As the test oscillator is tuned, a sharp dip in the grid current, as indicated on the grid-current meter, indicates that the test oscillator and the unknown

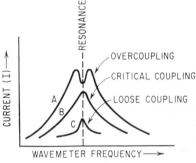

FIG. 10-9. Current flow at resonance for different degrees of coupling.

circuit are on about the same frequency. Coupling should be reduced until a sharp dip over a small portion of the dial is obtained.

By setting the grid-dip meter to the desired frequency, it may be used as a signal source. The external resonant circuit is then tuned for a meter dip.

In either use no power is required in the external tuned circuit; the receiver or transmitter which contains the tuned circuit to be tested is not turned on. Grid-dip

FIG. 10-10. Model-59 UHF megacycle meter is a grid-dip meter covering the range from 100 kc to 4.5 Mc, 2.2 to 420 Mc, and 420 to 940 Mc. (*Measurements Corp.*)

meters can be used to determine the resonant frequency of tuned circuits of all kinds, for measuring capacitance, inductance, or Q, as a marker with a sweep generator, for crystal-frequency checks, as a beat-frequency oscillator, as a receiver, as a signal generator, for transmitter tuning, and for other uses.

As a grid-dip oscillator the instrument is turned on and held near the test circuit. Tuning through the range produces a dip in grid current; reducing the coupling sharpens the dip. Frequency is read directly. If the instrument is coupled to the receiver input, it can serve as a signal source, either modulated or unmodulated.

By turning gain to minimum the grid-dip meter can function as a wavemeter (absorption-frequency meter). As a further function, the instrument is also an oscillating detector or heterodyne-frequency meter; earphones are plugged in, and the oscillator is coupled to the test-signal source. A beat note in the earphones or the meter in Fig. 10-10 is the indication.

Heterodyne-frequency Meters. A heterodyne-frequency meter, as in Fig. 10-11, is a continuously variable signal source with provision for accurate frequency measurement. It has greater flexibility than a crystal standard-frequency source, which provides only check points.

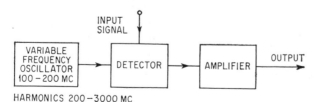

FIG. 10-11. Heterodyne-frequency-meter block diagram.

A crystal calibrator, a variable-frequency oscillator, a detector, and an amplifier are part of a heterodyne-frequency meter.

Fundamental frequencies, in this example, are from 100 to 200 Mc, and harmonics are between 100 and 3,000 Mc in a typical instrument. Over-all accuracy is usually better than 0.005 per cent; transmitters may be measured to this tolerance.[1]

Operating frequency is selected by the tuning dials. Actual frequency is determined by the dial readings as modified by any corrections because of calibration. Harmonic frequencies are the readings multiplied by the harmonic number.

Measurements are made directly; the unknown frequency is fed into the instrument from an external antenna. Settings are made for the tuning dial until the unknown-frequency zero beats as heard through the headphones connected to the audio-amplifier output. The reading is taken directly or multiplied by the appropriate integer if a harmonic is used.

Figure 10-12 shows a curve of the beat-note frequency plotted against the audible range. When the difference frequency between the two signals is above the audible range, no sound is heard. As the two frequencies are brought closer to each other (A), a high-pitched note is heard in the headphones. This tone gradually decreases in frequency to B, where it is replaced by a series of rapid clicks, and the difference frequency is then only a few cycles per second. At C, the clicks have stopped completely, the two original frequencies are equal to one

[1] With accurate calibration against the crystal-signal source.

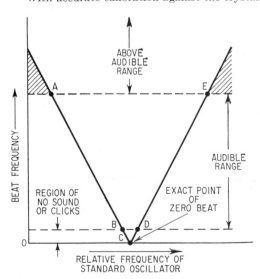

FIG. 10-12. Zero-beat diagram showing the point at which both signals are the same frequency.

another, and this is the exact point of zero beat. As the oscillator frequency is varied beyond the zero-beat point, the number of clicks increases to point D. A low-pitched tone again is heard at this point, and varying the frequency in the same direction causes a gradual increase in frequency until point E is reached, where the beat note is again inaudible.

Calibration using an external crystal oscillator is simple. Harmonics of the crystal frequency may be used. Some heterodyne-frequency meters use a VFO to locate the approximate frequency of the test signal and a crystal-controlled oscillator to determine the exact frequency.

A heterodyne-frequency meter is a versatile instrument—is, in effect, an accurate calibrated receiver—and it is used for rapid checking of transmitter frequencies within the limitations of the instrument accuracy.

The Gertsch frequency meter FM-3, as in Fig. 10-13, is available in several models, and it exceeds the FCC requirements over the frequency range from 20 to 1,000 Mc. It is direct-reading with an accuracy of 0.001 per cent. Model FM-3 is portable, and it has a battery power supply; model FM-3PS-3 has an a-c power supply; model FM-3-3R is a rack-mounted unit with the a-c power supply.

The fundamental frequency range is from 20 to 40 Mc; harmonics are

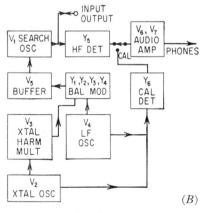

Fig. 10-13. Frequency meter FM-3 combined with a peak-modulation meter DM-1 in A; block diagram of the frequency meter in B. (*Gertsch.*)

(A)

used above 40 Mc and up to 1,000 Mc. Beyond this frequency, special techniques are required. The meter reading can be reset with an accuracy of 0.0005 per cent. A crystal oscillator at 1 Mc is the internal source of calibration, and signals from WWV, on another external source, can be used to check the calibration. Auxiliary outputs at each 1-Mc point from 1 to 20 Mc are also available. Modulation is AM of 30 per cent at 1,000 cps if desired.

This instrument and the block diagram are shown in Fig. 10-13. V_1 is the high-frequency, or search, oscillator from 20 to 40 Mc. V_2 is the 1-Mc crystal oscillator which feeds the harmonic multiplier V_3. V_4 is a low-frequency oscillator covering the range from 1 to 2 Mc. The difference frequency between the crystal harmonic and the low-frequency oscillator is fed from the balanced modulator to the buffer, V_5. Because V_1 and V_5 share a common tank circuit, V_1 is locked to the frequency of V_5. Y_5 is the high-frequency detector, V_6 and V_7 make up the audio amplifier, and Y_6 is a calibration detector used to calibrate the low-frequency oscillator against the crystal oscillator.

Operation of the frequency meter is as follows: The search oscillator is tuned to match the unknown frequency. Only the search oscillator, the high-frequency detector, and the audio amplifier are active. The other circuits are not used. The search oscillator, or one of the harmonics, is used to obtain a frequency reading through the beat note, detected and amplified.

The crystal harmonic is selected by the tuned harmonic multiplier. Only the desired harmonic is used, and the others are attenuated. The low-frequency oscillator is then tuned through the range until the difference frequency from the balanced modulator (difference between the crystal harmonic and the low-frequency oscillator) begins to approach that of the search oscillator. The buffer, driven by the balanced modulator, will begin to pull the search oscillator from the frequency to which it was set; this will be heard as a rising note in the earphones.

The search oscillator will lock on to the difference frequency, and tuning of the low-frequency oscillator is continued until there is a frequency match. The search oscillator is being used only as a means to identify the unknown signal roughly. The accurate determination is actually done by the crystal oscillator through the control of the search oscillator. The search oscillator also serves to amplify the difference frequency coming from the balanced modulator.

As a signal source, the procedure is reversed, and the output RF signal is again controlled by the crystal-oscillator accuracy. Calibration of the low-frequency oscillator by means of the calibrated detector and the 1-Mc crystal permits accurate readings. Modulation of the search oscillator is provided for identification wherever this is required. A plate-current meter is used to assist in properly tuning the crystal harmonic.

This operation permits high accuracy and high resettability; both of these are important for portable field use.

Interpolating-frequency Meters. These are designed to be used with another heterodyne meter or directly with a receiver, provided only that the calibration of the receiver is accurate with enough selectivity to separate close signals. Accuracy of 0.0025 per cent or better can be obtained depending upon how closely the variable oscillator is adjusted to the crystal frequency.

In terms of function as in Fig. 10-14 there is a variable signal with a range from 1,000 to 1,010 kc followed by a multivibrator divider for 100 kc and a multivibrator-harmonic generator for 1 Mc. As the heart of the instrument, there is a crystal oscillator at f_1, or 950 kc, and a stable LC oscillator covering the range f_2 from 50 to 60 kc. These two signals are fed to a modulator which mixes (heterodynes) them and produces $f_1 + f_2$ and $f_1 - f_2$. This then feeds a filter which selects the sum of the two. The 10-kc spread of the variable oscillator can have 1,000 dial divisions, which is 1 per cent; this means that the multivibrator harmonics are also 1 per cent.

However, complete coverage is provided only above the 100th harmonic. The filter output (the sum of the fixed and variable oscillators) is the 1-Mc fundamental with a range from 1 to 1.01 Mc, or 1 per cent. The 5th harmonic of this is from 5 to 5.05 Mc, the 20th harmonic is from 20 to 20.20 Mc, and so on up the scale. Complete coverage, however, is not obtained until the 100th harmonic and above.

The 100-kc multivibrator, as shown in Table 10-1, provides complete coverage above its 100th harmonic. The harmonics and their range are indicated at some significant frequencies. Here also, below the 100th harmonic (the 50th, for example), there are gaps in coverage.

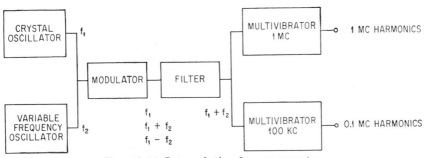

Fig. 10-14. Interpolation-frequency meter.

TABLE 10-1. OUTPUT FROM THE 100-KC MULTIVIBRATOR

Harmonic	Range, Mc
50	5.000– 5.050
51	5.100– 5.151
52	5.200– 5.252
100	10.000–10.100
101	10.100–10.201
102	10.200–10.302
103	10.300–10.403
250	25.000–25.250
251	25.100–25.351
252	25.200–25.452

This coverage becomes complete, as shown, above 10 Mc with an increasing overlap as the frequency is increased. Harmonics of this 100-kc source reach well into the 25- to 54-Mc band. Here the overlap extends so that not every harmonic is required. Since the 250th extends to 25.250 Mc and the 252nd begins at 25.200 Mc, there is complete coverage, with overlap, without using the 251st harmonic.

Table 10-2 shows the frequency range of the 1-Mc multivibrator.

TABLE 10-2. RANGE OF HARMONICS FROM THE 1-MC MULTIVIBRATOR

Harmonic	Range, Mc
100	100.00–101.00
101	101.00–102.01
102	102.00–103.02
50	50.00– 50.50
51	51.00– 51.51
52	52.00– 52.52
144	144.00–145.44
145	145.00–146.45
146	146.00–147.46
.	. .
.	. .
.	. .
172	172.00–173.72
173	173.00–174.73
174	174.00–175.74

Measurements of an unknown transmitter frequency may be made with an instrument of the heterodyne-frequency type, where the instrument oscillator is zero beat against the unknown; the interpolating-frequency meter then is substituted for the unknown signal. The variable oscillator of this highly accurate instrument is then set to zero beat at the same setting as the unknown.   The difference between the heterodyne-frequency dial and the interpolating-frequency meter provides an increment to be added to the original reading for a more accurate result.

10-6. Modulation Meters

The FCC has limits on a transmitter bandwidth, which is a function of the modulation.   Because of this, the modulation deviation must be measured accurately.   There are two methods for measuring this deviation: A modulation meter can be used, or a frequency meter can measure carrier nulls.

A modulation meter is a calibrated receiver, as in Figs. 10-15 and 10-16, which is tuned to the carrier center frequency.   Output from

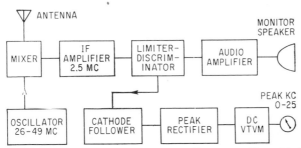

Fig. 10-15. Modulation-meter block diagram.   (*Lampkin.*)

Fig. 10-16. Lampkin model-205 modulation meter.   (*Lampkin.*)

the FM detector of the instrument is calibrated in deviation, as measured in kilocycles, and displayed on a meter. The FCC requires a certain fixed maximum *peak* deviation which can only be read by a peak indicator. Most voltmeters read rms and not peak, but the meter can be calibrated in peak volts. An oscilloscope may be used to provide a visual indication, since this always indicates true peak values of any waveshape.

Human voices in an audio system have a variety of complex waveshapes. Because of this, average-reading indications should never be used for measurements of modulation deviation.

A modulation meter measures the carrier swing during modulation. The best method of measuring the FM modulation is by the use of a direct-reading monitor, although there are other methods for laboratory use, such as a spectrum analyzer with a visual display. In FM the bandwidth of the transmitted signal is a function of *both* the frequency and the amplitude of the audio signal. The carrier deviation (change from the carrier frequency with no modulation) is a measure of the total bandwidth, which exceeds the carrier deviation because there are sidebands beyond the maximum carrier swing. But, in mobile radio, there is only a small amount of power in these extreme sidebands.

A modulation meter is a receiver with special provision for measuring the carrier modulation; the receiver is tuned to the transmitter to be tested. Voltage developed across the FM detector is measured on a peak-reading voltmeter. An RC network with a long time constant is arranged at the output of the detector, so that the capacitor charges to peak values of modulation. This voltage is read on the VTVM, which is calibrated in kilocycles of deviation.

The modulation meter provides for a simple direct measurement of transmitter modulation by a three-way check: indication of the peak deviation on the calibrated meter, a visual indication on an oscilloscope, and an audible indication. This instrument is essentially a calibrated receiver with a built-in VTVM; the instrument covers any transmitter from 25 to 500 Mc. It indicates peak deviations, either positive or negative, on a meter with a full-scale reading of 25 kc peak.

The received signal (from the transmitter under test) and the local oscillator are heterodyned in the mixer stage. A range from 26 to 49 Mc is available from the oscillator, and the difference between this signal, or one of its harmonics, converts the received signal to the IF of 2.5 Mc. After limiting, the received signal is detected by the discriminator. A cathode follower, fed by the audio signal, is used to charge an RC circuit to peak values for meter indications. Audio is also fed from the limiter to an amplifier and monitoring speaker. This audio is convenient as a tuning aid, a monitor of the signal quality, and as a means of communication with the transmitter. A provision is also made for an oscilloscope connection across the discriminator output.

The selector switch is turned to modulation after the instrument is allowed to warm up. This connects the VTVM to the audio peak rectifier output. Even without an antenna the internal noise will provide a peak Kc (deviation) reading, so the *Quiet* switch is provided. This allows the modulation zero-adjust control to reduce the peak Kc reading to zero, because the mixer plate is shorted when the *Quiet* switch is depressed. When a signal is received during test, the receiver noise will be quieted.

An antenna is then connected, and the transmitter signal, without modulation, is received. The selector switch is set to tune maximum, and the instrument is tuned to the transmitter signal. There will be several points where the milliammeter (peak kilocycles per second), now reading limiter-grid current, has indications because of harmonics. However, this is no problem, because the tuning is adjusted for maximum meter reading; the peak-kilocycles-per-second meter is an indication of field strength. For close adjustment of tuning, the selector is set at tune zero, and the milliammeter (now a VTVM) reads the discriminator output. Fine tuning adjustments are made for a balanced deflection in both negative and positive positions of the modulation-polarity switch.

The selector switch is set to modulation and the transmitter modulated with the desired tone; peak deviation is then read directly on the meter at both positions of the polarity switch.

10-7. Radio Test Sets

Mobile-radio test sets are test instruments designed for several different measurement and servicing functions. Typical units in use may combine a signal generator and a VTVM or a power meter and a frequency meter.

The characteristics vary widely, depending on the instrument. One may have a signal source for transmitter carrier-frequency measurement by heterodyning and several crystal-controlled IF signals for receiver alignment. This is the most common arrangement, but the instrument sometimes includes a deviation meter or a VTVM.

A convenient form for the test equipment needed for mobile radio is illustrated in Fig. 10-17.   This instrument measures voltage and current, AF power, RF power, and carrier deviation.   It is designed to be used with a signal generator.   This signal source covers the range of the mobile bands and includes AM and FM (deviations of 5 and 25 kc) as well as crystal signals at the IF frequencies for added flexibility in use.

The test set, having the signal generator as a signal source, has wide use as a servicing instrument.   Voltage and current are measured using the basic 50-μa meter.   The audio-power meter can be used to determine the signal-to-noise ratio of a receiver.   The ranges are from 300 μw to 3 watts at both 3 ohms and 600 ohms.   RF power is measured from 0 to 20 watts at 50 ohms.   Carrier deviation from 0 to 15 kc can be measured up to 500 Mc.   As usual, the transmitter deviation is measured by means of a superheterodyne receiver; the external signal generator acts as the local oscillator for the built-in receiver of the test set.

The instrument of this type is portable; transistors allow a compact unit, as in Fig. 10-18, with a battery power supply.   Because of the small drain of current the unit batteries have a long useful life.

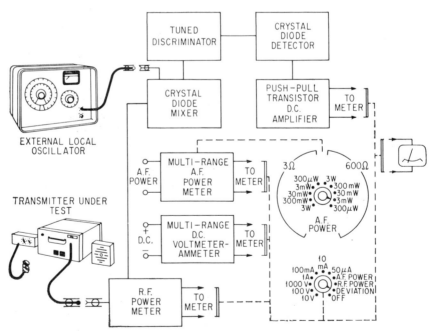

FIG. 10-17. Test-set diagram for type TF 1065.   (*Marconi.*)

FIG. 10-18. Transistorized-mobile-radio test set. (*DuMont*.)

10-8. Frequency Calibration

The precise frequency of test equipment and radios may be checked against frequency standards. The primary frequency standard is the National Bureau of Standards transmitter, WWV or WWVH. These signals are used as the standard frequencies for calibration of equipment and take the place of the crystal oscillator in a heterodyne-frequency meter. The other method is the crystal oscillator in a heterodyne-frequency meter or a secondary-frequency standard. This secondary-frequency standard can be used to check the accuracy of any oscillator within its frequency range.

The Crystal Calibrator. A crystal calibrator, or a secondary standard, is a stable source of crystal-controlled RF signals for the exact calibration of transmitters, receivers, and signal generators. A fixed-reference crystal-oscillator output signal is provided for check points at the crystal fundamental and harmonics. Multipliers for higher frequencies or dividers for lower frequencies provide accurate signals over a wide frequency range.

A crystal oscillator in a calibrator used as a secondary-frequency standard could have, as in Fig. 10-19, a 10-Mc fixed stable frequency

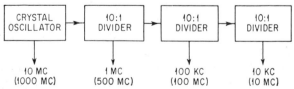

FIG. 10-19. Crystal-calibrator block diagram showing fundamental output frequency and harmonic limits.

as one output.   Harmonics of this signal then provide an output every 10 Mc up to 1,000 Mc.   Successive divisions by 10, from the fundamental 10 Mc, produce 1-Mc, 100-kc, and 10-kc signals; these are all used for calibration.   With constant room temperature the stability of the crystal oscillator is about 0.0001 per cent (one part per million per degree centigrade), which exceeds the FCC requirements.   Harmonic frequencies are available up to 1,000 Mc.   Because the 10-Mc harmonics are too far apart for adequate band coverage, dividers are also used.   Three frequency dividers provide 1-Mc, 100-kc, and 10-kc output signals.

While a frequency source of this type is quite useful in mobile radio for accurate check points, there is a limitation in the flexibility of the signal frequencies.   Table 10-3 indicates this; the three bands, 25 to 50 Mc, 144 to 174 Mc, and 450 to 470 Mc are shown in the first column. Harmonics of the 10-Mc oscillator, in the second column, do cover all three bands but only with a frequency separation of 10 Mc.   As indicated, check points for frequency measurement are available, but, for points in between, multiples of 10 Mc for the divider output are required.   Harmonics up to 1,000 Mc can be used.

In the third column the output of the first divider (every 1 Mc) is shown; these harmonics are useful to 500 Mc.   The output from the 100-kc divider is useful to 100 Mc.   The 10-kc output is only useful to 10 Mc.   With available check points, as at every 1 Mc, the usable signals, of course, occur 10 times as often.   With the 1-Mc signal, for example, between 25 Mc and 26 Mc no points are available.   But from the 100-kc divider there are points from every 0.1 Mc as 25.0, 25.1, 25.2, . . . , 25.9, 26.0.   The amplitude of the divider harmonics falls off above 1,000 Mc (10-Mc signal), 500 Mc (1-Mc signal), 100 Mc (100-kc signal), and 10 Mc (10-kc signal).

Four positions are available for the single output: 1 Mc, 10 Mc, 100 kc, and 10 kc; but the outputs are rich in harmonics.   No tuning control (other than the calibration) is available, because this instrument is designed for use as a crystal-oscillator harmonic generator.

A crystal calibrator has many uses.   Because it is limited to harmonics (or subharmonics through dividers), it cannot tune over an entire band, but it can be used to check a VFO signal generator.   The two are mixed to obtain zero beat, and the signal generator is adjusted to match the crystal signal.   Thus, within the accuracy of the reading the signal generator is correct.

A calibrator can also be used as a signal source for receiver alignment or as a signal against which to measure a transmitter carrier provided one of the output signals is at the correct frequency.

TABLE 10-3. CRYSTAL-CALIBRATOR SIGNALS

	10 Mc (1,000 Mc)	1 Mc (500 Mc)	100 kc (100 Mc)
25	—*	25	25
25.1	—	—	25.1
25.2	—	—	25.2
26	—	26	·†
			·
27	—	27	·
30	30	·	·
		·	·
40	40	·	·
50	50	·	·
		·	·
52	—	52	·
53	—	53	·
			·
			53.8
			53.9
54	—	54	54.0
60	60	—	
144	—	144	—
145	—	145	
		·	
150	150	·	
		·	
160	160	·	
		·	
170	170	·	
		173	
174	—	174	
450	450	450	
451	—	451	
		·	
		·	
		·	
459	—	459	
460	460	460	
461	—	461	
		·	
		·	
469	—	469	
470	470	470	

* A dash (—) indicates no coverage.
† A dot (·) indicates complete coverage.

Some instruments also have provisions for measurement: a hetero-dyne detector and an amplifier.   With a strong signal the detector and audio amplifier are sufficient.   Both the crystal (or divider) signal and the unknown signal are fed into the detector, just as the RF signal and local oscillator signal are mixed in a superheterodyne receiver. Zero beat will be obtained when there is zero-frequency difference.   If a superheterodyne receiver is used to monitor a transmitter, this crystal oscillator is first used to zero beat as the receiver input.   The unknown signal is then substituted for the input to obtain the same zero beat and is therefore at the same frequency.

Primary Frequency Standards.   The standard-frequency stations WWV and WWVH are operated by the Central Radio Propagation Laboratory of the National Bureau of Standards.   Station WWV is located at Beltsville, Maryland (near Washington, D.C.), and WWVH is on the island of Maui, Hawaiian Islands.   Both stations broadcast continuously on the carrier frequencies shown below in megacycles:

WWV	2.5	5	10	15	20	25
WWVH	5	10	15			

The carrier frequencies at WWV are derived from the average of eight precision quartz-crystal oscillators which are operated con-tinuously.   These oscillators all operate on 100 kc from battery power and are housed in vaults 25 ft below the earth's surface.   The tem-perature and humidity of these vaults are carefully controlled to ensure maximum frequency stability.   The frequencies of the oscil-lators are compared continually among themselves and are checked against the basic frequency standard, the period of the earth's rotation.

The frequency standards at WWVH are similar to those used at WWV and are maintained in agreement with WWV signals to within 2 parts in 100 million by comparison.

From most points in the continental United States, the standard-frequency broadcasts of WWV can be received on relatively simple communications-type receivers.   Under normal propagation condi-tions, such receivers are capable of receiving WWV or WWVH trans-missions on several of the standard frequencies, thus permitting good flexibility of measurement.

These standards can be used for mobile radio in several ways: A special receiver, as in Fig. 10-20, may be used to calibrate secondary crystal oscillators as used in crystal calibrators or other crystal sources whose frequency or harmonic is related to a WWV frequency.   The

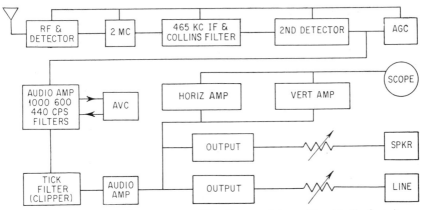

FIG. 10-20. Standard-frequency-calibration receiver. (*Specific Products.*)

receiver, as illustrated in Fig. 10-21, has two inputs, the standard and the unknown; visual and audible outputs are provided for comparison.

10-9. Power Measurement

Several methods are available for measuring the actual RF power output from a transmitter. A dummy antenna is used to replace the radiating antenna; the impedance match is important. A thermocouple can be used to measure the RF current, from which the power can be calculated. Or at UHF a thermistor bridge can be used. A thermistor is a resistor with a negative temperature coefficient; the change in resistance as the RF heats the thermistor unbalances a bridge. This current reading at unbalance may also be used to calculate the power output.

However, one of the best methods for rapid and accurate results is quite simple: An RF wattmeter is connected to the transmitter cable in place of the normal antenna. A matched resistive load terminates the calibrated cable between the antenna and the wattmeter. A crystal detector rectifies a portion of the RF output, and the d-c voltmeter is calibrated to read directly in watts.

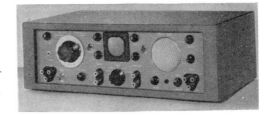

FIG. 10-21. Model-WWVC receiver. (*Specific Products.*)

10-10. Miscellaneous Equipment

A receiver for portable use with a meter indicator is a field-strength meter for tuning transmitters, adjusting antennas, and measuring interference and undesired transmitter-harmonic radiation.   Readings are taken at several positions in a circle to reduce error.

A relative-strength meter indicates only the increase or decrease in a received signal.   More complex instruments have a calibrated oscillator, so that the absolute field strength can be measured and read.

Vibrators which are used in power supplies of mobile radios of vehicles are sometimes a source of trouble and require testing.   A replacement by another vibrator which is known to be good is one method for servicing.   A vibrator tester is another.

The vibrator to be tested is inserted; the source voltage for the vibrator is reduced to check upon the starting characteristics.   Excessive current indicates a shorted unit.   If the vibrator starts at reduced voltage, the voltage is then stepped up to normal operation.   The output voltage is an indication of the relative quality of the tested vibrator.

For repairs and testing of a vehicle radio, a power source is required to take the place of the car battery for low-powered radio.   This is the battery eliminator, which is a d-c power source operated from the a-c line.

Other test equipment includes Q meters, bridges, crystal test sets, and instruments for testing batteries and generators.

CHAPTER 11

SERVICING

11-1. Introduction to Servicing

Servicing, the adjustment and repair of mobile and base-station radio with test instruments, has several aspects. These include measurements of the transmitter as required by the FCC, routine maintenance, and the actual repair of equipment defects.

1. *FCC checks.* These are the measurements and readings of carrier frequency, carrier maximum deviation (under normal modulation), and power input to the final RF power amplifier of the transmitter.

2. *Preventive maintenance.* Many failures can be prevented by a routine maintenance procedure. This is not required by the FCC, but many service organizations follow certain routine checks to locate trouble before it causes an interruption in operation.

3. *Alignment, trouble shooting, and repair.* Radio equipment which requires the location and repair of defects falls into this class.

This chapter is divided into these three parts.

In the following servicing discussions, general steps are given which apply to many different models, and specific models are used for illustrations. The procedures will apply in most cases, but the specific instructions, supplied with each test instrument, are a valuable source of information. The careful reading of these instructions will help the user to get the most out of each instrument.

FCC CHECKS

11-2. Measurements

Frequency, modulation, and power of the transmitter must be measured and recorded.

These are specific items included in the FCC requirements for maintenance. The important requirements are listed below:

1. *Frequency.* The operating frequency must be measured when

(1) the transmitter is installed, (2) change is made in the transmitter which affects the operating frequency, and (3) at regular intervals. The regular intervals must not exceed 1 month when the transmitter is not crystal-controlled or 6 months when the transmitter is crystal-controlled. Below an operating frequency of 50 Mc the tolerance is 0.01 per cent, and above 50 Mc the tolerance is 0.005 per cent of the assigned frequency for most transmitters. Closer tolerances for transmitters, under narrow-band operation as proposed by the FCC, will be required: 0.002 per cent (25 to 50 Mc) and 0.0005 per cent (50 to 1,000 Mc).

2. *Modulation.* A modulation check is required at the same time the frequency is measured. For FM transmitters the frequency of the carrier must not change more than 15 kc from the assigned center frequency. Narrow-band standards call for 5-kc deviation. For AM transmitters modulation must be between 70 per cent and 100 per cent (for negative peaks of modulation).

3. *Power.* The plate power input (plate current times plate voltage) must also be measured, at the times specified above, and must never exceed the licensed value.

11-3. Measurement of the Transmitter Frequency

If a transmitter is in operation, the steps for measurement using a heterodyne-frequency meter are:

1. Turn on the transmitter, without modulation, only during the actual measurement to prevent interference.

2. Attach an antenna to the input of the heterodyne-frequency meter. The antenna length will depend upon the signal strength, the interference, and the characteristics of the meter.

3. Carefully tune the meter to the proper frequency, and note the dial setting for the zero beat, or null point. A steady modulation of the transmitter by a single frequency sometimes helps locate the exact null under difficult conditions.

4. Read the exact heterodyne-meter frequency; the percentage of error (or deviation) is given by

$$\frac{\Delta f}{F} (100) = \text{per cent of error}$$

where F = actual carrier frequency

Δf = difference between actual carrier and assigned value

For example, if the assigned frequency is 51.230 Mc and the actual reading is 51.232 Mc, then Δf is 0.002 Mc (2 kc), and the deviation from the correct frequency is 0.0039 per cent.

11-4. Measurement of Modulation-frequency Deviation

There are several possible methods for measuring the deviation during normal modulation. Two such methods are given here.

The equipment required for the first method includes:

1. Modulation meter with a peak-modulation indication; the meter (a receiver type of instrument) should have direct-reading scales for the center (carrier) frequency.

2. Transmitter which has been adjusted to the correct assigned carrier frequency.

3. Audio oscillator for the source of the modulating signal. (A normal voice-modulation check must also be made; a signal generator will *not* show the voice peaks.)

The steps in measurement are:

1. Turn on the transmitter and the modulation meter. (Turn off the transmitter as soon as the test is completed to prevent interference.)

2. Attach an antenna of the proper length to the meter input. An antenna cut the resonant length for the center of the band is normally used.

3. Tune the modulation meter to the carrier frequency while the transmitter is not being modulated.

4. Modulate the transmitter with a 1,000-cycle note from the audio oscillator. This will allow a *preliminary* adjustment of the transmitter modulation level, but actual voice transmission is the only way to check on the actual voice peaks.

5. Adjust the transmitter so that the modulation peaks do not exceed the limitations of the FCC.

6. Use a normal speaking voice and a microphone to check voice peaks during voice transmission. As in Fig. 11-1 the voice waveshape is complex and has peaks which do not occur in a pure sine wave. For this reason the voice check is suggested.

The carrier-disappearance method is the second one which is used.

The FM carrier "disappears" under certain conditions of modula-

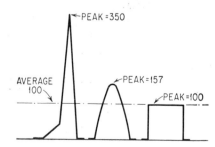

FIG. 11-1. Complex waveshapes.

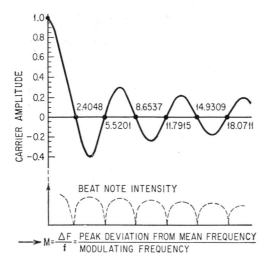

FIG. 11-2. Modulation index.

tion.   Variations in carrier amplitude are shown in Fig. 11-2. M is the modulation index, and the product of $M \times f$ (where f is the audio frequency of modulation) is the deviation, ΔF.   Thus

$$M = \frac{\Delta F}{f}$$

Negative values of carrier amplitude indicate only a change in the phase of the carrier from the original phase.   Where M crosses zero, the carrier amplitude falls to zero; this can be used as a measure of the frequency deviation.   By proper choice of the modulating frequency, the carrier disappearance, or null point, can be made to correspond to the desired deviation.   Figure 11-3 illustrates the sideband power; as M increases, the carrier power decreases.

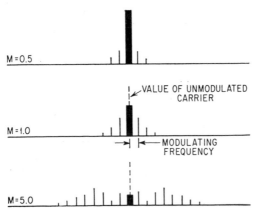

FIG. 11-3. Decrease of the carrier amplitude.

For example, if an audio signal of 2,495 cycles is used for the modulating voltage, the carrier component of the resultant signal will disappear (fall to zero amplitude) at a modulation index (M) of 2.4048 at 6-kc deviation. Other values are shown in Table 11-1.

TABLE 11-1. DEVIATION CONDITIONS
(Modulation frequency, in kilocycles per second)

Null	M	6-kc deviation	15-kc deviation	75-kc deviation
1	2.4048	2.4950	6.2375	31.187
2	5.5201	1.0869	2.7173	13.586
3	8.6537	0.69332	1.7333	8.665
4	11.7915	0.5088	1.2721	6.3605
5	14.9309	0.4018	1.0046	5.0230
6	18.0711	0.3320	0.83005	4.1502

The necessary equipment includes:

1. Audio oscillator with accurate calibration and low harmonic content to prevent spurious readings.

2. Stable and accurate frequency meter or receiver (AM) with a stable local oscillator.

3. Transmitter to be tested. This must be adjusted for no audio clipping and for linear modulation over the desired deviation range.

For the determination of the proper deviation:

1. Choose a modulation frequency as high as possible (within the transmitter audio band) which will result in the desired deviation swing. From the table, 6,237 cycles (for 15-kc deviation) and 2,495 cycles (for 6-kc deviation) are examples; both have an M of 2.4048.

2. Modulate the transmitter with the audio signal, and couple the transmitter to the frequency meter or receiver. Adjust the transmitter modulation for maximum deviation as in Fig. 11-4.

3. Adjust the audio signal *as accurately as possible,* as the entire method depends on this accuracy; set the audio output to zero.

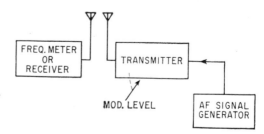

FIG. 11-4. Transmitter adjustment.

4. Tune the frequency meter (or receiver) close to the transmitter carrier for a low-frequency audio beat note.

5. Advance the audio-signal level until the carrier zero beat disappears. If nulls other than the first are to be used, carefully advance the audio level while counting the nulls.

6. When the proper null is reached, advance the transmitter limiter until the carrier (and its beat note) just reappears. This means the limiter, which controls the amount of modulation, is properly set.

7. If the transmitter does not have a limiter adjustment but it has a modulation control, the steps are valid as above; in this case an oscilloscope is used to monitor the transmitter output. Audio level is advanced until limiting begins as seen on the oscilloscope. The oscilloscope is then removed, and the modulation level is advanced until the proper carrier null is reached. Vertical gain must be kept low to prevent overloading the vertical amplifiers, which appears as limiting.

An oscilloscope can be an aid in observing the point where audio clipping starts. Measurements should only be made at the transmitter output; multipliers multiply the deviation as well as the carrier frequency, which means greater care is required if, for some reason, the deviation must be measured at a stage other than the final power amplifier.

11-5. Transmitter Power Input

The third operating characteristic of a transmitter which is important is the input power to the final stage. FCC rules and regulations state: "The license of each station shall employ a suitable procedure to determine that the plate power input to the final radio frequency stage of each base station or fixed transmitter . . . does not exceed the maximum figure specified on the current station authorization."

The power input to the final RF stage of a transmitter is the product of plate current and plate voltage:

$$\text{Power input} = \text{plate voltage} \times \text{plate current}$$

where power input is in watts, plate voltage in volts, and plate current in amperes.

In some cases the plate current cannot be measured directly. The cathode current can be used in the formula; the value of power input will exceed the plate power input by the screen-grid input plus the control-grid input.

The plate current may be derived from the cathode current by means of the formula

$$I_p = I_c - I_{sg} - I_g$$

where I_p is the plate current, I_c the cathode current, I_{sg} the screen-grid current, and I_g the control-grid current.

Screen-grid current (I_{sg}) cannot always be metered conveniently. It can be calculated by

$$I_{sg} = \frac{V_{rsg}}{R_{sg}}$$

where V_{rsg} is the voltage across the screen resistor and R_{sg} is the resistance of the screen resistor.

PREVENTIVE MAINTENANCE

11-6. Preventive-maintenance Check List

The FCC requirements and corrective measures for adjusting to the required frequency and deviation limits have been discussed above. But many service organizations find other routine checks are of assistance in catching trouble before it starts. The job of the mobile-radio technician is to repair transmitters and receivers and keep them operating properly by locating possible problems.

Routine preventive maintenance and checking also covers those items required by the FCC. Among the items on this preventive-maintenance list for the transmitter are:

1. Operating frequency
2. Modulation swing (deviation from the center frequency during modulation)
3. Tuning of the multipliers and the final stage
4. Power input of the final
5. Operating voltages including plate supply voltage
6. Inspection for any loose, damaged, or broken parts caused by vibration
7. Power-source inspection, including battery, voltage regulator, and vibrator (or dynamotor)
8. Relay inspection and maintenance
9. Inspection of cable connections
10. Inspection of antenna
11. Receiver tuning, adjustments, and sensitivity

For these items the required instruments include a frequency meter, a VTVM, a modulation meter, an RF signal generator, and an AF signal generator.

A scheduled check list is given in Table 11-2. This is suggested as a check list to be used for an over-all record every time the required FCC measurements are made.

This table is one type of check list, but this does not replace the forms required by the FCC as required by law.

At every routine FCC check the items on this chart are also measured or inspected.

TABLE 11-2. RADIO-INSPECTION RECORD

1. Call letters		Agency	Date	
2. Equipment		Model	Freq.	Mc
3. Operation	Meas. freq.	Dev.	Dev.	kc
a. Power		Final RF		A
b. Recvr. vol.		Squelch	Sens.	
c. B volt.		Mike		
d. Tx tune		Term. volt.		
4. Inspection:	Mike:	Cables	Ant.	
	Relays	Pwr. source	Pwr. sup.	
5. Base station only:		Twr. height_____	Gas press._____	
Aux. pwr._____				
6. Adjustments				
7. Tubes replaced:				
8. Components replaced:				
9. Equipment replaced:				
10. Signature:_____				

The parts of a radio set can also be considered as falling into four groups. Preventive maintenance applies to both base stations and mobiles and covers the four general parts of the system: the primary power source, the cabling, the receiver-transmitter, and the associated equipment.

1. *Primary power source.* For a fixed (base) station this includes the power-line feeders, the fuses and relays, and the switches. There is little to check concerning the input power except for variations in line voltage.

Power for a radio in a vehicle comes from the battery-generator system. Every inspection should include these items. The battery condition and water level should be checked; the terminals should be clean and secure. Generators have an extra burden in vehicles with mobile radios, and they should be inspected; the brushes and the fanbelt drive are important. Voltage regulators require checking; tighten connections and note the condition of the wires.

In any type of radio set the fuses and fuse holders should be examined and cleaned, if necessary, using fine sandpaper, not steel wool. Power cables should be checked for breaks, and the plug connections must be kept clean.

2. *Cables.* These include all connecting wiring between units of the radio, from the power source to the radio (as above) and the antenna transmission line.

All connecting cables should be examined for signs of wear, weathering, or poor mating of the plugs. This is particularly important where equipment is mounted in the trunk, on top of cabs, or other places where the cables can be damaged. Relay contacts should be examined and burnished if required. The amount of attention they require depends upon the use the equipment receives.

An antenna inspection is also a part of routine maintenance. The location of an antenna on a vehicle is always a compromise between best operation and antenna protection. Physical damage to antennas is common, particularly for long antennas extending beyond the top of the car or truck roof.

3. *Receiver-transmitter.* The entire unit should be cleaned and inspected carefully for broken parts, and the tubes should be checked. Each tube should be properly seated in its socket.

A measure of the receiver and the transmitter terminal and operating voltages is a significant operational check together with the measure of the receiver sensitivity and local oscillator frequency and the transmitter output power, frequency, deviation, and audio output.

A transmitter will require a slight retuning to adjust for the changes in tube characteristics and the aging of other parts. The manufacturer's instructions for this readjustment should be followed.

Mobile radios are rugged and usually designed for their use in vehicles. However, because of the conditions under which they operate an over-all visual inspection can uncover points of possible trouble.

The power supply, whether it is a vibrator, a dynamotor, or a rectifier and filter, requires inspection. Brushes, connections, capacitors, and vibrators are all important items. Vibrators, as an example, should be replaced when their voltage output begins to drop off.

4. *Associated equipment.* This includes all other accessory items such as selective calling, speaker amplifiers, remote-control devices, and the like. All of these should be checked for proper operation and inspected for broken or worn parts.

ALIGNMENT, TROUBLE SHOOTING, AND REPAIR

11-7. Alignment and Tuning

Alignment, the adjustment of tuned circuits, requires an accurate signal source and an oscilloscope.

Checking the response of tuned circuits, or alignment, can be done in two ways:

The point-by-point method uses a number of individual frequencies whose amplitude of response is measured and plotted. From the resultant curve, the bandwidth and tuning may be calculated.

Visual alignment is faster, more accurate, and much more widely used. An FM signal generator and an oscilloscope are required. Any FM signal generator can be used provided it covers the proper frequency bands (including all the receiver RF and IF stages) and has provision for the modulating signal to be supplied as sweep (or sync) for the oscilloscope. Accurate marker signals are required to check the exact response.

An oscilloscope is required for visual alignment of tuned circuits, which is rarely required in mobile radio unless parts have been replaced, because the mobile equipment is well designed for its intended purpose and withstands normal shock, vibration, and use without requiring realignment.

An oscilloscope presents the circuit response, as in Fig. 11-5, usually by taking the modulating voltage also as a horizontal sweep and the response of the circuit as the vertical input. The swept signal has the same center frequency as the circuit to be aligned, and the deviation of this signal is greater than the bandwidth of the aligned circuit. A detecting probe permits the RF signal to be picked up from any point for the vertical input to the oscilloscope.

An accurate signal generator or crystal source, operating at the carrier frequency, can be used for transmitter-frequency measurement (by heterodyning) and for receiver adjustment. But, because of the

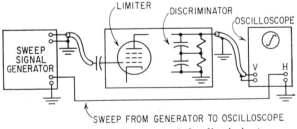

FIG. 11-5. Visual alignment of the discriminator.

sharp narrow-band characteristics of the receiver IF stages, special care is required.

11-8. Receiver-alignment Procedure

Figure 11-6 shows a triple-superheterodyne receiver. A change in the receiver frequency of operation can be made by changing the crystal (Y_1 for a single channel receiver or both Y_1 and Y_2 for a two-channel receiver), the RF-stage tuning, and the crystal-multiplier chain tuning. The two-channel receiver has the RF tuning between

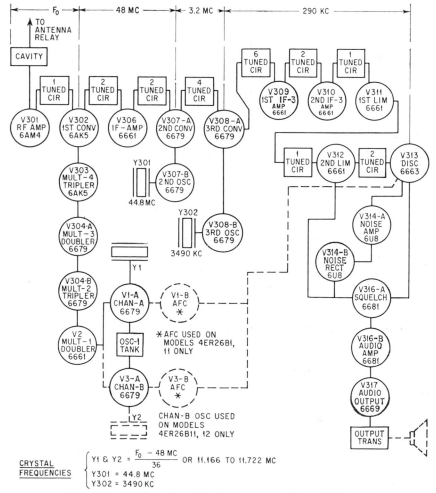

Fig. 11-6. UHF-receiver block diagram. (*General Electric.*)

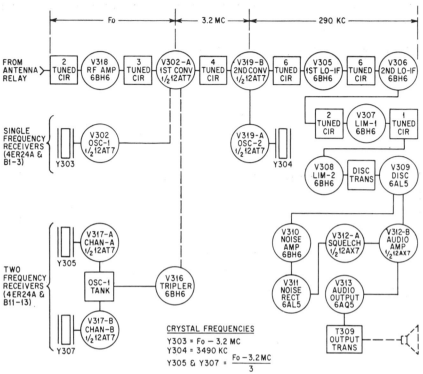

FIG. 11-7. Low-band-receiver block diagram.   (*General Electric.*)

the two frequencies to be received. Figure 11-7 shows a double superheterodyne, and a typical receiver is shown in Fig. 11-8.

Both the discriminator and the IF stages often will require alignment after component replacement in the circuits.

For *discriminator* alignment (Fig. 11-9) the test instruments required are a voltmeter, with at least 20,000 ohms per volt sensitivity and a

FIG. 11-8. Receiver construction. (*General Electric.*)

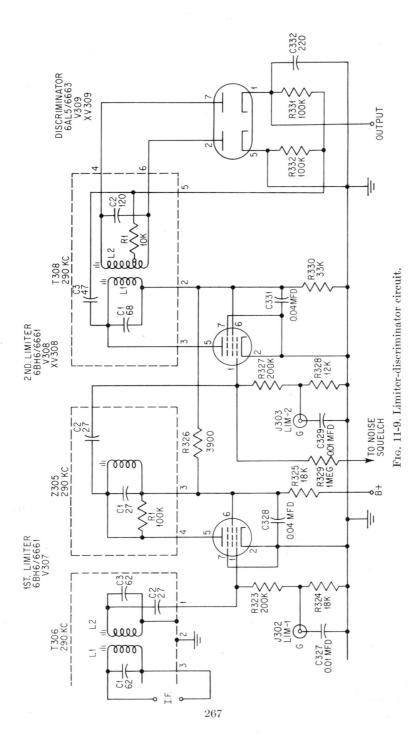

Fig. 11-9. Limiter-discriminator circuit.

267

0- to 3-volt scale (preferably a VTVM), and a signal generator accurate to ±0.002 per cent at 290 kc, which is the third IF.   Preferably this is a sweep-signal generator.

The purpose of a triple conversion, as in this receiver, is to provide for sharp selectivity; a transmitter signal may be used for discriminator alignment.   But this transmitter signal must be accurate.   In a 450-Mc transmitter, for example, 0.002 per cent accuracy (9 kc above or below) is not nearly enough for this purpose.   Many transmitters multiply the crystal frequency by 36 or more.   An error of 1 kc, at the crystal frequency, would produce a 36-kc error in the transmitter output.   Using this as an alignment signal for the discriminator could hardly result in good receiver performance.   While 36 kc is only about 0.008 per cent at the carrier frequency, it is more than 12 per cent of the 290 kc IF and is outside the passband for this low IF.

The steps for alignment are:

1. Apply the 290-kc signal generator to the grid of the stage (limiter) preceding the discriminator as in Fig. 11-9.   Both the receiver and generator must be on long enough to reach proper operating condition.

2. Remove the local oscillator crystal to prevent interference.

3. Connect the indicator to the discriminator output.

4. Adjust the discriminator secondary for zero output.

5. Apply a sweep generator (if available) to the first limiter grid. Set the unmodulated signal for zero discriminator output.

6. Use a 60-cycle sweep with 100-kc deviation; observe the characteristic S-shaped discriminator output on the oscilloscope, as in Fig. 11-10.   Narrow the deviation if necessary.

7. Adjust the discriminator primary for a symmetrical curve with a linear slope between the positive and negative peaks.

8. If a sweep-signal generator is not available, it is possible to use an unmodulated carrier signal.   Changing this 10 kc above and below will permit symmetrical voltage to be developed at the discriminator output.   Any change in either the primary or secondary affects the other, so successive adjustments must be made.

Normally the *IF amplifiers* will require alignment only if components have been replaced.

The equipment required includes an oscilloscope and an accurate signal generator (preferably of the sweep type).

The data supplied by the manufacturer is most useful in IF alignment.   The crystal for each IF strip (in a double or triple superheterodyne) should be removed to prevent interfering signals.   A sweep oscillator covers the IF passband, and the IF response is shown on the oscilloscope, as in Fig. 11-11.

A special technique is the use of a crystal calibrator.   A sweep-

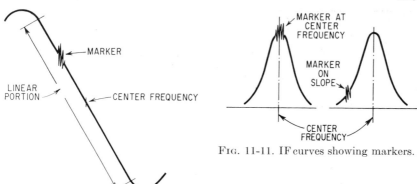

FIG. 11-10. Discriminator curve showing markers.

FIG. 11-11. IF curves showing markers.

signal generator may be heterodyned to produce an accurate alignment source, because the crystal oscillator in the calibrator is stable and accurate. Because of this the sweep-signal generator does not have to have the center frequency of the IF amplifiers; this can be obtained by heterodyning. But the generator still must be accurate enough to produce a precise alignment.

11-9. Transmitter-tuning Adjustment

A crystal-controlled transmitter, in proper operating condition, can normally be tuned by adjusting the tuned circuits to resonance. Only a voltmeter is required for adjustment. Figure 11-12 is a low-band

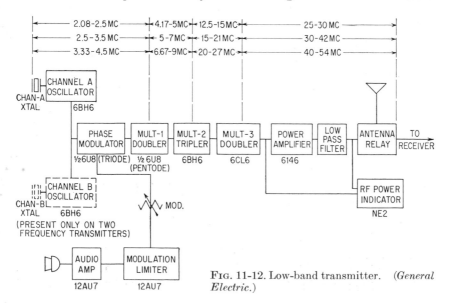

FIG. 11-12. Low-band transmitter. (*General Electric.*)

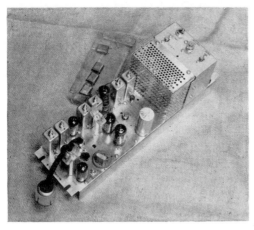

FIG. 11-13. Transmitter construction. (*General Electric.*)

transmitter block diagram and Fig. 11-13 is a typical transmitter.

Frequency-measuring instruments of the required accuracy can be used to measure the final carrier frequency as a check.

Tuning should, again, follow the manufacturer's recommendations. Most transmitters have voltage jacks for tuning purposes. If the jack is located in the grid circuit, it is tuned for maximum reading. When a multiplier (or any class-C stage) is tuned through resonance, there will be a *maximum* grid drive and maximum resulting grid current when the grid circuit is tuned to resonance. If, as in a power-amplifier stage, there is a plate jack, the tuning is adjusted for *minimum* reading, because a plate circuit tuned to resonance will provide minimum plate current because of the high impedance in series with the plate.

In any transmitter the power amplifier can draw excessive plate current if it is detuned. Because of this two precautions are taken: The PA plate voltage (or screen voltage) is reduced until the transmitter is at least roughly tuned, and the transmitter is not keyed, except for very short periods, until approximate tuning is done.

The equipment required includes a voltmeter (20,000 ohms per volt) with a 0- to 3-volt scale, a heterodyne-frequency meter for measuring the output frequency, a wavemeter for the frequency of each multiplier, and an alignment screwdriver.

The general procedure is to adjust each multiplier for resonance and the power amplifier for maximum output (within the allowable power) and greatest transfer of energy to the antenna.

The tuning steps are as follows [see Fig. 11-12 (low-band), Fig. 3-39 (high-band), and Fig. 3-40 (UHF)]:

1. Check the crystal (or crystals) for proper connections. Choose the lower frequency if two crystals are used for dual-channel operation.

2. Use the normal antenna, or properly load the transmitter. Set

the power amplifier *Tune-Operate* switch on tune, which lowers the screen voltage to protect the amplifier tubes during tuning. Adjust antenna coupling to load the amplifier.

3. Turn on power, allow warm-up, and read the first multiplier grid with transmitter keyed. A proper negative voltage indicates the crystal oscillator and the modulator are operating.

4. With the meter in multiplier 2, the plate of multiplier 1 is tuned for maximum. The multipliers are tuned, in sequence, from the modulator to the power amplifier.

5. Any large change in transmitter frequency, such as the replacement of a crystal by one of a frequency different by 1 per cent or greater, will require a preliminary tuning by an absorption wavemeter to obtain the correct approximate frequency.

6. Tune the last multiplier plate for maximum reading at PA-grid jack.

7. Tune PA plate for *minimum* cathode-PA jack reading.

8. Switch to operate (*Tune-Operate* switch) and retune the last multiplier plate for minimum PA-cathode reading. Tune PA plate and *Antenna Tuning* for minimum cathode-PA reading.

9. Adjust *Antenna Coupling* for proper loading on cathode PA and repeak *Antenna Tuning*.

10. Retune the last multiplier plate, PA grid, and *Antenna Coupling* until there is no further change in cathode-PA reading.

11. Check the output frequency with an accurate heterodyne-frequency meter, and adjust *Frequency Control* (crystal oscillator) for the exact crystal frequency.

11-10. Use of a Crystal Calibrator

A crystal signal source can be used to check the frequency of signal generators, receivers, and transmitters. Signal generators can, of course, be tuned over a wide range, but special crystals will be required for fixed-frequency radio receivers and transmitters.

Crystal calibrators, because of their greater inherent accuracy than variable-frequency oscillators in signal generators, have a distinct value for calibration of signal generators, transmitters, and receivers.

Signal Generators. If the calibrator has an internal detector and amplifier, the procedure is this:

1. Turn on the crystal calibrator, so that an unmodulated RF is provided.

2. Feed in the signal generator to the calibrator after it has been on long enough to reach the proper operating temperature.

3. Attach earphones to the calibrator audio output.

4. Tune the signal generator to just below the desired check point; assume this to be 50 Mc.

5. The calibrator is turned to the 10-Mc position.

6. As the signal is brought to 50 Mc, the best note in the earphones will disappear. Tuning the signal generator on either side of this point will cause the beat note to increase in frequency until it is above audibility. The carrier is beating against the 5th crystal harmonic. Note: Any harmonic of the crystal signal or the generator output will also cause beat notes, but if the signal generator is approximately correct, the other crystal-calibrator beat notes will be at 50 Mc and 60 Mc (for a 10-Mc crystal), and there will be no difficulty in finding the correct point.

7. The dial reading of the signal generator may be recorded, so that it can be used for a correction factor for the signal-generator RF output. The signal generator may be adjusted to this exact frequency, but this does not assure equal accuracy between check points.

8. The calibrator is then set for 1 Mc, and harmonics of this output are available. Going up in frequency, the signal generator will provide beat notes and calibration points at 51, 52, 53, and 54 Mc.

9. If the calibrator has a 100-kc or 250-kc output, this can be used in the same manner to check points between the 1-Mc points.

Receiver Calibration. Turn on modulation of the calibrator, and attach to the output a short piece of wire, which will act as an antenna and means of coupling the calibrator and receiver.

The correct amount of coupling will have to be determined experimentally. A short wire to the antenna connector on the receiver may be desirable to effect sufficient coupling to the calibrator. Above 30 Mc a properly terminated coaxial line between the output jack and receiver input should be used to prevent standing waves.

Connect a pair of headphones to the output terminal of the receiver under test. It is also desirable to connect the receiver to an output meter to provide a visual indication.

Use a frequency most suitable for the receiver under test. For example, it will be convenient first to determine the location of 10-Mc harmonics.

Tune the receiver to the fundamental, or required, harmonic of the oscillator for a maximum volume in the headphones of the receiver. Exact tuning may be easier with the use of an output meter.

Always reduce gain to minimize the effect of too much receiver gain.

Transmitter Calibration. Use earphones from the calibrator with an unmodulated signal output.

Connect a short piece of wire to the input. Placing this wire in proximity to the transmitter will usually be sufficient to obtain a beat note, as the transmitter frequency is tuned through a harmonic or subharmonic of the calibrator.

11-11. Trouble Shooting

If a receiver or a transmitter is inoperative, there are several possible approaches to trouble shooting; one method is signal tracing, where a modulated signal is followed through the equipment until it is lost.

Any RF signal source which can be modulated can be used if the operating frequency is correct. In a receiver a detector probe is connected to a voltmeter or an oscilloscope. The test signal is applied as the receiver input and traced through to find the inoperative stage, if the local oscillator is operating properly. AM can be used up to the limiter and detector.

This function can be accomplished by various commercial signal tracers. Some of these instruments permit the monitoring of the receiver at several locations at the same time. Detector probes for demodulators of the RF signal are required. These may be constructed or purchased.

There are two general methods of using signal generators for servicing: signal substitution and signal tracing. When a receiver develops trouble and the cause of the defect is not immediately apparent, the first step is to test the tubes. If this does not clear up the trouble, the standard procedure in trouble shooting is to find the defective stage by either the signal-substitution or the signal-tracing method.

In signal substitution the signals from the generators are applied to each stage of the receiver to determine whether the stage can pass the signal. To check the operation of the audio section, an AF signal is injected at the grid of the audio output stage. If the stage passes the signal, it is assumed to be in working order, and the generator is moved to the plate of the preceding audio stage, then to the grid, until the entire audio section has been covered. If the signal is passed along and amplified from each point, the AF stages are operating, and the IF stages should be checked.

A modulated IF signal is applied to the IF section, starting with the plate of the last stage, then back to the mixer plate, listening for the modulation output at the speaker. If the IF stages pass the signal, the mixer, oscillator, and RF stages must be checked. Apply the modulated RF signal to the grid of the mixer stage, and note whether the signal appears at the receiver output. If this stage is operating, work back through the RF stages to the antenna terminal. When the signal does not appear at the output of the mixer, the oscillator stage should be checked for operation.   A simple way to determine oscillator operation is to check the negative voltage on the grid.   The minimum usually necessary for operation is −5 volts; however, the amount of negative voltage varies with different receivers.   If any stage fails to pass a signal when using signal substitution, the trouble is localized in that stage.   The individual parts for that stage should then be checked for defects.

The second method for localizing trouble is signal tracing.   This method is similar to signal substitution, but the procedure starts at the antenna terminals of the receiver instead of the audio output stage.

In signal tracing, a signal generator supplying a modulated RF signal of predetermined amplitude is connected to the antenna terminals of the receiver.   This signal is then followed, or traced, through various stages of the receiver by connecting an indicating device first to the input and then to the output of each succeeding stage.   The point where the signal disappears indicates the defective stage, and the individual parts within that stage should be checked.

Indicator units used in signal tracing should be suitable for the circuit under test.   An output meter, speaker, or an oscilloscope can be used.

Locating system troubles can be done in the following steps.   Isolate the trouble to either the transmitter or the receiver.   If neither operates, the power supply is probably the defective part.

1. Receiver.   An inoperative receiver should first be checked for the proper operating (supply) voltages and then for the condition of the tubes.   Many receivers will have jacks for measuring test voltages.

If the tubes are checked out and the supply voltages are normal, the receiver is then broken down into sections.   A signal generator can be used as a signal source for tracing.

2. Transmitter.   Again the first step should be checking the condition of the tubes and the measured voltages.   A signal generator can be used as a substitute for the crystal signal; this will locate a defect in the crystal-oscillator stage.   Assuming the above check is no help in locating the trouble, a signal source is used starting from the last RF amplifier and moving forward while receiving the transmitter signal.

An audio signal used to modulate the transmitter will isolate any trouble in the modulator or audio-amplifier stages.   Remaining receiver stages (squelch, AFC, selective-calling) can be isolated one by one to find any defect in a single stage.

After the defect has been traced to a single stage, the serviceman falls back to the schematic diagram, which will assist him in locating the defective component by voltage and resistance measurements.

Signal tracers are effective in isolating troubles to a single stage.

Component-parts replacement requires normal care to see that parts of the same electrical characteristics are used. Usually alignment (receiver) or tuning (transmitter) will not be required except when IF transformers, ratio-detector transformers, or other critical parts are replaced. An operational check should always be made after any replacement of circuit parts.

A suggested test setup is illustrated in Fig. 11-14. The receiver-transmitter unit is the focal point; all other equipment is on, or part of, the test bench. A_2 is the receiver test meter which is attached, by a selector switch, to the receiver test points; A_3 is the same for the transmitter. Both are 0- to 50-μa meters. A d-c power supply is provided for the range from 4 to 15 volts with 80 amp at 6 volts and 40 amp at 12 volts. Meters are provided for current, A_1, and voltage, E_1. An a-c source can also be provided for base-station testing.

By using a coaxial switch the several inputs can be provided for the antenna transmission line. A coaxial switch has three antennas, one for each band, by which the common point (S) is fed to the unit coaxial

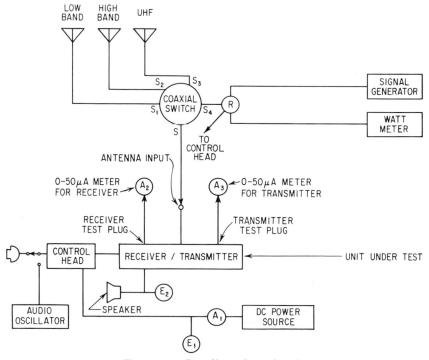

FIG. 11-14. Coordinated test bench.

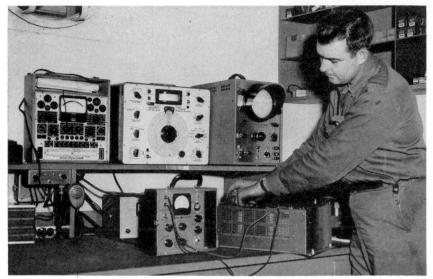

FIG. 11-15. Measuring mobile-transmitter operation.   (*General Electric.*)

line which normally goes to the antenna.   A fourth position (S_4) leads to a coaxial relay which is attached to the control head.   When the transmitter is keyed, by the push-to-talk button, the plate supply is transferred from the receiver to the transmitter, and the antenna relay operates.   In the operating equipment this relay changes the antenna from the receiver to the transmitter; in this test arrangement the relay is tied to the control head.   In transmit position the wattmeter monitors the RF output power.   In receive the signal generator provides the RF signal input to the receiver.

For test purposes there is a choice of four receiver inputs: the three antennas or the signal source.   The transmitter can only be connected to the wattmeter.

Two inputs for the transmitter are the microphone and the audio oscillator.   A two-position selector switch is provided.   If a voltmeter, E_2, is across the audio line, the audio level may be continuously measured.

An integrated test bench requires careful planning and modification of the control wiring as in Fig. 11-15, as well as standard test cords for the models of transmitters and receivers which will be tested.   But, together with the proper test equipment, the bench permits rapid servicing.

APPENDIX A

TABLE A-1. THE IMPORTANT MOBILE-RADIO FREQUENCY BANDS
FOR COMMERCIAL USE

(New systems after Aug. 1, 1958; all systems after Oct. 31, 1963)

Band, mc	Range,* miles	Channel spacing		Frequency tolerance, per cent	Deviation, kc
		Old	New		
25–50	25–60	40	20	0.002	5
152–162	10–30	60	15†	0.0005	5
450–470	10–25	100	50	0.0005	15

* Range is comparative only. It depends upon transmission conditions and the power output.

† Every other channel is in use; the spacing is thus 30 kc.

TABLE A-2. OTHER FREQUENCY BANDS RELATED TO COMMERCIAL
MOBILE RADIO

Band, Mc	Service	Notes
1.6–5.0	Restricted to special commercial use	Long-range of 25–50 miles or more.
72.0–76.0	Point-to-point use	Use must not cause television interference.
118.0–132.0	Airport service	Ground-to-ground at airports (AM, not FM).
132.0–144.0 162.0–174.0	Reserved for government use	
462.55–463.20 464.75–464.95 465.05–466.45 (460.05–460.95 also presently used)	Citizens' band (A)	Maximum power 60 watts, FM and AM, stations 50 kc apart, for two-way radio telephone.
465.00*	Citizens' band (B)	Maximum power 5 watts, AM or FM for voice or remote control, stations 10 kc apart.
26.995, 27.045, 27.095, 27.145, 27.195, and 27.255	Citizens' band (C)	Maximum power 5 watts (except on 27.255, where it is 30 watts), on-off carrier or AM tone only, NOT for radio-telephone, for mobile-radio control only.
26.965–27.035 27.005–27.085 27.105–27.135 27.155–27.185 27.205–27.255	Citizens' band (D)	Maximum power 5 watts, AM two-way radio-telephone, stations 10 kc apart.

* Also, any frequency in the 464.75- to 466.45-Mc or the 462.55- to 463.20-Mc
bands *to class-A standards*, but with only 5 watts.

APPENDIX B

FCC INFORMATION

Several types of information are available on two-way radio. The FCC rules and regulations, as an example, are now prepared in a new form.

RULES AND REGULATIONS

According to the FCC notice of Apr. 22, 1959, the Government Printing Office will print and sell volumes of FCC rules and regulations by categories, with amendments. Under this arrangement, the commission will, as each such volume becomes available, no longer maintain a mailing list for amendments and other changes to the rule parts concerned. This mailing will be made by the Superintendent of Documents.

The first issue of this type combines four rule parts: Part 9, Aviation Services; Part 10, Public Safety Radio Services; Part 11, Industrial Radio Services; and Part 16, Land Transportation Radio Services, in a single book, volume V.

The commission has discontinued its mailing lists for amendments and changes to the rules contained in volume V, and the Superintendent of Documents will no longer sell such rule parts individually.

Under the new arrangement, it will not be possible either to purchase these rule parts separately or to receive only amendments to the rules of a single radio service involved. Because of the volume grouping, purchasers will receive changes to the rules of all the services contained in that combination.

RADIO-LICENSE LISTINGS

Official FCC listings of mobile and base-station assignments are available from the Communication Engineering Book Co., Monterey, Massachusetts.

Each of the four registries listed below is revised and brought up to date annually from official license files at Washington, D.C., by permission of the Federal Communications Commission. These are the only listings published of radio-communications systems, as the FCC does not issue any similar records.

New services and changes: In the Public Safety Registry, the new Local Government Service has been added. The Common Carrier Registry is now known as the Common Carrier and New Services Registry, for it includes the Business Service, Manufacturers Service, and Telephone Maintenance Service, newly authorized by the FCC. The Low Power Industrial Service listing has been deleted from the Industrial Registry, since those systems have been moved to the Business Service, and they now appear in the Common Carrier and New Services Registry.

Listing by names of licensees shows:

1. Name and address of licensee
2. Location of each fixed transmitter
3. Number of mobile and portable units authorized
4. Operating frequencies of fixed, mobile, and portable transmitters, including relay, operational, and control transmitters
5. Call letters
6. Make of equipment used

Listing of operating frequencies shows:

1. Operating frequency
2. Location of transmitters
3. Service for which operation is authorized

Additional information on each transmitter and its location can be found by referring to the listing by means of licensees.

1959 Registry of Common Carrier and New Services and STL Radio and TV Systems

Revised annually and issued in July, 1959, listing systems in the following services:

Business Service

Manufacturers Service

One-way Signaling (radio paging)

Individuals Using CC Base Station

Common Carrier Mobile

Miscellaneous Common Carrier

Telephone Maintenance

STL for Radio and TV Broadcasting

1959 Registry of Public Safety Systems

Revised annually and issued in October, 1959, listing systems in the following services:

Police (state, county, municipal)
Fire (county, municipal)
Local Government
Highway Maintenance

Forestry Conservation
Special Emergency (relief organ-
    izations, doctors, veterinarians,
    ambulances, school buses)

1959 Registry of Industrial Systems

Revised annually and issued in January, 1959, listing systems in the following services:

Special Industrial
Forest Products
Power Utility

Petroleum and Gas
Relay Press and Motion Picture
VHF Maritime

1959 Registry of Transportation Systems

Revised annually and issued in April, 1959, listing systems in the following services:

Railroad
Taxi
Auto Emergency
Intercity Bus

Highway Trucks
Urban Transit
Motor Carrier

INDEX